STRING FIGURES

AND OTHER MONOGRAPHS

STRING FIGURES
BY W. W. R. BALL

METHODS AND THEORIES FOR THE SOLUTION OF PROBLEMS OF GEOMETRICAL CONSTRUCTION
BY J. PETERSEN

NON-EUCLIDEAN PLANE GEOMETRY AND TRIGONOMETRY
BY H. S. CARSLAW

A HISTORY OF THE LOGARITHMIC SLIDE RULE
BY F. CAJORI

CHELSEA PUBLISHING COMPANY
NEW YORK
1960

STRING FIGURES WAS ORIGINALLY PUBLISHED BY W. HEFFER
& SONS, LTD.

METHODS AND THEORIES FOR THE SOLUTION
OF PROBLEMS OF GEOMETRICAL CONSTRUCTION
WAS ORIGINALLY PUBLISHED BY ANDR. FRED. HOST & SON

NON-EUCLIDEAN PLANE GEOMETRY AND TRIG-
ONOMETRY WAS ORIGINALLY PUBLISHED BY LONGMANS,
GREEN AND CO.

A HISTORY OF THE LOGARITHMIC SLIDE RULE
WAS ORIGINALLY PUBLISHED BY THE ENGINEERING NEWS PUBLISHING
COMPANY

LIBRARY OF CONGRESS CATALOGUE CARD NO. 59-11780

PRINTED IN THE UNITED STATES OF AMERICA

EDITOR'S PREFACE

This work, like its companion volume, *Squaring the Circle, and other Monographs* by Hobson et al., consists of a reprint in one volume of several books on mathematics that were originally published as separate volumes.

The reason for the selection of the four books that comprise this volume is that each is a valuable and important work and that each is of interest to a fairly wide circle of mathematicians and students.

The reason for their inclusion in a single volume is neither learned nor recondite. The reason is purely economic: Reprinted separately, the books would have to be priced at not much less than the price of the whole present volume (if they could be so reprinted at all). Anyone who buys the book for the sake of one of the four volumes that it contains will surely find the other three of interest and will consider them to be a worthwhile and welcome addition to his library.

STRING FIGURES

BY

W. W. ROUSE BALL

Fellow of Trinity College, Cambridge.

Third Edition.

Prefatory Note.

THE making of String Figures is a game common among primitive people. Its study by men of science is a recent development, their researches have, however, already justified its description as a hobby, pleasing to most people and readily mastered. The following pages contain a lecture which I gave in 1920 at the Royal Institution, London, on these figures and their history (Proceedings, Vol. xxiii. pp. 77–110); to it I have appended full directions for the construction of several easy typical designs, arranged roughly in order of difficulty, and, for those who wish to go further, lists of additional patterns and references. The only expense necessary to anyone who takes up the pastime is the acquisition of a piece of good string some seven feet long; with that and this booklet to aid him, he will have at his command an amusement that may occupy many a vacant hour.

I have avoided as far as is practicable the use of technical terms, but for the convenience of those who consult other works I have added to the index of this, the third edition a glossary of terms in common use.

W. W. ROUSE BALL

Trinity College, Cambridge.

Contents.

A Lecture on String Figures.

I have chosen as the subject for this Lecture *String Figures*, which I present to you as a world-wide amusement of primitive man, and as being in themselves interesting to most people. In the course of the evening you will see how such figures are actually made, but before coming to that I must say something about their nature and history. I hope you will bear with me if I introduce them to you in my own way.

A string figure is usually made by taking a piece of good flexible string, such as macrami thread, about six-and-a-half feet long, knotting the ends so as to make it into a closed loop, and then weaving or twisting this loop on the fingers so as to produce a pleasing design.

Having taken up the loop of string in some defined way, the subsequent weaving may be effected either with the aid of another operator, each player in turn taking the string from the other, or by the single player making a series of movements, such as dropping a loop from one finger, transferring a loop from one finger to another, picking up a string with one finger and then returning the finger to its original position carrying the string with it, and so on ; unless I state the contrary it is to be assumed that it is with figures made in the second way that I am concerned to-night. In general, after each step, the hands are separated so as to make the string tight ; and normally the hands are held upright with the fingers pointing upwards and the palms approximately facing one another. [These movements were illustrated by the formation of one or two string figures.] Nothing more is required in most constructions, though many other small movements, notably slight rotations of the wrists, while not necessary, give neatness of manipulation and add to the effectiveness of the display.

These figures, when shown to a few spectators in a room, always prove, as far as my experience goes, interesting alike to young and old ; but their attractiveness, their fascination I might almost say, is not permanent unless people can be induced to construct them for themselves. I can hardly propose—and that is a difficulty inherent in lecturing on the subject —I can hardly propose that for the first time, now and here, without individual help, you should make the designs you will see later. To enjoy the occupation, however, you must be able to make them, and, bold though I may seem, I venture to assert that if once you acquire this knowledge you will find pleasure in applying it.

It is a truism, and in fact a truth as well, that all sensible people have hobbies. I am not alone in finding that collecting string figures is an agreeable hobby, and it may be added a very cheap one, while friends who have learnt how to make them tell me that in convalescence and during tedious journeys the amusement has helped to while away many a long hour ; moreover the figures are easy to weave, they have a history, and they are capable of numerous varieties. Thus even in England the game may prove well worth the time spent in learning to play it ; and admittedly to the very few who travel among aborigines it may sometimes be of real service.

It would be absurd to talk about string figures if you do not know what they are ; so before I go any further let me show

you what is meant by the term.   These figures may be divided
into three classes, α, β, γ, according as (α) the production of a
design, or (β) the illustration of some action or story, or (γ) the
creation of a surprise effect is the object desired ; it will be
desirable to begin by giving one or two examples of each
class.

The designs reproduced in figures 1 and 2 are well-known
forms which will serve as illustrations of figures in Class A.
Like all those given in this booklet they are drawn as seen
by the person who makes them.

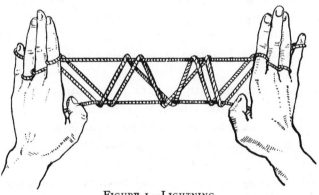

FIGURE 1—LIGHTNING.

The first of them, a zig-zag pattern, termed *Lightning*, is
due to the Navaho Indians who live in the far West, on the
Mexican border of Arizona, where the customs of the Red Man
have not yet been destroyed by civilization and law. [The
figure as shown by the Lecturer was made by successive movements, as set out in the next paragraph.]   The construction is
simple, and no digital skill is involved.   You see the final
result appears suddenly, almost dramatically, and I regard

this as an excellent feature of it. Observe also that the production of the figure is rapid. Timing myself, I find I take about six seconds to make it. I think quickness, which comes easily as soon as one knows the moves, adds finish to the working and is worth cultivating.

In making the figure, this is what I did. *First*, I put the string in the form of a figure of eight, one oval (preferably small) lying away from me, and the other towards me, and the strings crossing in the middle of the figure ; I then put my index-fingers down into the far oval, and my thumbs down into the near oval ; next I separated the hands and then turned them up into their normal position with the thumbs and fingers well spread out, thus causing the strings of the loops on the thumbs and index-fingers to cross one another : this is called the *Navaho Opening*. *Second*, I bent each thumb away from me over two strings, and with its back picked up from below the next string (i.e. in the language expounded later, the ulnar index string), and, as usually follows and is assumed to be the case unless the contrary is stated, returned the thumbs to their former positions. *Third*, I bent each mid-finger towards me over one string, and with its back picked up from below the next string. *Fourth*, I bent each ring-finger towards me over one string, and with its back picked up from below the next string. *Fifth*, I bent each little-finger towards me over one string, and with its back picked up from below the next string. *Sixth*, I moved my thumbs away from me, and placed their tips in the spaces by the little-fingers, their fronts resting on the near little-finger string ; this released the thumb loops. *Lastly*, I threw the loops thus released over the other strings, and at the same time with the thumbs pressed down the near little-finger string sharply and as far as possible, and the figure flashed out.

The description is lengthy, but in my opinion it is not desirable to labour at making this extremely concise. As is the case in many of these figures, the resulting pattern is shown stretched or hung on parallel horizontal strings, and to present it effectively it is desirable to keep these strings widely separated. To those who know something of these figures the construction is easy, and a boy of eight or nine, if taught practically, can learn it in a few minutes; none the less, a novice of more mature years will be well advised to begin with even simpler forms, some of which are given below in the addendum.

The next diagram is of a design, known as a *Tent Flap* or

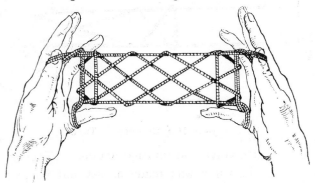

FIGURE 2—A TENT FLAP.

Door, due to the Apache Red Indians. [The figure as shown by the Lecturer was made as set out below on page 31.] The tribe is now almost extinct, but the figure is familiar to various Indians, who are said to have originally got it from Apaches living on the Reservation Lands maintained by the United States Government. This also is a figure in Class A.

The two designs, represented in figures 3 and 4, will serve as examples of figures in Class B. The first of them is supposed to represent a *Man Climbing a Tree*, his arms and feet (or perhaps his tree-band and feet) clasping the tree trunk. It is derived from the Blacks in Queensland; since only a drawing of the design was brought away, it is impossible to be certain how it was made by the aborigines, but the construction I am about to employ has been suggested, and is probably correct, since

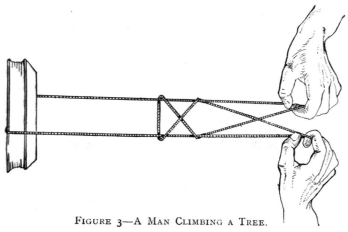

FIGURE 3—A MAN CLIMBING A TREE.

it is simple and involves no unusual actions. [The figure as shown by the Lecturer was made as set out on page 52.] In the figure thus obtained (which is here drawn as seen sideways) I pull with my index-fingers, and then the part which represents the man moves up the part which represents the tree trunk. Such motion is characteristic of figures of this kind; hence such results are often used as a framework for stories—two warriors fighting, a hammock breaking and its occupant falling out, and so on.

String Illustrations of Stories may be employed as examples of Class B. The well-known representation of the *Yam Theft* will serve as a specimen. [The construction as shown by the Lecturer was made as set out below on page 49, the final form being shown in the accompanying diagram.] You can tell the story much as you like. In one version of it the thumb loop represents the owner of a yam patch. He is supposed to be asleep. The loops successively taken up from the dorsal string and put on the fingers represent

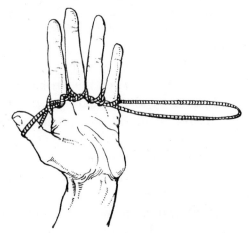

FIGURE 4—THE YAM THIEF.

the yams dug up by a thief, and tied up in bags ready for carrying off. The loop coming off the thumb represents the owner waking and going to see what is the matter. He looks down the back of the hand, sees the yams collected for removal, notices that the dorsal string holds them tight, and looks about for the thief. The thief, who may be represented by a loop on the pendant palmar string, coming back for his booty, sees the owner, whereupon (pulling that string) he disappears with all the yams. There is a well known British specimen of such a string story which deals with the misadventures of a thief who stole some tallow candles.

There is yet a third class, which I call Class Γ, of string figures to which primitive man is very partial ; these are string paradoxes, where the unexpected happens. Take this as an example. Here is a loop of string, held for convenience by my left hand high up. Obviously if I twist my right hand round one string of the loop and pull with the left hand, the right hand will be caught. If I give the right hand a twist round the other string of the loop, it is generally still more firmly caught. The problem is to give this additional twist so that the string runs free when the left hand is pulled. This can easily be effected by what is known in certain South Pacific Isles as the *Lizard Twist*. [This was shown and explained.] There is no trickery ; the movements are simple, yet I predict that few people, even if they have seen the twist, will succeed when they first attempt to make it. String paradoxes or puzzles of this kind are widely known, and are generally amusing. To show them, to be shown them, and above all to show pleasure in them, often lead to friendly intercourse with primitive folk, but they are different in kind from the figures about which I wish to talk. I put them, then, on one side as not relevant to my subject to-night, and come back to the formation as practised to-day of string designs in classes α and β.

The study of string figures is new, and its history a short one. I may dispose of the story prior to 1902 very briefly. From about the middle of the nineteenth century onwards we find occasional notices by travellers in wild countries of the fact that the natives made, with a piece of string, forms different from and far more elaborate than the Cat's Cradle of our nurseries, but (with the exception of two examples described in France in 1888 and two in America in 1900) no details were given of how they were constructed, and in only a few cases near the end of the century were drawings kept of the patterns produced. There are more accounts of the Cat's Cradle familiar to children in England ; indeed they stretch back to the eighteenth century, for there is an allusion to it in English literature as long ago as 1768, and Charles Lamb refers to it as played at Christ's Hospital in his school-days. It is, however, a dull amusement, producing, as usually presented, merely four or five designs of little interest ; here, too, before the present century, no description was available which would enable anyone previously ignorant of the Cradle to make it. Outside Britain, in the nineteenth century it was known in Northern Europe, and travellers in Victorian times mention it as practised in Korea, China, and the Asiatic Isles

We may say that before 1902 the whole matter of string figures was regarded as a pastime of children and savages, hardly worth mention and not worth consideration. To-day, when serious attention is given to folk-lore and the histories of games, such things are looked at from a different stand-point. The study of string figures came about in this way. In 1898, Rivers and Haddon organised an anthropological expedition to the Torres Straits, and, among other things, they brought back information about string patterns there current, together with some thirty examples. Some of these designs were made to the chanting of sing-songs, some were connected with tribal stories, and some were devised as amusements, but everything suggested that here was a custom worth investigation.

This conclusion showed the need of having an unambiguous nomenclature which would allow anyone acquainted with it to describe a string figure in such a way as to permit of its reproduction by an intelligent reader.   The terms introduced are taken from anatomy, and there is nothing recondite about them, but it is necessary to know them if you want to understand recent writers on the subject.   Here they are:—

The part of a string which lies across the palm of the hand is described as *palmar*, the part lying across the back of the hand as *dorsal*.

Anything on the thumb side of the hand is called *radial*, anything on the little-finger side is called *ulnar*. Since a string passing round a finger or fingers forms a loop, each such loop is composed of a radial string, and an ulnar string.

Of two strings or loops on the same finger, the one nearer the palm of the hand is called *proximal*, and the one nearer the finger tip is called *distal*.

These six adjectives, palmar and dorsal, radial and ulnar, proximal and distal, together with the names of the parts of the hands, fingers, wrists, etc., enable us to state exactly the relative place of every string in a figure held on the hands.

This nomenclature is framed so as to define the position of strings on a hand by reference to the hand, and not by terms like near and far, lower and upper, which may mean quite different things according as to how it is held.   At the same time, if the hands are held upright, and with the palms facing each other, which I regard as their normal position, we may conveniently use *near* and *far* instead of radial and ulnar, and *lower* and *upper* instead of proximal and distal. It is, however, well to make it a rule that this every-day language is used only when the hands are in their normal position or when there can be no doubt as to the meaning; when there is no ambiguity I prefer to employ these ordinary words rather than the technical terms.

Precision of language, which was necessary if the subject was to be treated scientifically, was introduced only in 1902. Subsequent research has strengthened the interest taken in string figures, and in anthropological expeditions to-day they are among the matters on which information is sought. In particular Haddon has continued to stimulate enquiry, and to him we owe several of the patterns discovered. It is not too much to say that he is the creator of the science, and to his enthusiasm many owe their introduction to it.

The Americans took up the investigation warmly, and in Philadelphia a valuable collection of drawings of string figures has been formed which will permanently preserve the patterns discovered. The results of the earlier work in America are embodied in a handsome volume published in New York in 1906, containing full descriptions of about a hundred string figures, chiefly collected in North America and New Guinea, though with some examples from Africa, the Philippines, and other scattered localities. In it also are given drawings of more than another hundred finished patterns from Oceania and Queensland. Unfortunately Mrs. Jayne, to whose liberality and initiative the book was due, died shortly after its publication.

Further examples from places where the amusement was already known to exist, and collections from Africa and India, have since been issued, and show that the construction of string figures is widely practised where primitive man is still found. Examples also have been reported from South America, but as yet this immense area is an almost unworked field, the only well-known South American instance being a *Mosquito* or *Fly*—an example of Class B.   [The figure as shown by the Lecturer was made as set out below on page 45.]   The insect with its body and wings appears between the hands. Of course in such a position the natural thing is to try to squash it.   To do this you clap your hands sharply together, then drawing them apart quickly and at the same time releasing the little-fingers, you will find that here, as usually happens in life, you have failed, and the fly has gone.

In 1911 K. Haddon published in London an excellent account, employing the customary technical terms, of several results.   Later, in 1914, P. Hambruch printed at Hamburg a long memoir on the subject, with special regard to the patterns found at Nauru in Micronesia, the home of some of the most skilful native exponents of the art, and then a German possession.   Of course the outbreak of war in 1914 put a stop to researches of this kind, as of so many others[1].   Hence, up to to-day (1920), the serious study of the subject covers only twelve years—namely, from 1902 to 1914—and as yet few save specialists know much about it; but materials increase rapidly, and the number of recorded specimens, which in 1902 was less than fifty, already runs to some hundreds.

[1] Before the end of the war, work on the subject had recommenced; and in particular I note R. H. Compton's interesting paper in the Journal of the Royal Anthropological Institute, vol. 49 (printed subsequently to the delivery of my Lecture), giving an account and the workings of 25 figures, including *The Caterpillar*, *The Ebbing Tide*, and *The Porker*, collected by him from Lifu and New Caledonia.   The workings of these three figures are given below.

I may sum up the result of the work of these twelve years by saying that the evidence does not justify us in asserting dogmatically that all primitive people play and always have played at making string figures ; but we may say that the game was at one time common among a large number of them. The formation of these designs is natural, for there are not many sedentary occupations open to uncivilized man during his long leisure hours, and to toy with a piece of string is an obvious recreation[1]. What, however, is striking, is the immense variety of well-defined patterns already discovered, and their distribution in different parts of the world.

The search for and collection of designs was begun just in time. The development of such branches of anthropology as are concerned with the amusements of primitive man is a tragic story. Put on a scientific basis only at the extreme close of the nineteenth century, already the materials for research are fast disappearing. Everywhere and ever more eagerly the white man seeks for new fields to explore, and his intercourse with aboriginals remorselessly destroys recreations such as those here described; under his influence everything tends to become uniform and colourless. Ethnologists tell us that these primitive games are now being discarded by adults, and survive only among the children; it would really seem that their continuance is almost incompatible with civilization as we know it, and I suspect that this is why, until recently, when Cat's Cradle was imported from Asia, there were in European literature, covering centuries of cultured life, no allusions to string figures.

---

[1] A correspondent, writing to me from the Gold Coast in 1921 on figures found there, informed me that besides their normal use for illustrating stories or indicating objects a few forms (thrown, so to speak, at the spectator) are sometimes employed as signs of good-humoured abuse—an interesting local development.

Among existing aborigines, it is usually the women who teach the pastime to the children, and in most cases now-a-days the lads and men, though familiar with the methods used, do not of their own accord make designs in the presence of strangers. Hence the amusement may easily escape the attention of travellers; no doubt, also, many of these would take no interest in such figures even if they saw them. Moreover, in wild countries the natives are shy, and think that the white man will laugh at these simple games; thus an exhibition is not made unless encouraged by sympathetic advances, but if patterns are shown no secret is made about the method of construction, which is not treated as a tribal secret. To this open revelation of methods of weaving there is one reported exception mentioned by F. Boas, and referred to later. When figures are displayed, it does not follow that it is easy to take down or follow the rapid sequence of moves made by the operator, so the collection of records may involve a good deal of gentle diplomacy.

I can give an illustration of this reluctance to show figures unless they are asked for. A few years ago a traveller, near the Victoria Falls in Africa, met a high official of the Government, and, enquiring about various customs of the natives, asked if any string games were known in that part of the country. The officer said, " No "; he had never heard of them, he had lived for years among these people, had constantly seen them at work and at play, and was confident that nothing of the kind could exist without his knowledge. After their talk the visitor strolled to where the police escort waited, and taking out of his pocket a piece of string (without which to-day no self-respecting anthropologist ought to travel), made to their obvious pleasure a couple of string figures. He then tossed the string to a black orderly, who made other patterns. In fact these natives were acquainted with various forms, and when their questioner disguising his deeper knowledge, showed interest, they were delighted and readily exhibited to him such designs as they knew. One of these is worth reproducing here, for it represents (what is rare in such

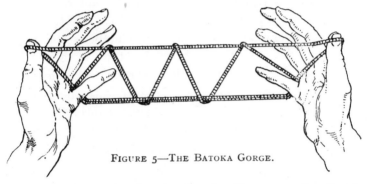

FIGURE 5—THE BATOKA GORGE.

designs) a place, namely the Batoka Gorge on the Zambesi River below the Victoria Falls. [The figure as shown by the Lecturer was made as set out below on page 29.] This incident suggests, what I believe is the truth, that the best way of finding out native figures is to make some oneself, and then challenge the natives to do better if they can; for this, no extensive acquaintance with their language is necessary, a very obvious advantage in opening communications on so technical a matter.

Apart from collectors, who naturally find pleasure in getting specimens of what they collect, travellers in uncivilized countries, even if uninterested in string figures, will find some knowledge of them a useful equipment. A native is apt to distrust a missionary, a prospector, and a trader ; but a stranger, who exhibits what may well be taken to be one of the innocent games of his own people, offers credentials to which a friendly response is, as far as experience goes, invariably made. Who, indeed, would attribute evil intentions to one who comes armed only with a piece of string, and seems chiefly interested in amusements similar to those familiar to the onlookers in their childhood ? This is not a matter of mere conjecture. I know of more than one definite instance where cordial relations were thus immediately established.

Of course from the beginning of the study of these figures the question arose of their possible relation to historical and religious traditions. Until now, however, with the exception of a few isolated facts, no evidence of such connection has been found. Indeed the only traces of it so far recorded are that in New Zealand the forms are associated with mythical heroes and the invention of the game is attributed to Maui, the first man ; that various designs common to many of the Polynesians are often made to the accompaniment of ancient chants ; that the Eskimo, too, have songs connected with particular patterns, have a prejudice against boys playing the game for fear it should lead to their getting entangled with harpoon lines, and hold that such figures, if made at all should be constructed in the autumn so as to entangle the sun in the string and delay the advent of the long winter night. Further, Boas asserts that among the natives of Vancouver Island the form known as " Threading a Closed Loop " is used instead of a password by members of a certain secret society to recognise fellow-members. These facts, interesting though they be, do not come to much, and it would seem that as yet there is no substantial evidence that the construction of string figures is other than a recreation. I say " as yet," for new discoveries may at any time alter our views on this question.

Now let me put aside these historical questions, and consider the patterns actually made and their making. In opening the subject I remarked that for constructing string figures two methods are commonly applied ; these are known respectively as the *Asiatic* and the *Oceanic*. In the former, two players are required, of whom one at each move takes the string from the other ; in the latter, normally, only one player is required, who weaves the pattern with his fingers, using, if need be, his feet and teeth to assist him.

The Asiatic method lends itself to many varieties, but as far as I am aware these have not been developed, and broadly speaking this method is known to us almost only in the classical form, common in the English nursery, of Cat's Cradle. This form occurs in Korea, Japan, the Asiatic Islands, China, and Northern Europe, and the result is a figure of Class A. The weaving begins by the first player twisting the string round the four fingers of each hand, so as to make two dorsal strings and one palmar string ; next picking up the string lying on the palm of each hand with the back of the mid-finger of the other hand, he draws the hands apart. In England, the four fundamental figures, which can be made in succession, are termed the cradle, a snuffer-tray, cat's-eye, and fish-in-a-dish. These are shown in the diagram given below on page 41; the method of construction is widely known, see below, p. 40 *et seq*, and I need not display it here. Another figure, called a pound of candles, is usually (though unnecessarily) interpolated: a few other designs and an arrangement for a See-Sawing movement can also be

introduced. That is all. In Korea the four fundamental
figures are designated a hearse, a chess-board, a cow's-eye, a
rice-pestle, and the interpolated figure chop-sticks. In other
places other names are given.

I need not describe Cat's Cradle further. As usually
played, it leads only to a fixed sequence of four or five forms ;
there are three or four standard moves, and by using these in
various orders other forms can be obtained. No skill is
required, and probably to-day ethnologists are the only people
of mature age who concern themselves with it. It is believed to
have had its origin in Eastern Asia, and to have been thence
conveyed to Northern Europe, perhaps by tea traders. A map
of the localities in which it is practised shows a band of marks
along the east and north of Asia and the north of Europe
From England, with its unceasing output of emigrants,
missionaries, and venturers, it has probably been carried to
other localities, but I do not think it is common outside the
places I have named.

Oceanic examples of Classes A and B are more interesting
and far more widely spread. They occur among the Eskimo,
and the natives in America (North and South), Oceania, Australasia, Africa, and India, though the last-named country, as we
might expect from its ancient civilization, has not given us
many designs. In this form there is almost invariably only
one player. The figures produced are numerous, and many of
them can be made, and are made, in more than one way. In
this country only one Oceanic construction, known as the
Leashing of Lochiel's Dogs, has been discovered. [The figure
as shown by the Lecturer was made as set out below on
page 33.] This, in some places termed *Crow's Feet*, is the most

widely distributed of string designs as yet catalogued. It may be indigenous in Great Britain, but in a sea-surrounded

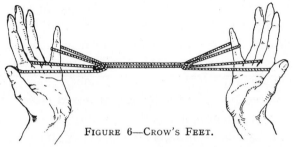

FIGURE 6—CROW'S FEET.

land like this, having ship communication with all parts of the world, it seems more likely that it is an importation.

Recently I came across an instance of how such figures may be introduced here. A friend of mine, then living at an inland town, showed me a well-known figure, sometimes called a *Fishing Net*, sometimes *Quadruple Diamonds*, which has been

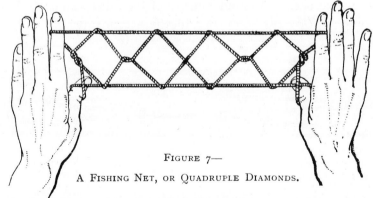

FIGURE 7—
A FISHING NET, OR QUADRUPLE DIAMONDS.

found in Africa, Oceania, and America, but was said to be unknown in Europe. [The figure as shown by the Lecturer was made as set out below on page 36.] This figure he had learnt here in boyhood, and therefore supposed it to be an English production. On enquiry we found that his nurse had taught it to him, and as a result of further talk it seemed that she had got it from a sailor to whom she had been engaged to be married; the conclusion that the latter had learnt it in the course of his voyages seems a safe one. The figure in question is typical of the numerous patterns made of diamond-shaped lozenges strung between two parallel strings, arranged either in single rows (of one or two or more, as the case may be) or in the form of rows side by side as in figure 2, see above, page 5.

A remarkable feature in the Oceanic examples is that a large number of the figures begin in one way. In this the tips of the thumbs and little-fingers of each hand are put together, and then from below into the loop of string ; next the digits are separated, and the hands drawn apart (this is called the *First Position*); and, lastly, the palmar loop on each hand is picked up by the back of the index-finger of the other hand : this is known as *Opening A* or *B*. In the accompanying diagram

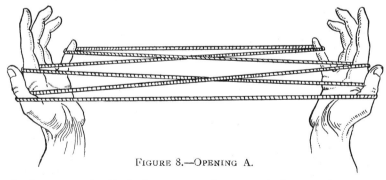

FIGURE 8.—OPENING A.

the loops on the little-fingers are drawn as being on the tips of the fingers: this is done to make the diagram clearer, but in working it is more usual to keep that loop near the base of the little-fingers. The fact that such a normal (and not very obvious) opening exists all over the world suggests either that the game was played by the ancestors of the existing races before they were widely dispersed, or that in the long series of past generations there has been more occasional intercourse between natives of distant localities than was formerly suspected, and of course a single stray voyager, whether travelling on his own initiative or driven from home by some unhappy chance, might serve to carry with him the methods of making such figures traditional among his own folk. Either view implies a long history, perhaps extending over thousands of years.

In *Opening A* the left palmar string is taken up before the right palmar string. If the right palmar string is taken up by the left index finger before the left palmar string is taken up by the right index finger we obtain *Opening B*. In most Oceanic figures it is immaterial whether we begin with Opening A or Opening B.

There is also another movement, known as *Navahoing*, which occurs in the construction of many figures. This is when we have on a finger two loops, one proximal and the other distal, and the proximal loop is pulled over the distal loop, then over the tip of the finger, and then dropped on the palmar side of the hand. This movement is not uncommon. It was first discovered among the Navaho Indians : hence it is called *Navahoing the Loop*.

And now having talked at large about the subject, I want to spend the remaining time in showing you a few of the more interesting of these Oceanic figures. [Some figures illustrative of different openings and actions were then shown, and their histories briefly given.]   I had originally intended to conclude by showing lantern slides of natives displaying various figures; but I can do better, for Mrs. Rishbeth, whose adventurous travels among aboriginees are well known, has kindly consented to come to London to show us various examples, most of which have never before been exhibited in public.   [Mrs. Rishbeth then showed fourteen examples of string figures.]

In selecting these constructions as the subject of this Lecture I have been venturesome, but I plead guilty to liking to wander in the outlying fields of science, and, as I have found pleasure in String Figures and their history, I hoped that others might do the same.

Addendum.

String designs have little interest except to those who know how to make them. Their construction however is not a difficult operation, and to smooth the path of would-be learners I add these notes on figures I made in the Lecture, together with a few other typical ones. When figures are made by different peoples there are often slight differences in the workings, and in such cases I select whichever construction I consider simplest; in my opinion, there is no objection to varying petty details. When once learnt, all string figures are easy, and with the exception of Cat's Cradle, the Ebbing Tide, and the Porker, none of those here described should, when mastered, take more than a few seconds to construct. To any who may find my language ambiguous, I may say that in my directions the words *near, far, above,* and *below,* may, if it be thought clearer, be replaced by the words *radial, ulnar, distal,* and *proximal,* respectively. In the following descriptions, a knowledge of the First Position and of Opening A (see above, page 20), of the Navaho Opening (see page 4), and of the Navahoing Movement (see page 21) is assumed.

The operations are facilitated if the string is smooth, flexible, and not very thin: crochetted doubled silk is almost ideal. I venture to add that generally if, in the weaving, a mistake is made, or a loop accidentally dropped, it is well not to try to correct the error, but to start again from the beginning. Also when two loops are on one digit, it is desirable to keep each clear of the other.

I have selected these examples in nearly equal numbers from the two standard classes, and placed those in each class roughly in order of difficulty ; I advise the novice to mix his diet, and not to learn all those in one class before he begins to make those in the other.

For the benefit of any reader who has mastered the constructions here presented and wishes to go further I have, at the end of each class, mentioned a few additional figures in it, and in my notes on Authorities, have stated where descriptions of them can be found.

CLASS A. Of figures in Class A, I choose the following as being interesting and easy.—a *Fish Spear*, an *Outrigged Canoe*, a *Moth*, a *Frame-work for a Hut*, the *Batoka Gorge*, *Carrying Wood*, a *Tent Flap*, *Crow's Feet*, *Lightning*, *Little Fishes*, the *Veiled Sun*, a *Fishing Net*, a *Butterfly*, the *Laia Fruit*, and *Cat's Cradle*.

1. *A FISH SPEAR* (Class A). This is one of the simplest of String Figures, and its construction requires no skill. It is widely distributed, being found in New Guinea and the adjoining regions, and along the Western side of North America. The result is said to represent a three-pronged spear, the handle being held by the right index and the ends of the three prongs resting on the left hand. In British Columbia the figure is known as *Pitching a Tent*, the six strings from the left hand being taken to represent a frame work of six poles tied together at their tops.

It is made thus :—*First*, Take up the string in the form of the First Position. *Second*, With the back of the right index pick up, from below, the string which lies across the palm of the left hand, give it a couple of twists by rotating the right index, and return. *Third*, Pass the left index through the loop on the right index, then with its back pick up, from below, the string which lies across the palm of the right hand, and return.

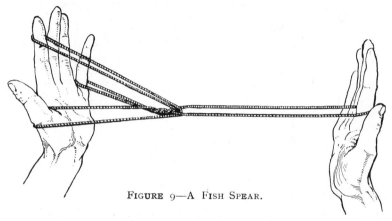

FIGURE 9—A FISH SPEAR.

Lastly, Release the right thumb and little-finger, and extend, that is, draw the hands apart as far as practicable into their normal position.

The working may be summarised thus :—Opening A, except that the right index, after picking up the left palmar string, gives it two twists. Release right thumb and little-finger, and extend.

2. *AN OUTRIGGED CANOE* (Class A). This also is very easy to construct, though it is uninteresting except as an introduction to the subject. It comes to us from New Caledonia.

It is made thus :—*First*, Opening A. *Second*, Bend each thumb away from you over two strings, pick up on its back the far index string, and return. *Third*, Navaho the loops on the thumbs. *Lastly*, Release the little-fingers, and extend. For diagram see over-page.

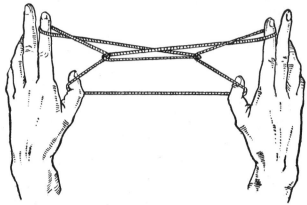

FIGURE 10.—AN OUTRIGGED CANOE.

3. *A MOTH* (Class A). This is interesting as an example of a Zulu construction; it was discovered in 1905. The full length of the string is not needed, and the figure is best presented by using the string doubled. The construction is easy, and follows typical lines.

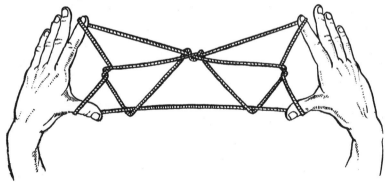

FIGURE 11.—A MOTH.

It is made thus:—*First*, Opening A. *Second*, Release the thumbs. *Third*, Pass each thumb over both strings of the index loop, and with its back pick up, from below, the near little-finger string. *Fourth*, Release the little-fingers. *Fifth*, Pass each thumb over one string, and with its back pick up, from below, the near index string. *Sixth*, Navaho the thumb strings and extend. *Lastly*, Put each index finger downwards into the loop hung on the string running from the far side of the thumb to the near side of the index-finger, thus allowing the existing index loops to slip off ; extend, the fingers pointing downwards. This shows the insect with its wings outspread.

Some of the Zulus describe the resulting figure as a pair of spectacles, and putting it up to the face look through two of the holes.

4   *A FRAME WORK FOR A HUT* (Class A). This figure is supposed to represent eight poles tied together at their tops, forming a frame-work for a tent or hut.   If the design is turned upside down it might well represent a *Parachute*.

In Central Africa, it is constructed thus:—*First*, Holding the left hand horizontal, pointing to the right, and palm downwards place the string on it in the First Position, giving a long loop hanging down in front of the hand. *Second*, With the right thumb and index take up the string lying on the back of the left thumb, pull it over the back of that hand, and let it hang in a short loop on the far side of the hand. *Third*, Pull the short loop through the long one, and loop it over the left index : draw tight, and raise the left hand into its normal position. *Fourth*, With the right thumb and index, pick up the string which is on the near side of the left little-finger, taking hold of it as close to the little-finger as possible, pull it out, and loop it over the left thumb. *Lastly*, With the right thumb and index take hold of that string on the back of the hand which runs across the knuckles, pull it over the left fingers on to the front of the hand, and draw it away from the left hand : this movement can be assisted by working the left hand.

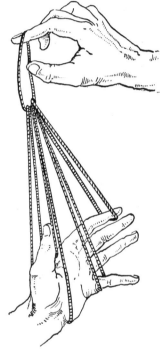

FIGURE 12—A FRAME WORK FOR A HUT.

Among the Red Indians a similar figure called a *Hogan* is made by a different process, thus:—*First*, Put the left index and mid-finger through the loop, a short piece of string resting across the back of the hand and a long loop hanging down in front. *Second*, Put the right index, from the near side, under the near string between the left index and mid-finger, over the cross string at the back of the hand, and with its tip pick up the cross string, and return ; extend, and release the right index. *Third*, Put the right hand from the near side under the near hanging string into the pendant loop, and then with the right thumb and index take hold of the two strings between the left index and mid-finger, return through the pendant loop, and extend; release the right hand. *Fourth*, Bend the left thumb from you, and with its back pick up below the knot the near index string; bend the left little-finger towards you, and with its back pick up below the knot the far mid-finger string. *Lastly*, With the right thumb and index pick up that string on the left palm which goes across and over the two other strings on that palm ; pull with the right hand, and the figure is formed.

5. *THE BATOKA GORGE* (Class A) ; for diagram, see page 15, figure 5. In my Lecture I mentioned and showed this figure, and I have nothing to add to what I there said. It is interesting from the way in which it was discovered, and as being one of the few recorded attempts to represent geographical features by a string pattern. The construction is peculiar to the natives near the Victoria Falls in Africa.

It is made thus :—*First*, Hold the right hand horizontal, pointing away from you and with its palm facing downwards; rest the string on the right wrist so that two equal loops hang freely down, one on its radial side, the other on its ulnar side. *Second*, Pass the left hand from left to right through both loops, and bring both hands into their normal positions. *Third*, Bend each little-finger towards you, and with its back pick up both the strings which cross each other in the centre of the figure. *Fourth,* Throw the near wrist string away from you over both hands to their far side. *Fifth,* Bend each thumb away from you, and with its back pick up the corresponding oblique near little-finger string. *Lastly,* Take each far wrist string and (keeping the other strings unaltered in position) pass it over the hand to the near side of the wrist. Extend the hands, and the figure, representing a bird's-eye view of the zig-zag course of the river through the gorge, will appear.

6. *CARRYING WOOD* (Class A). This is a figure made by Mexican Indians. The construction is simple, and the result pleasing. The result is supposed to show poles lying on a sledge.

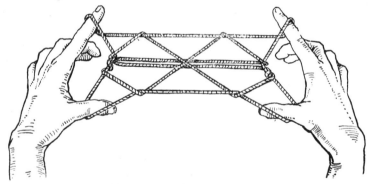

FIGURE 13.—CARRYING WOOD.

It is made thus :—*First,* Opening A. *Second,* Pass the thumb and index-finger of each hand above the index loop, and put them, from below, into the little-finger loop. Release the little-finger, thus transferring the little-finger loop to the thumb and index-finger. *Third,* Navaho the loops on the thumbs and index-fingers, but keep the strings hanging loose. There is now a string hanging in front of the figure and running straight across it. *Lastly*, Put each thumb away from you over this cross string, let the loops on each thumb slip off, and extend with the thumbs pointing away from you and the palms facing outwards.

7. *A TENT FLAP* (Class A); for diagram, see page 5, figure 2. I have in my Lecture mentioned and delineated this figure, and I need not here repeat what is there set out. The design is familiar to most of the Mexican Indians, who attribute its origin to the Apaches, a tribe now almost extinct. The result shows a pretty piece of string network which looks like a *Hurdle*, but is said to have been intended to represent the flap, or perhaps lacing, covering the opening to a tent; it has alternative descriptive names, such as a *Poncho*, a *Sling*, a *Net*, and so on.

There is a touch of romance in the story of its discovery. In September, 1904, Haddon, on his way to England, stopping one night at Philadelphia with H. H. Furness, expressed to Mrs. Jayne, the daughter of his host, his regret that he had no time to go to the St. Louis Exposition, where he understood he might meet some Mexican Indians whose tribal customs had not been investigated, and the talk drifted on to String Figures, a subject of which his fellow guests then knew nothing. The next morning Haddon sailed for Liverpool, and Mrs. Jayne, with characteristic American energy, went to St. Louis, found the Red Indians in question, and from them learnt, among other things, how to make the Tent Flap. That beginning of her interest in the subject, which in its early days owed much to her enterprise.

It is made thus :—*First*, Opening A. *Second*, Lift the loops off the index-fingers, pass them over their corresponding hands on to the wrists, thus making them dorsal strings. *Third*, Bend each thumb away from you over one string, and with its back pick up from below the next string, and return. *Fourth*, Bend each little-finger towards you, and with its back pick up the next string. *Fifth*, Grasp with the left hand all the strings in the centre of the figure where they cross, pass this bunch of strings from the palmar side between the right thumb and index-finger so that the bunch lies along the arm, with the left thumb and index-finger take hold of the two loops on the right thumb, draw them over the tip of the right thumb, let the bunch of strings also slip over the right thumb to the palmar side, and then replace the two loops on the right thumb ; make a similar movement with the other hand. *Lastly*, Lift the wrist loops over the hands, letting them fall on the front or palmar sides of the hands, rub the hands together, separate them, and the figure will appear.

The working may be summarized thus :—Opening A. Index strings over the hands on to the wrists. Each thumb over one and picks up one. Each little-finger picks up one. Thumb loops over groups of strings. Wrist loops over hands. Extend.

8. *CROW'S FEET* (Class A) ; for diagram, see page 19, figure 6. This figure, also, is mentioned and delineated in my Lecture, and I have nothing more to say about it. It is the most generally spread of string patterns at present known, occurring in Africa, Australasia, the Pacific Isles, America, and sporadically elsewhere. It may be native to

Great Britain, where it is called the *Leashing of Lochiel's Dogs,* but it seems more likely that it was introduced here by sailors. It has many alternative names.

It is made thus :—*First,* Opening A. *Second,* Insert the four fingers of each hand from above into the corresponding thumb loops, and throw the near thumb string over the closed thumbs and fingers on to the backs of the hands. *Third,* Transfer each index-finger loop to the corresponding thumb. *Fourth,* Transfer each dorsal loop to one of the free digits of that hand, for choice I prefer the index-finger. *Fifth,* Pass each near little-finger string from below through the corresponding index-finger loop, place it on the far side of the little-finger, and Navaho the far little-finger strings. *Lastly,* Release the thumbs and extend. In the working of this figure in different places there are many small variations.

If the middle strings of the final figure are held by the teeth, the hands placed horizontally with their palms upmost, and the strings stretched, the result closely resembles the figure of *Two Hogans,* as made in Arizona, representing the poles of two small tents side by side.

9. *LIGHTNING* (Class A) : for diagram, see page 3, figure 1. In my Lecture I described and showed this figure, and gave its construction; I need not here repeat this. It was obtained from Red Indians who live on the border of Arizona, where ethnologists have been fortunate in finding natives able to describe old tribal customs and amusements; it has also been found in New Caledonia. It is an excellent example, but the last movement may present difficulty to a beginner.

The working may be summarized thus :—The Navaho

Opening. Each thumb over two and picks up one. Each mid-finger over one and picks up one. Each ring-finger over one, and picks up one. Each little-finger over one, and picks up one. Release thumbs, put them into the spaces by the little-fingers, and rest them on the near little-finger string. Throw the loose hanging strings to the back of the figure, press down the thumbs, and turn the hands to face away from you.

10. *LITTLE FISHES* (Class A). This figure was obtained in the Torres Straits ; the final pattern somewhat resembles Lightning. The first movement in the construction is unusual.

It is made thus :—*First*, Insert the index-fingers, pointing upwards, into the loop of string so that the far index string

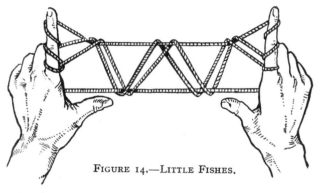

FIGURE 14.—LITTLE FISHES.

is short and straight ; next, take hold of each side of this far index string between the tips of the corresponding thumb and index-finger and form with it a small upright ring, say, by carrying the part of string held by the left hand towards you and to the right over the right hand string ; put the index-fingers away from you into this ring, and separate the hands ;

this is called the *Murray Opening*. *Second*, Bend each thumb over the lower near index string, and with its back pick up, from below, the lower far index string; then bend each thumb over the upper near index string, and with its back pick up, from below, the upper far index string ; next, bend each little-finger over the upper near index string, and with its back pick up, from below, the lower near index string. Extend. *Lastly*, Pass the tip of each index-finger away from you and close to the base of the little-finger into the triangle resting on that finger, and bending the index-finger towards you and then upwards, pick up with its back the upper near index string ; turn the palms from you, thus releasing the thumbs, and extend.

The natives make the figure to a sing-song chant, " Little fishes swim round to Waier Waier in the channel, to Waier Waier in the channel," and so on.

The working may be summarised thus :—Murray Opening. Each thumb over one string of the lower loop, picks up the next, then over one string of the upper loop, and picks up the next.   Each little-finger over one and picks up one.   Each index-finger from above into far triangle, and picks up on its back the upper near index string.   Rotate, release thumbs, and extend.

11. *THE VEILED SUN* or *AN ECLIPSE* (Class A). This is a widely distributed figure known in the Torres Straits as the *Mouth*, and in Queensland as the *Veiled Sun*.   It also occurs in the Andaman Isles, in the Caroline Isles as one stage in a figure known as *Carrying Stone-Money*, and in Central Africa as one stage in a figure known as the *Eclipsed Moon*. In native practice, these continuations involve taking the design completely off the hands, placing it on the knees, and

re-arranging the strings ; in my opinion such constructions are not to be commended.

The Eclipse is made thus :—*First*, Opening A. *Second*, Take the far little-finger string in the mouth, bring it over the other loops, and release the little-fingers. *Third*, Pass each little-finger over both strings of the index loop, and on its back

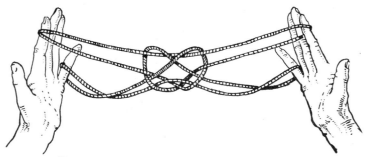

FIGURE 15.—THE VEILED SUN OR AN ECLIPSE.

pick up the far thumb string ; return, and release the thumbs. *Fourth*, Insert each index-finger, from below and close to the mouth into the mouth loop, release the mouth, and extend. *Lastly*, Navaho the index loops. In making this figure the strings should be kept rather loose. The working affords a good example of the way in which the mouth may be used to facilitate a construction.

12. *A FISHING NET* (Class A) ; for diagram, see page 19 figure 7. This figure is mentioned and delineated in my Lecture. It has been found in Africa, Oregon, and the Hawaiian Isles. In some places it is called *Quadruple Diamonds*, in others a *Ladder*, and in others a *Fence*.

It is made thus :—*First*, Opening A. *Second*, Release the thumbs, then bend them away from you under four strings, and with their backs pick up the far little-finger string, and return. *Third*, Bend each thumb away from you over one string, and with its back pick up the next string. *Fourth*, Release the little-fingers, then bend each of them towards you over one string, and with its back pick up the next string. *Fifth*, Release the thumbs, then bend each of them away from you over two strings, and with its back pick up the next string. *Sixth*, Pick up from the base of each index-finger the near index string, and put it over the corresponding thumb, and Navaho the thumb loops. *Seventh*, Put each index-finger from above into the adjacent triangle, whose sides are formed by the radial little-finger string twisting round the two strings of the thumb loop. *Lastly*, Rotate the hands so as to face away from you (thus causing the little-finger loops and the lower index loops to fall off, the thumbs to point away from you, and the index-fingers to point upwards), and separate the hands.

The working may be summarized thus :—Opening A. Release thumbs. Each thumb under all the strings, and picks up the far string. Each thumb over one, and picks up one. Release little-fingers. Each little-finger over one, and picks up one. Release thumbs. Each thumb over two and picks up one. Each near index string on tip of corresponding thumb. Navaho the loops on the thumbs. Index-fingers in triangles. Rotate the hands, releasing little-fingers, and extend.

13. *A BUTTERFLY* (Class A). This, like Lightning, is a Navaho figure ; it was first obtained by Jayne in 1904. It represents the insect with its wings up. The working is more simple than the description suggests.

The figure is made thus :—*First*, Take up the string in the

Navaho way, that is make the first movement as when forming Lightning. *Second,* Twist each index loop by rotating the index-finger down toward you and up again four or five times. *Third,* Bend each thumb away from you over one string, with its back pick up the next string, and Navaho the thumb loops. *Fourth,* Put the tip of the index-finger of one hand against the

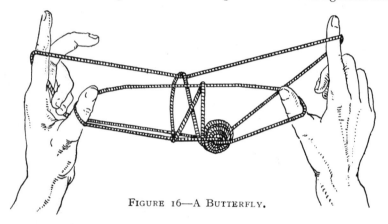

FIGURE 16—A BUTTERFLY.

tip of the index-finger of the other hand and similarly put the tips of the thumbs together ; then slip the right index loop on to the tip of the left index-finger and the right thumb loop on to the tip of the left thumb, thus freeing the right hand. *Fifth,* Put the tips of the right index-finger and thumb against the left thumb between the two strings on that hand, then slip the right index-finger away from you under the loop on the tip of the left thumb, and slip the right thumb towards you under the loop at the base of the left thumb. *Sixth,* With the right thumb and index-finger lift both loops from the left index-finger ; then put the left index-finger away from you into the loop previously on the tip of that finger, and the left thumb towards you into the loop previously at the base of that finger. *Lastly*, Draw the hands apart and when the strings have partially rolled up in the middle of the figure, use the free fingers of each hand to pull down the far index string and the near thumb string. The butterfly will now appear ; its wings being held up by the string extended between the widely separated thumbs and index-fingers.

The working may be summarized thus :—Navaho Opening. Twist index loops. Each thumb over one and picks up one. Navaho the thumb loops. Take up figure afresh with thumbs and index-fingers, and extend.

14. *THE LAIA FRUIT* (Class A). This was found by T. T. Barnard in the New Hebrides in 1923. The result is a pyramid with an hexagonal base; it is an effective design and easy to make, but being in three dimensions does not lend itself well to illustration by a diagram.

It is made thus:—*First*, Opening A. *Second*, Insert the four fingers of each hand from above into the corresponding thumb loops, throw the near thumb string over the closed thumbs and fingers on to the backs of the hands, and put the thumbs into the wrist loop. *Third*, Turn the right thumb down under both the wrist strings, pass it from below into the little finger loop, with its back pick up the far little finger string, and return. *Fourth*, Insert the left thumb, from the near side and from below, into the right thumb loop (close to the thumb), and extend. *Fifth*, Transfer the index loops to the little-fingers. *Sixth*, With each little-finger take up the corresponding far thumb string. *Seventh*, With each index-finger take up from below both the near little finger strings, and release the thumbs. *Lastly*, With the back of each thumb take up from below that near index string which is a continuation of the near wrist string, release the little fingers, and extend.

The same figure though differently placed on the hands can be made by interchanging all the movements from back to front and vice versa: for instance, using the little-fingers instead of the thumbs, substituting far for near, and so on: in this form it is known as the *Laia Flower*.

15. *CAT'S CRADLE* (Class A).   The various forms of this figure are made successively by two persons, P and Q, each of whom in turn takes the string off the hands of the other, and draws his hands apart so as to stretch the string. I have dealt with its history in my Lecture.

In the following description the terms *near* and *far* refer to the player from whom the string is being taken.   In the nursery form of this game there are four standard forms, delineated below.   Normally these are made as follows :—

The weaving begins by P twisting the string round the four fingers of each hand so as to make two dorsal strings and one palmar string, next picking up the string on the palm of each hand with the back of the mid-finger of the other hand, and then drawing the hands apart ; this forms the *Cradle*.   The figure comprises two horizontal strings, over each of which are crossed strings, each cross has four angles, which we may describe, with reference to P, as the right and left, upper and lower.

In the second stage, Q (facing P) inserts, from the side of the figure nearest P, his right thumb in to the left angle of the near cross and his right index-finger into the right angle of this cross ; and from the side of the figure farthest from P, his left

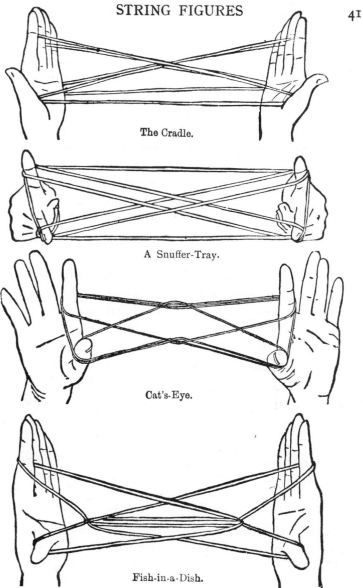

The Cradle.

A Snuffer-Tray.

Cat's-Eye.

Fish-in-a-Dish.

FIGURE 17—CAT'S CRADLE: THE FOUR STANDARD FIGURES.

thumb into the left angle of the far cross, and his left index-finger into the right angle of this cross. Next, Q with the tips of the thumbs and index-fingers, takes hold of each cross pulls it away from the centre of the figure, over and beyond the corresponding horizontal string, and continuing the motion carries the cross round this string ; Q then turns his thumbs and fingers upwards through a right angle, thus passing the cross between the two horizontal strings, which causes the thumbs and index-finger of each hand (still holding the crossed strings) to be brought against the horizontal strings. Lastly, Q having pushed his fingers up, releases the crosses by separating his index-fingers from his thumbs, and drawing his hands apart removes the string from P's hand. This pattern is called a *Snuffer-Tray* ; the diagram on page 41 represents it as seen by P. The figure lies in a horizontal plane, and comprises two two straight strings and four crosses. Of these crosses we are only concerned with those at the sides of the figure, and in each of them the angles may be described, with reference to Q, as right and left, near and far.

In the third stage, P (facing Q) inserts, from below, his left thumb into the left angle of the side cross farthest from Q, and his left index-finger into the right angle of this cross, his right thumb into the left angle of the side cross nearest Q and his right index-finger into the right angle of this cross. Next, P with the tips of his thumbs and index-fingers, takes hold of each cross, pulls it down, separates his hands, thus bringing each cross below its corresponding horizontal string, and continuing the motion carries the cross outside, round, and above this string. P then turns each thumb and finger towards the centre of the figure between the two horizontal strings, through two right angles, taking these strings with them. Lastly P pushes his fingers down, separates the index-fingers from the thumbs, and then drawing his hands apart, removes the figure from Q's hand. The resulting figure is known as *Cat's Eye*; the diagram on page 41 shows it as seen by Q, after the figure has been made. It lies in a horizontal plane with P's fingers pointing downwards and comprises four crosses; of these crosses we are only concerned with those at the sides of the figure, and in each of them the angles may be described with reference to P as right and left, near and far.

In the final stage, Q, inserts, from above, his left thumb into the left angle of the cross farthest P, his left index-finger into the right angle of this cross, and his right thumb into the left angle of the cross nearest P, and his right index-finger into the right angle of this cross. Next, Q turns each hand inwards towards the centre of the figure, through two right angles, and as he does so catches the sides of the centre diamond on the thumb and index-fingers; and the end of this motion the thumbs and fingers will be pointing upwards. Lastly, Q draws his hands apart, and thus takes the figure off P's hands. The diagram on page 41 represents the pattern as seen by Q This forms *Fish-in-a-dish*, the fish being represented by the two parallel lines in the middle of the design, and the dish by the diamond-shaped figure on which they rest.

16. *OTHER FIGURES IN CLASS A*. Numerous other easy and attractive figures in class A will be found in Jayne accompanied by full workings and much historical information ; as good examples I pick out *Double Diamonds*, a simplified form of the Fishing Net described above, the net having two meshes instead of four, found among the Oklahoma Indians

and in Hawaii ; *Two Chiefs* or *Two Caterpillars* side by side, from Uap in the Caroline Isles ; and the *Square*, a modern invention. An instructive group of figures is afforded by *Meshed Networks* ; one form of such a pattern, as made in West Africa, is called a *Face Mark*, and another very similar figure, as made by Red Indians, is known as *Many Stars* ; of these the general design is obtained most simply by the negro method, but the American working may be easily altered so as to give slight variations in the final pattern, thus introducing the operator to the amusement of making new figures. Another good design is *Circles and Triangles*, from the Natiks in the Caroline Isles, in which a series of loops are gracefully intertwined.

Of effective but harder examples, here commended by me with more hesitation, I may mention a *Rabbit*, from Red Indians in Oregon ; a *Sea-Gull* from the Eskimo ; *Two Elks* from the Klamath Indians ; and *Tree Burial*, from Papua.

References for the workings of these additional figures are given below under the heading, " Authorities."

CLASS B. Of figures in class B, I select the following as being easy and interesting :—the *Mosquito* or *Fly*, a *Siberian House*, the *Elusive Loop*, *Fluttering Wings*, the *Yam Thief* or *Uprooting the Alou*, *Throwing a Spear*, a *Man Climbing a Tree*, the *Sleeper*, a *Well*, a *Fence*, a *Salmon-Net*, the *Caterpillar*, the *Ebbing Tide*, and the *Porker*.

17. *THE MOSQUITO OR FLY* (Class B). This is one of the easiest of the β constructions. I worked it in my Lecture in its South American form. Figures resembling it, and somewhat similarly made, have been found in many places, but the variety here given is the simplest of them. The result shows the

insect with its body midway between the hands and its wings spread out.

It is made thus :—*First*, Put the thumbs, held upright, into the loop of string, and extend. *Second*, Move the left hand to face away from you; then turn it counter-clockwise under the strings and up towards you into its normal position, thus giving two dorsal strings, and no palmar string. *Third*, Pass

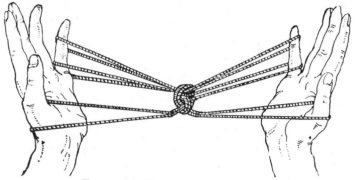

FIGURE 18—THE MOSQUITO OR FLY.

the right hand between you and the left hand, then put the right little-finger from above under the dorsal strings, pick them up, and return. *Fourth*, Put the left little-finger on the right palm, and pass it towards you under the two strings on the right thumb, pick them up, and return. *Lastly*, Lift the dorsal strings on the left hand over the digits, and extend. This is the Mosquito or Fly.

Next its proboscis (or some part of its anatomy) is shown by releasing the little-fingers. To try to catch the insect, clap your hands together: on drawing them apart quickly and as far as possible, it will always be found that it has escaped, in fact the display of the proboscis destroyed the figure.

Ethnologists, more conservative than primitive men, deem it undesirable or worse to vary recorded methods, so with hesitation I add that the Indians might have made the conclusion more effective by not displaying the proboscis and thus not destroying the mosquito as a definite creation; in this case, as before, on trying to squash it, you clap your hands sharply together, then drawing them apart quickly and at the same time releasing the little-fingers, it will have disappeared. Of course with a mosquito or fly between one's hands the most natural thing is to try to squash it, but often, as here represented, without success.

The knot in the figure midway between the hands may also be taken to represent a coco-nut, and Compton reports that in Lifu, in a similar figure, the last movement is used to illustrate efforts to crush the shell. The unskilful person, when clapping his hands and not releasing his little-fingers, fails, for on separating his hands the nut remains visible. But when the skilled native tries, then on clapping his hands and simultaneously releasing his little-fingers, he succeeds, for on separating his hands the nut is broken and gone.

18. *A SIBERIAN HOUSE* (Class B). This was obtained from the Eskimo, who are experts in making string figures.

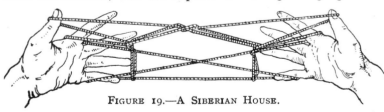

FIGURE 19.—A SIBERIAN HOUSE.

It is made thus :—*First*, Opening A. *Second*, Insert the four fingers of each hand from above into the corresponding thumb loops, and throw the near thumb string over the closed thumbs and fingers on to the backs of the hands. *Third*, Bend each thumb from you over one string, under all the others, and with its back pick up the far string which comes round from the back of the hand. *Lastly*, Pull the dorsal string, which lies on the back of each hand, over the fingers on to the front of that hand, and extend. This is the House.

There are two boys inside the house. If you do not see them, release the index fingers, and draw the hands apart. The house will then break up, and the boys will be seen escaping, one from each side.

19. *THE ELUSIVE LOOP* (Class B). This consists in making a loop, representing (say) a yam, to be offered to a hungry applicant. The operator causes the yam to disappear unless it is seized sufficiently promptly ; hence a contest in rapidity between the operator and the applicant. Alternatively you can display the yam, and when the applicant asks for food make it disappear, remarking that you have none, or if you prefer, none for him. There are figures of this type common in all countries, and any of them will answer the purpose of the game.

A simple construction, common in Great Britain (and best illustrated with a loop of string some two to two-and-a-half feet long) is as follows :—*First*, Put the four fingers of the left hand, held vertically with its palm facing you, into the loop, giving a short straight piece of string across the palm of the hand and a loose loop at its back, and hook, from below, into this dorsal loop the right index-finger. *Second*, Bring the right index-finger vertically over the left hand so as to make that string of the dorsal loop which is next the left index-finger pass between the left index and middle fingers and that string of the loop which is next the left little-finger pass between the left little and ring fingers, thus forming one loop on the left index-finger and another on the left little-finger. *Third*, Move the right index-finger so as to bring the two strings hooked on it (keeping the ulnar above the radial string) between the left index-finger and thumb, and then round the thumb ; next pass the left little-finger, from below, between these strings (the former radial string being ulnar to it), and then carry the right index-finger to the right in front of the left hand. *Fourth*, Turn the right index-finger clockwise through two right angles, thus putting a twist on the loop held by it, and then transfer this loop to the left index-finger, releasing the right index-finger. *Lastly*, with the right thumb and index-finger lift the two loops off the left thumb and put them, from the front, between the left middle and ring fingers. The loop thus placed on the back of the left hand is the Elusive Loop. On pulling the left palmar string this loop will disappear, and the string come free off the hand

20. *FLUTTERING WINGS* (Class B). This comes from Murray Island, where the movements are described as those of a tern.

It is made thus:—*First*, Opening A. *Second*, Put the foot (or a heavy book) over the far string so as to hold it down. *Third*, With the back of each little-finger pick up, from below, the far index-finger string; and Navaho the little-finger loops. *Fourth*, With the back of each thumb pick up, from below, the near index-finger string; and Navaho the thumb loops. *Lastly*, Release the index-fingers.

In the resulting figure the long loop on the foot (or book) is supposed to represent the extended neck and body of the bird, and the index and thumb loops its wings. By rotating the wrists the wings flutter.

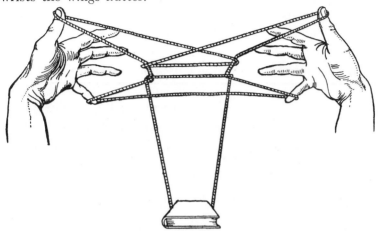

FIGURE 20.—FLUTTERING WINGS.

21. *THE YAM THIEF* (Class B). This is a good illustration of a string story ; one version of it is given in my Lecture, and a drawing of the final arrangement also appears there, see page 7, figure 4. Among some tribes the result is said to represent the flight of a row of birds sitting on a rail and suddenly disturbed; among others it is used to illustrate a story about a cat and a mouse. In Lifu it is called *Uprooting the Alou*; the strings on the hand representing the root; and the palmar string a shoot of that tree. Someone, representing a strong stupid man, takes hold of the shoot, and though he pulls for all he is worth and is encouraged by the shouts of the onlookers, he cannot move the root: then someone else, representing the traditional cunning village clown, takes hold of the shoot and (the thumb loop being released) the root comes up easily, to the ostensible astonishment of the spectators. This

design is widely distributed, and has been found in Africa, America, Oceania, Siberia, and Japan.

The figure is made thus :—*First*, Hold the left hand open with the palm facing you, the thumb upright and the fingers pointing to the right and slightly upwards. With the right hand, loop the string over the left thumb, crossing the strings if you like, and let one string hang down over the palm and the other over the back of the hand—we may call these the palmar and the dorsal strings. *Second*, Pass the right index-finger from below under the palmar string, and then between the left thumb and index-finger, and with its front tip hook up a loop of the dorsal string; pull this loop between the left thumb and index-finger back on to the left palm; then with the right index-finger give the loop one twist clockwise, and put it over the palmar string on to the left index-finger; pull the two pendant strings so as to tighten the loops on the thumb and index-finger. *Third*, In the same way pass the right index-finger from below under the pendant palmar string, and then between the left index and middle fingers, and with its front tip hook up another piece of the pendant dorsal string; pull this loop back on to the left palm, and with the right index-finger give the loop one twist clockwise, and put it over the palmar string on the left mid-finger. *Fourth*, In the same way, working between the middle and ring fingers, hook up another loop of the pendant dorsal string, and put it on the left ring-finger. *Fifth*, In the same way, working between the ring and little-fingers, pick up another loop of the pendant dorsal string, and put it on left little-finger. *Sixth*, Take off the left thumb loop, and hold it between the left thumb and index-finger ; and, for the sake of effect, to show that the loops are still on the fingers, pull the pendant dorsal string. *Lastly,* Pull the pendant palmar string, and the figure will come off the hand.

22. *THROWING A SPEAR* (Class B). This is a rather dull figure, but is easy to construct; it has been found in Queensland, Africa, and the Torres Straits. In some places it is known as a *Canoe.*

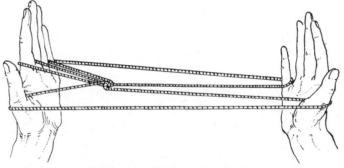

FIGURE 21—THROWING A SPEAR.

It is made thus :—*First,* Opening A. *Second,* Transfer the right index loop to the tip of the left index, and pass the original left index string over this on to the right index. *Lastly,* Release the right index and extend, bringing the right thumb and little-finger close together. We thus get a spear with a heavy handle on the right hand, and three prongs resting on the left hand.

To throw the spear from one hand to the other pass the right index from below under the string just dropped from the right index, up to the left index, and with its back pick up this string. Release the left index, and the spear flies to the other hand. This can be repeated over and over again.

23. *A MAN CLIMBING A TREE* (Class B); for diagram, see page 6, figure 3. This is a figure derived from the Blacks in Queensland, and is one of the most effective examples of class B. It is described and delineated in my Lecture. It is suggested that the two upright strings represent the trunk of a tree and the loops which move up these strings represent the arms and feet (or tree band and feet) of a man climbing up it.

It is made thus :—*First*, Opening A. *Second*, Bend each little-finger towards you over four strings, with its back pick up the next string, and return. *Third*, Navaho the little-finger loops. *Fourth*, Bend each index-finger over the palmar string and between the two strings of the loop on that finger and press its tip on the palm. *Fifth*, Holding the strings loosely, slip the loops off the thumbs; then still keeping the tips of the index-fingers on the palms, separate the hands, thus causing the loops near the bases of those fingers to slip over the knuckles and so off the fingers. *Lastly*, Put the far little finger string under one foot, or under a heavy book, release the little-fingers, and pull gently with the index-fingers, after hooking their tips into the string they hold. This makes the "man" climb up the "tree."

24. *THE SLEEPER* (Class B). This is a Torres Straits figure, in my opinion dull in itself and not suggestive of the supposed object, but experience shows, pleasing to some people.

It is made thus :—*First*, Opening A. *Second*, Pass each thumb from you over the far thumb string and under both strings of the index loop ; pick up on its back the near little-finger string, and return the thumb under the index loop.

Third, Pass each little-finger towards you over the far index string, under the near index string, pick up on its back the far thumb string (not the palmar string), and return the little-

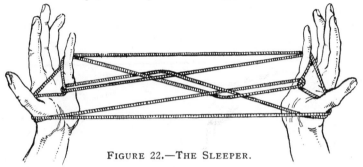

FIGURE 22.—THE SLEEPER.

finger under the near index string. *Lastly,* Release the index-fingers, and extend.

This gives a figure supposed to represent a bed or hammock with a man lying on it. Having reached this stage the natives sing " Man on a bed, man on a bed, lies asleep, lies asleep, bed breaks," and on the word " breaks " they release the little-fingers with unpleasant results to the suppositious sleeper.

25. *A WELL* (Class B). This figure has been found in Lifu, Murray Isle, and Mabuiag It is also known as a *Canoe* and as a *Nest*.

It is made thus :—*First,* Opening A. *Second,* Insert each index-finger from above, into the little-finger loop ; bend the finger down over the far index and near little-finger strings ; then, hooking these strings on it, pass it between the far thumb and near index strings, and let the index loops slip off. Release the little-fingers. *Third,* Insert each little-finger, from above, into the index loops, and with it pull down the two far index strings, bringing the hands into their normal position.

Fourth, Give a twist to each thumb loop by taking hold of the far thumb string, pulling the loop off the thumb, and then replacing the loop on the thumb with this string on the near side of the thumb. *Lastly*, With the back of each thumb pick up the lower part of the string passing obliquely from the near

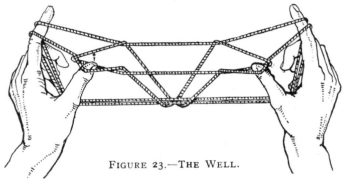

FIGURE 23.—THE WELL.

side of the index-finger to the two bottom strings, and pull it through the thumb loop, thus allowing that loop to slip off.

The inverted pyramid in the centre of the figure represents the Well. The Well can be filled by slacking the little-fingers, and pulling the thumb and index strings ; this movement raises the bottom of the Well.

The working may be summarized thus :—Opening A. Each index hooks far index and little-finger strings, and carries them between the thumb and index strings. Little-fingers pull down the far index strings. Twist to thumb loops. Each thumb picks up the oblique string, and pulls it through the thumb loop.

26. *A FENCE* (Class B). In the Loyalty Isles the natives continue the construction to make a figure known as a Fence Round the Well. This is really a figure in class A, but since

it is a continuation of one in class B it is, perhaps somewhat illogically, treated as being in the latter class.

It is made thus :—*First*, Make the Well. *Second*, Bend each thumb away from you close to the index-finger under the two near index strings, and with its back pick up these two strings. *Third*, Navaho the lowest string on each thumb, that

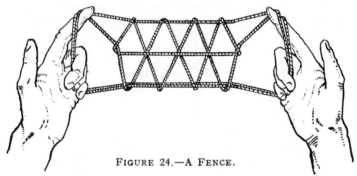

FIGURE 24.—A FENCE.

is, lift it over the two strings on the tip of the thumb, and drop it on the palmar side of the hand. *Fourth*, Release gently the little and index-fingers, thus allowing the figure to hang loosely on the thumbs. *Lastly*, Put the four fingers of each hand towards you into the thumb loops close to the thumbs ; press the middle, ring, and little fingers on the palm ; release the thumbs, raise the index-fingers, and extend.

The working may be summarized thus :—Make the Well. Each thumb picks up the two near index strings, and returns through the thumb loops. Release all fingers. All fingers of each hand through the thumb loops ; release thumbs ; raise the index fingers.

A similar figure made by the Yöruba negroes in West Africa is taken to show a corpse (represented by the straight

cross string) being taken in a canoe or sledge (represented by
the network) for burial.

27. *A SALMON NET* (Class B). A *Salmon Net,* or *Triple
Diamonds,* or *Caroline Diamonds* is a net-work of three meshes
placed side by side ; it may be of negro origin, but comes to
us from the Natiks in the Caroline Isles.

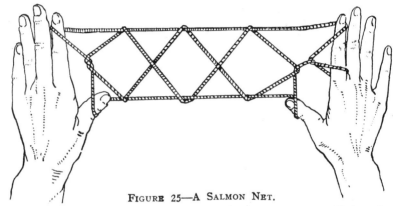

FIGURE 25—A SALMON NET.

It is made thus :—*First,* Opening A. *Second,* Take the
right hand out of the string, and put the tips of the right
thumb and little-finger together from the right side into the
left index loop, extend, and release the left index. *Third,*
With the back of the right index-finger pick up the string on the
palm of the left hand. *Fourth,* Bend each thumb from you
over one string, and with its back pick up the next string,
keeping it on the tip of the thumb. *Fifth,* Bend each index-
finger towards you, and with the extreme tip of its back pick up
the next string. *Sixth,* Navaho the thumb loops. *Lastly,*
Release the little-fingers, rotating the hands so as to face
away from you, and extend ; beginners sometimes find this
last movement difficult.

At the end, an onlooker puts his hand, representing a salmon, in the middle mesh. It escapes if the left hand is released and the right hand moved away, but is caught if the right hand is released and the left hand moved away.

28. *THE CATERPILLAR* (Class B). This design is known in North Australia, and various places in Southern Oceania; it is described by Jayne under the name *One Chief*.

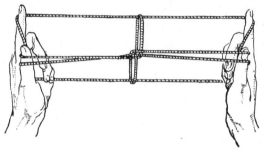

FIGURE 26—THE CATERPILLAR.

The result shows the outline of what may be taken to be a caterpillar, which can be made to loop itself up, and so crawl forwards.

The Caterpillar is made thus:—*First*, Take up the string in the form of the First Position (see p. 20), and then put a loop round the left thumb. *Second*, With the back of the right index pick up the left thumb loop; pass the left index through the right index loop and, with its back, pick up the right palmar string; pass the right index through the left index loop, and with its back, pick up the left palmar string. *Third*, Release the left hand; hold the right hand horizontal and palm downwards, and put the loop which is nearer the tip of the right index over the loop which is nearer the base of that finger. *Fourth*, Put the left little-finger and thumb towards you between the two loops on the right index and resting on the joint of the finger ; and, with the back of the left little-finger, pick up the adjacent loop now nearer the base of the right index, and with the back of the left thumb, pick up the adjacent loop now nearer the tip of the right index ; extend, thus pulling both loops off the right index. *Fifth*, Transfer each thumb loop to the corresponding index-finger, and then transfer it back again by putting the thumb from outside into the loop. (The effect of this is to turn the thumb loops over.) *Sixth*, Bend each thumb from you over one string, and, with its back, pick up the next string. *Seventh*, Put each index-finger over the palmar string under the far thumb string, and, with its back, pick up on the far tip of the finger the latter string, hold it against the index-finger by the mid-finger, erect the index fingers, thus bringing the string connecting their tips to the top of the figure, and rotate the wrists away from you. *Lastly*. Keeping the thumbs and index-fingers close together, bend down the little and ring fingers, and, with their tips, catch and stretch the far string, thus making sure that it is brought to the bottom of the figure. Extend flat on the knee, and the caterpillar appears.

If the wrists are now turned so as to move the palms of the hands upwards, the caterpillar will contract. Then turn them back to their former position, and he elongates. Repeat the action, and he walks down the leg.

29. *THE EBBING TIDE* (Class B). This was obtained from Lifu where it is known as *Sardines*. It has also been found in Queensland under the name *Shrimps*, in Papua under the name of the *Coral Reef*, and in Mebu where it is used to illustrate the passing of men along a road. It and the next

figure are not difficult, but take somewhat longer to make than those I have previously described : that is a defect. They are, however, so excellent of their kind that I put them among my selected examples, and commend them to my readers.

The construction involves an initial movement followed by the Lifu movement, each comprising four steps.

Initial Movement : (i.) Navaho Opening, as in Lightning. (ii.) Pass each little-finger over one string and with its back pick up, from below, the near index string; release the index-fingers. (iii.) Bend each thumb over one string, and with its back pick up, from below, the near little-finger string. (iv.) With the back of the tip of each index-finger pick up, from below, the far thumb string, with the thumb press the part of this string now on the near side of the index-finger against it, and turn the palms away from you. This step is known as the "Caroline Extension." At the end of this movement we get two widely separated parallel strings, one at the top and the other at the bottom of the figure, and in front of them across the middle of the figure two strings close together. The figure represents high tide.

The Lifu Movement : (i.) Release the thumbs ; pass each thumb under the index and little-finger loops, and, then from below, into the index loop. (ii.) Rotate each thumb away from you downwards, and then up, thus picking up on its back the far index string, and putting a twist on each thumb loop; release the index-fingers. (iii.) With the back of each thumb pick up, from below, the near little-finger string. (iv.) Make the Caroline Extension. At the end of this movement, we get two diamonds representing two rocks which appear as the tide ebbs.

Repeating the Lifu Movement we get four rocks, and every further repetition of it shows two more rocks. In Mebu, the successive results are said to represent an empty path, two men walking along it, then four men, and so on. In Kiwi, the same story is told about women.

The Flowing Tide. In my Lecture a continuation of the figure was shown by Mrs. Rishbeth, by which it was transformed, so that each further repetition of the Lifu Movement caused two rocks to disappear, and finally there was again high tide. To effect this we interpolate at the end of one of the Lifu Movements the following *Reversing Movement*, with the object of turning the whole figure counter-clockwise through two right angles. (i.) Release the index-fingers and extend, spreading out the fingers. (ii.) Take the two near left thumb strings in the mouth (or preferably, if wearing the usual garments of civilized man, hang these strings on the top button of the jacket or waistcoat), and release the left hand. (iii.) Put the left thumb and little-finger, tip to tip, against those of the right hand, and slip the loops from the right hand on to the corresponding digits of the left hand. (iv.) With the left thumb and index-finger, take hold from the right of the two strings on the right side of the button and close to it, and lift them off the button, allowing them to hang vertically as parts of two loops: then, turning these strings round counter-clockwise through two right angles, put the right little-finger away from you into the pendant loop originally on the left little-finger, and the right thumb away from you into both these pendant loops; release the two strings held by the left hand and taken off the button; bring the hands into their normal position, and extend. This fourth step requires care ; if correctly performed, the same string is now ulnar to (i.e. the far string of) both the little-fingers, and the figure is symmetrically placed on the two hands, there being two radial strings on each thumb. (v.) Make the Caroline Extension, and you get a figure resembling that from which you started at the beginning of the Reversing Movement. Every successive Lifu Movement will now cause two rocks to disappear, until finally we come again to high tide.

This is an excellent example of a String Figure ; the working showing successively high tide, the gradual ebb, dead low water, and then the reverse flow, until we again get high tide. If you then continue to make the Lifu Movement the tide will again ebb.

30. *THE PORKER* (Class B). This figure was obtained from Lifu by R. H. Compton; it is also known in Uvea. The result is particularly effective.

It is made thus :—*First*, Make Little Fishes (see page 34), giving a W-shaped pattern. *Second*, With the back of each thumb take up the corresponding outer arm of the W ; release from each index-finger the three loops on it, and extend. *Third*, Pass each index-finger, from below, into the corresponding thumb loop, and on its back take up the far thumb string, letting its continuation slip off the thumb. *Fourth*, Pass the thumbs under the index loops (thus releasing the thumb loops), over the far little-finger string, then with its back pick up the latter string and return below the whole figure. You now have a loop on each thumb, index, and little finger, the near string of each thumb loop passing below the far string of that loop, crossing the palm below the index loop, passing below the near string of the little-finger loop, and becoming the far

string of the little-finger loop. The resulting figure is said to
represent the outline of a long low island near Lifu, having
three headlands at each end.

Fifth, We have next to put the thumb and little-finger
loops on each hand above the strings· of the index loop. To
effect this, we pass the right thumb and index-finger, from
above, through the left index loop ; lift the left thumb loop
off that digit, bring it up through the left index loop, and replace it unaltered on the left thumb ; do the same with the left
little-finger loop. Make corresponding movements with the
other hand. *Sixth*, Take each index loop, and put it over the
whole hand on to the back of the wrist. [Thus placed, these
strings serve to make the legs of the porker.] With the right
thumb and index-finger, take hold of the far left thumb and
near left little-finger strings, and remove the left hand. With
the left thumb and index-finger take hold of these two strings
where they are held by the right thumb and index-finger,
releasing them from the right hand. With the left thumb and
index-finger take hold also of the two corresponding right-hand
strings, and remove the right hand. The left thumb and index-
finger now grasp four loops, namely, the two original thumb
loops and the two original little-finger loops.

Seventh, Pass the right thumb and little-finger towards the
left hand and between the two original thumb loops, and
separating these digits take up on their backs these two loops.
With the right thumb and index-finger take hold of the two
other loops held by the left thumb and index-finger, and
release the left hand. Pass the left thumb and little-finger
between the two original little-finger loops, and separating these
digits take up on their backs these two loops. Extend. *Lastly*,

With the tips of the index and middle fingers of the right hand hold and slightly raise the two middle strings going to that hand ; release the right thumb and little-finger ; then pass the middle, ring, and little-fingers of the right hand below and round the two strings going to the right hand, and let the index-finger follow them. These two strings are now hooked on and held by the four fingers of the right hand. You now have a quadruped as represented in the diagram on the cover

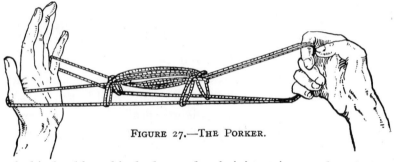

FIGURE 27.—THE PORKER.

of this booklet ; his body made of eight strings and each leg of two strings. By gently pulling the two upper strings on the right hand the porker walks towards the right, by pulling the two lower strings, he walks to the left. During his progress you can address him in whatever terms you deem suitable. The final figure is slightly improved if, at the end of the last movement, we raise, with the tip of the mid-finger of the left hand, the two middle strings going to that hand, and hold them in place by pressing the index finger against them   This step, however, is not essential to the working, and is not given by Compton.

31. *OTHER FIGURES IN CLASS B.* Other excellent examples in class B are the following:—*Two Lads,* from New

Caledonia; in this the two lads run out of shelter, and then when frightened run back again, and continue such advances and retreats as often as is wished. *Two Eyes*, if I may give them that name, from the Yörúba Negroes in West Africa; in this the eyes alternately open and close. *Two Boys Fighting for an Arrow*, from Red Indians in Oregon: in this two loops representing the boys are held by the index-fingers; if a twig be put into the middle of the completed figure, the index-fingers released, and the figure extended, the loops move forward and catch the twig. *A Sea Snake*, from Murray Isle, in which the snake appears twisted round two parallel strings, and on slowly separating the hands he swims as the string unwinds. The *Setting Sun*, also from Murray Isle, in which the rayed sun slowly sinks below the horizon   And lastly, *Tallow Dips*, an indigenous British figure, dealing with the misadventures of a thief who stole a bunch of candle-dips, was arrested, and finally hanged

More difficult, and in my opinion not well suited to beginners, are the following :—*The Fighting Lions*, from Bulawayo in East Africa, in which two loops representing lions alternately approach each other and then draw back, while the natives chant something representing the roaring of the lions. The *Head Hunters*, which, like so many of these designs, comes from Murray Isle. The construction leads to two twisted loops representing two warriors. On extending the hands the two men meet in the middle, and, on working the hands carefully, one loop breaks up, leaving only a kink representing the head of the defeated warrior. On continuing the extension, the victorious loop travels forward pushing in front of it the head of the victim.   By making a knot in the string come into one of the twists we can make sure that that warrior shall be successful ; and this knowledge may be useful, since usually, before the game begins, the tribes from which the warriors come are mentioned—slimness in such matters is not confined to white men. An *Alaskan River,* from British Columbia: this shows the course of a river, the appearance of a mosquito, and then a man fishing from a boat.

References for the workings of these additional figures are given under the heading, "Authorities."

Authorities.

The following notes give references to the sources from which the figures above described are taken. The excellent works by Jayne and Haddon, namely, "String Figures," by C. F. Jayne, pp. xxiv. + 408, New York, 1906, and "Cat's Cradles from Many Lands," by K. Haddon, pp. xvi. + 96, London, 1911, mentioned in my Lecture, are more accessible than the articles in which the discoveries of these figures were first announced, and accordingly, when practicable, I refer, by choice, to these books (in which the sources of information are quoted) rather than to the original memoirs. Comparing the two authors, Jayne, like the present writer, uses, as far as may be, ordinary language, while Haddon is more concise, and following modern ethnologists, freely employs technical terms ; Jayne usually gives a diagram showing the positions of the hands and string after each step, while Haddon generally gives only the final arrangement of the string, not showing the hands.

1. *A Fish Spear* : see Jayne, p. 32, and Haddon, p. 7.

2. *An Outrigged Canoe* : see R. H. Compton, Journal of the Royal Anthropological Institute, vol. 49, p. 210, a paper excellent in form, and instructive alike to the novice and the expert.

3. *A Moth* : see Journal of the Royal Anthropological Institute, vol. xxxvi, p. 149.

4. *A Frame-Work for a Hut* : for this, as made in Central Africa, see W. A. Cunnington, Journal of the Royal Anthropological Institute, vol. xxxvi, p. 124, and Haddon, p. 29 ; and as made by the Red Indians, see Jayne, p. 243, and Haddon, p. 47.

5. *The Batoka Gorge* : see Haddon, p. 40.

6. *Carrying Wood* : see Jayne, p. 66, and Haddon, p. 46.

7. *A Tent Flap* : see Jayne, p. 12.

8. *Crow's Feet* : see Jayne, p. 116, and Haddon, p. 73.

9. *Lightning* : see Jayne, p. 216, Haddon, p. 51, and Compton, *loc. cit.* p. 232.

10. *Little Fishes* : see Jayne, p. 233, and Haddon, p. 12.

11. *The Veiled Sun* : see Jayne, p. 160, and Haddon, p. 32

12. *A Fishing Net* : see Jayne, p. 24, and Haddon, p. 36. For a Net with two meshes see Double Diamonds, Jayne, p. 28, and for alternative constructions, Jayne, pp. 129, 228, 323. One mesh of a net can be made as shown in Jayne, pp. 64, 65, 391, 392. A way of making three meshes in line is given in my Salmon Net. In the Ebbing Tide we get successively 2, 4, 6, 8 meshes in line.

13. *A Butterfly* : see Jayne, p. 219.

14. *The Laia Fruit* : this was given to me by the discoverer.

15. *Cat's Cradle* : see my Mathematical Recreations, ninth edition, pp. 350-356, and Jayne, pp. 324-336.

16. Concerning other Figures in Class A mentioned above, for the history and working of *Double Diamonds*, see Jayne, p. 28 ; of *Two Chiefs*, see Jayne, p. 188 ; of a *Square*, see Jayne, p. 392 ; of a *Face-Mark*, see Haddon, p. 37 ; of *Many Stars*, see Jayne, p. 48, and Haddon, p. 50 ; and of *Circles and Triangles*, see Jayne, p. 146. For those of a *Rabbit*, see Jayne, p. 79 ; of a *Sea Gull*, see Haddon, p. 57 ; of *Two Elks*, see Jayne, p. 74 ; and of *Tree Burial*, see Rishbeth, Appendix to my Lecture as printed in the Proceedings of the Royal Institution, p. 98.

17. *The Mosquito* : this is a common pattern, for the working given above see F. E. Lutz, Anthropological Papers, Amer. Mus. of Nat. Hist., vol. xii., New York, 1912.

18. *A Siberian House* : see Haddon, p. 53.

19. *The Elusive Loop* : the construction given in the text has been common in England for more than half-a-century. A different design is given by Jayne, p. 352.

20. *Fluttering Wings* : see Haddon, p. 10.

21. *The Yam Thief* : this construction is widely known, see Man, 1902, pp. 141, 153 ; Jayne, p. 340, Haddon, p. 80, and Compton, *loc. cit.* p. 233.

22. *Throwing a Spear* : see Jayne, p. 131, and Haddon, p. 8.

23. *A Man Climbing a Tree* : see Haddon, p. 69.

24. *The Sleeper* : see Jayne, p. 192, and Haddon, p. 11.

25. *A Well* : see Jayne, p. 85, and Haddon, p. 17.

26. *A Fence* : see Jayne, p. 88, and Haddon, p. 19.

27. *A Salmon Net* : see Jayne, p. 142.

28. *The Caterpillar* : see Jayne, p. 253, and Compton, *loc. cit.* p. 228.

29. *The Ebbing Tide* : see Compton, *loc. cit.* p. 224, and for the Reversing Movement, Rishbeth in the Appendix to my Lecture, *loc cit.* pp. 101—2.

30. *The Porker* : see Compton, *loc. cit.* p. 229.

31. Concerning other Figures in Class B mentioned above, for the history and working of *Two Lads*: see Compton, *loc. cit.* p. 207 of *Two Eyes*, see Journal of the Royal Anthropological Institute, vol. xxxvi., p. 135, No. 7; of *Two Boys Fighting for an Arrow*, see Jayne, p. 317 ; of a *Sea Snake*, see Jayne, p. 34, and Haddon, p. 16 ; of the *Setting Sun*, see Jayne, p. 21, and Haddon, p. 24 ; and of *Tallow Dips*, see Jayne, p. 248, and Haddon, p. 74. For those of the *Fighting Lions*, see Journal of the Royal Anthropological Institute, vol. xxxvi., p. 146, and Haddon, p. 41 ; of the *Head Hunters*, see Jayne, p. 16, and Haddon, p. 22, and of an *Alaskan River*, see the Appendix to my Lecture, *loc. cit.* pp. 102—3.

32. I have not dealt in this paper with examples in Class Γ. Here, however, are ten examples with references, for any reader who may like to try them ; the *Lizard Twist*, see Jayne, p. 337, or Haddon, p. 80 ; the *Chippewa Release*, see Jayne, p. 346, or Haddon, p. 87 ; *Cheating the Halter*, see Jayne, p. 339, Haddon, p. 86, or R. H. Compton, *loc cit.* p. 234; the *Threading of a Closed Loop*, see Jayne, p. 354, or Haddon, p. 89 ; the *Fly on the Nose*, see Jayne, p. 348, or Haddon, p. 83; the *Joining the Ends of a Cut String*, see almost any book on easy conjuring or parlour tricks, for instance, Hoffmann's Modern Magic, p. 317 ; the *Interlaced Handcuffs or Fetters*, see Hoffmann's Puzzles, p. 349 ; the *Button Hole Trick* (otherwise worked with a key or ring threaded on a closed loop), see Tom Tit's Scientific Amusements, London, 1919, p. 404 ; the *Knife in the Tree*, Ibid, 399 ; and the *Reversed Twist*, Ibid, p. 400.

Index and Glossary.

The Index includes a Glossary of the terms in common use.

METHODS AND THEORIES

FOR THE SOLUTION OF

PROBLEMS OF GEOMETRICAL CONSTRUCTIONS

APPLIED TO 410 PROBLEMS

BY

JULIUS PETERSEN,

PROFESSOR AT THE ROYAL POLYTECHNIC SCHOOL AT COPENHAGEN
AND MEMBER OF THE ROYAL DANISH SOCIETY OF SCIENCE.

TRANSLATED BY

SOPHUS HAAGENSEN, CAND. POLYT. C. E.

(AUTHORIZED ENGLISH EDITION.)

CONTENTS.

PREFACE.

As early as several centuries before Christ geometry had attained a high degree of development. Owing to the slower progress of the algebra, which since has assisted geometry so much, the ancients were almost exclusively confined to the pure geometrical method of solving problems of construction; consequently the solution of these problems played an important part in their works. Although the modern mathematicians have kept up their interest in this branch of their science, the development of the means of treating this class of problems rationally has been comparatively slow. Apollonius f. inst. might as well as Steiner have solved Malfatti's problem had he known of it. Problems of construction have therefore by many been looked upon as a kind of riddles, which only a few, gifted with a special talent, could attempt to solve. The consequence has been that problems of construction have hardly gained any foothold in the schools, where they naturally ought to be cultivated; for no other problems serve as well to sharpen the faculty of observation and combination, and to make the thought clear and logical; no other kind of problems will prove as attractive to the student as those.

The present work is an attempt to teach the student how to attack a problem of construction.

Having solved a large number of examples, partly original and partly selected from the many existing collections,

I have tried to analyze the train of ideas, which led to the solution of each, and to classify these into general rules. If therefore my solutions differ from those of other authors and in cases may appear more complicated, it is because I have preferred methodical solutions to those bearing the stamp of pure accident.

Method is my principal object; the key to the solutions has in most cases only been indicated, while the detailed discussion has been left to the reader or the teacher.

Only few figures have been inserted; a figure is best understood and remembered when one has seen it in process of construction. My idea is to have the scholar work through the book and not simply peruse it.

„Methods and Theories" appeared for the first time in the danish language in 1866. It has therefore been thoroughly tried and I venture to say that it has successfully stood the test. There are many proofs of the beneficial influence it has exerted upon the study of geometry not only in Denmark but also in the other scandinavian countries. Encouraged by its success at home, I think I am justified in offering it to the larger circle of students abroad. I hope it will be found useful not only as a help for the instruction in the elementary geometry but also as a preparation for the study of the modern.

Copenhagen 1879.

JULIUS PETERSEN.

INTRODUCTION.

Propositions in Geometry appear in a double form; they either express, that a certain figure, drawn in a certain way, satisfies certain conditions, or they require a figure to be so constructed, that certain given conditions are satisfied. The first form is *the theorem* the second *the problem of construction.*

In solving problems of construction certain tools are used, viz: a straight edge, by which a straight line may be drawn through two points, and a pair of compasses by which a circle may be described from a given centre with a given radius. Any solution of a problem will therefore be a combination of these two operations.

Being thus restricted, it follows that many problems apparently simple can not be solved (f. inst. the trisecting of an angle, squaring of a circle etc.); in general it can be proved to be the case, where problems lead to equations, which can not be reduced to equations of the first or second degree.

A problem is more than determinate when more conditions than necessary for the solution are given; determinate when there is a finite, indeterminate when there is an infinite number of solutions.

In solving the determinate problem there must be stated:

The mode of proceeding,

The proof of its correctness and

The discussion, i. e. stating the limits of the given quantities in order to have 0, 1, 2 etc. solutions.

Among the indeterminate problems those are of special interest, where one additional condition will render the problem determinate. Although such a problem has an infinite number of solutions, any chance figure will not satisfy it; but all the solutions will group themselves in a way, depending upon the given conditions. Thus a point is determined by satisfying two conditions; if only one be given, it is indeterminate; but all points satisfying this one will fall in either a straight or a curved line; this is called *the locus* of the points satisfying this condition. Similarly with a figure, to the determination of which only one condition is wanting; any point of the figure will ordinarily have its locus.

In the Analytical Geometry we have a general method for the solutions of geometrical problems. It is however evident, that if one method has to be applied to problems of great diversity, one is often forced to use it in a roundabout way. Thus in the Analytical Geometry any point is determined by its position in reference to a pair of axes, which generally have nothing to do with the problem considered; besides, the geometrical sense of the equations is not always easily understood, and the equations are often so complicated, that their solution is practically impossible.

These difficulties in applying directly Descartes Geometry have led to the formation of special methods (divers coordinatesystems etc.) by means of which the solution of the single problem has been rendered more natural and elegant; but the difficulty is removed to the choice of the right method. By these methods a transition has been effected from the algebraic method to the pure geometrical, by which we try to obtain the solution of the problem through a geometrical investigation of the relations existing between the given elements of the figure and those to be found.

To simplify the investigation of these relations, the first measure will be to *draw a figure* representing the solved problem; the next will be to examine this figure by the aid of known geometrical theorems.

If it now appears that everything depends upon the deter mination of an unknown point (which is the case in a great many simple problems) the method to be applied follows immediately from the preceding, viz:

The two conditions, which the point must satisfy, are considered separately; to each of them will correspond a certain locus, and if this is a straight line or a circle the problem is solved; for as the point is situated in both loci, it must be their point of intersection.

If the loci are two straight lines, the problem has only one solution, and is only impossible in case the lines are parallel. Are the loci two circles or one circle and a straight line, the problem will have two solutions if they intersect, one if they touch and none if they have no points in common. There is a qualitative difference between the impossible solution in this last case and that of the parallel lines, where the impossibility is only a question of limit.

If the loci are other curves they can not directly be applied to the construction; the problem must then be differently considered. Still it is worth remarking, that a point, determined by a straight line and a conic section, can also be determined by a straight line and a circle; whereas the construction is impossible if the point is determined by two conic sections independent of each other.

The method, which here is applied to the simplest problems, can be extended to the more complicated. The rule is then as follows, viz:

Imagine one of the given conditions for the figure in quest of removed, and seek the loci of the points of the figure thus rendered indeterminate.

It is evidently of the greatest importance to know many loci, as far as they are straight lines or circles. In the first chapter the most important of these are therefore stated with a further development of the above rules.

If loci can not be directly applied, the rule will be as follows, viz:

Of the drawn figure try to form another, in which the relations between the given and sought elements are more convenient; the application of this rule will be discussed in the second chapter.

In the following a triangle is designated ABC; the sides are a, b and c. The altitude is h_a, a being the base; the median to A, or the line from A bisecting a, is m_a. v_A is the length of the line bisecting $\angle A$. R and r are the radii of the circumscribed and the inscribed circles, while r_a, r_b and r_c are the radii of the exscribed circles (r_a of the one touching the prolongations of b and c).

In the quadrilateral $ABCD$ the angular points follow in the order, in which they are mentioned.

$\angle (a, b)$ is the angle between the lines a and b.

FIRST CHAPTER.

L O C I.

A. LOCI OF POINTS.

a. *The locus of the points having a given distance from a given point is a circle, the centre of which is the given point, the given distance being its radius.*

App. 1. The locus of the ends of tangents of equal length to a certain circle is another concentric with the first.

App. 2. The locus of the intersection of tangents to a given circle enclosing a given angle is a circle concentric with the given.

App. 3. The loci of the centres of circles having a given radius and touching a given circle are two circles concentric with the given, and of which the radii are either the sum or the difference of the given radii.

b. *The loci of the points, which have a given distance from a given line, are two lines, parallel to the given line at the given distance.*

App. 1. The locus of the vertices of triangles having the same area and base is a line parallel to this, as the triangles must all have the same altitude.

c. *The locus of points equally distant from two given points, is a line perpendicular to and bisecting the line drawn between the two points.*

d. *The locus of points, equally distant from two given lines, is a system of two lines, forming a right angle and bisecting the angles between the given lines.*

e. *The locus of points, from which lines drawn to the ends of a given line, enclose a given angle, is an arc of a circle, in which the given line is a chord.* The arc is said to *contain* the given angle and the chord is *seen* under (subtends) the given angle from (at) all points of the arc.

If one point of the arc satisfies the given condition, they all must; for all the angles are angles at the circumference standing upon the same arc. As the angle of the segment is equal to the given, the mode of construction is thus determined: Lay down the given angle at one end of the chord; one leg will be a tangent; a perpendicular to this at the point of contact will contain the centre, which must also be in the perpendicular line bisecting the chord.

If the given angle is a right angle, the arc will be a semicircle.

Remark. If it is not known on which side of the given line the sought point is situated, two arcs containing the angle must be constructed, one on each side of the line. The two remaining arcs of the two circles contain the supplement of the given angle.

We may define the angle thus, that the whole circle will be the locus of the vertex. Let the two given points be A and B; we must not then speak of the angle *between* the two lines through A and B, but of the angle *from* the line through A *to* the line through B, meaning the angle described by a rotation of the line through A in a given direction. For every point C of the circumference the angle from AC to BC will then be equal to the angle from the tangent at A to AB.

App. 1. The locus of the middle points of chords through a given point, is a circle; for the angle between lines from the middle point to the given point and to the centre is a right angle.

App. 2. If in a circle triangles ABC with a common base AB are inscribed, and in these triangles circles are again inscribed, the locus for the centres of the latter will be an arc over AB having for its centre the middle point of arc AB; the rest of the circle is the locus of the centres of the circles touching AB and the prolongations of BC and AC. For AB is seen from the sought centres under angles respectively $R + \frac{1}{2}C$ and $R - \frac{1}{2}C$ and AB is seen from the middle point of $\smile AB$ under an angle $2R - C$.

f. *The locus of the points, the distances of which from two given points have a given ratio* $(m:n)$, *is a circle.*

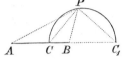

A and B are the given points, P one of the sought. Bisect $\angle APB$ and its adjacent angle by the lines PC and PC_1.

Then

$$\frac{AC}{CB} = \frac{AC_1}{BC_l} = \frac{m}{n}; \quad \angle CPC_1 = R.$$

Points C and C_1 divide the line AB in the given ratio and are the same for every P. As the line CC_1 is seen from P under a right angle, the locus of P must according to **e** be a circle having CC_1 for diameter.

Points C and C_1 are said to divide AB harmonically in the ratio $m:n$, and the problem is therefore reduced to this:

To divide a line harmonically in a given ratio.

This construction is shown in the figure. AD and BE are drawn parallel to each other and having

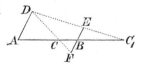

$$\frac{AD}{BE} = \frac{m}{n}.$$

Make $BF = BE$; draw lines DF and DE, which will intersect AB in the points sought.

c is a special case of **f**, namely for $m = n$.

g. *The locus of the points, from which the distances to two given lines have a given ratio* $(m:n)$, *is a system of two straight lines through the intersection of the given.*

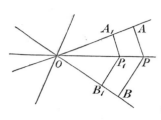

The given lines are OA and OB. If one point, P, has the required properties, all other points in the line OP must have the same; for

$$\frac{OP_1}{OP} = \frac{A_1 P_1}{AP} = \frac{B_1 P_1}{BP}$$

or

$$\frac{A_1 P_1}{B_1 P_1} = \frac{AP}{BP}.$$

Thus the line can be drawn if one point in it be known; this is easily found by **b**, any two distances, having the given ratio, being chosen.

The other line is drawn similarly in the angle adjacent to AOB. The four lines through O are called *harmonical rays*. They will intersect any line in 4 harmonical points.

d is a special case of **g**, m being $= n$.

App. 1. If two straight lines AB and CD are given, and a point P sought, so that $\triangle PAB$ and $\triangle PCD$ have a given ratio, the locus of P is the same as in **g**, the ratio of the altitudes being a constant.

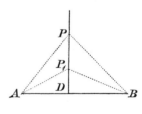

h. *The locus of the points, for which the squares of the distances from two given points have a constant difference a^2, is a straight line perpendicular to the line joining the given points.*

Be A and B the given points, P one of the sought. Every point of the line $PD \perp AB$ must satisfy the problem; take for instance P_1, and

$$\overline{AP_1}^2 = \overline{AD}^2 + \overline{P_1 D}^2; \quad \overline{BP_1}^2 = \overline{BD}^2 + \overline{P_1 D}^2;$$

thence

$$\overline{P_1 B}^2 - \overline{P_1 A}^2 = \overline{BD}^2 - \overline{AD}^2$$

and similarly

$$\overline{PB}^2 - \overline{PA}^2 = \overline{BD}^2 - \overline{AD}^2.$$

If any right-angled triangle be drawn having one cathetus $= a$, and from B and A as centres circles be described with the hypothenuse and the other cathetus as radii, then the sought line will go through the intersections of the two circles. The other cathetus must be made large enough for the circles to intersect. It is here understood that P has its greatest distance from A.

App. 1. The locus of the points, from which tangents of equal length can be drawn to two circles is a straight line perpendicular to the centerline, and is called *the radical axis* of the circles; by drawing a figure it is easily seen, that the points must have distances from the centres, the difference of the squares of which is equal to the difference of the squares of the radii. If the circles intersect, the radical axis will pass through their intersections. The three radical axes of three circles pass through the same point, *the radical centre*. The radical axis of two circles, which do not intersect, is thus easily determined by drawing any third circle intersecting both of the former.

App. 2. The locus of the centres of circles, which intersect two given circles in points diametrically opposite, is a line perpendicular to the centerline and having the same distance from one centre as the radical axis has from the other.

App. 3. The locus of the centres of circles, intersecting two given circles orthogonally (so that the tangents to the points of intersection are perpendicular to each other) is the radical axis of the circles.

i. *The locus of the points, for which the squares of the distances to two given points have a contant sum a^2, is a circle having its centre in the middle point of the line joining the given points.*

Let A and B represent the given points, P one of the sought. Draw the median PC and

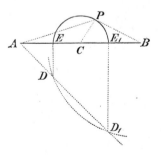

$$\overline{AP}^2 + \overline{BP}^2 = 2\overline{PC}^2 + \tfrac{1}{2}\overline{AB}^2$$

or $\qquad \overline{PC}^2 = \tfrac{1}{2}a^2 - \tfrac{1}{4}\overline{AB}^2.$

The sought points have consequently a constant distance from C. To find the points in the line AB, through which the circle passes, draw

$\angle\ BAD = 45°$. Describe from B a circle with radius a, intersecting line AD in the points D and D_1. Perpendiculars from these points to the line AB will give the sought points E and E_1; for

$$a^2 = \overline{DE}^2 + \overline{EB}^2 \text{ and } a^2 = \overline{D_1 E_1}^2 + \overline{E_1 B}^2$$

but
$$DE = AE \text{ and } D_1 E_1 = AE_1.$$

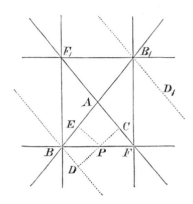

k. *The locus of the points, the distances of which from two given lines have a given sum or difference, is a system of four straight lines.*

The given lines be AB and AC, P one of the sought points, $PC + PE$ being equal to a. Produce CP to D making $PD = PE$, and the locus of D must be two lines parallel to AC and at the distance a there from. Be those BD and D_1B_1.

The sought points are all to be equidistant from AE and one of these lines; consequently they are situated in the four lines bisecting the angles at their intersections. This is also the solution of the problem taking the difference of the distances equal to a; by an examination of the figure it is easily seen, that for the four limited parts BF, FB_1, B_1F_1 and F_1B the sum and for the other unlimited parts the difference of the distances is a.

Remark. If we take CP positiv or negativ according to the situation of P on one or the other side of the given line AF, and likewise we take EP positiv or negativ according to the situation of P in regard to AB, we shall obtain a whole straight line as the locus; having for the four lines respectively:

$$CP + EP = a; \quad CP - EP = a;$$
$$- CP + EP = a; \quad - CP - EP = a.$$

By the aid of these loci the following problems are easily solved; the two conditions, which the sought point must satisfy being considered separately, two loci of the point shall be obtained.

EXAMPLES.

1. To find a point equidistant from three given points (**c**).
2. To find a point equidistant from three given lines (**d**).
3. To construct a triangle, the three sides being given (**a**). To describe a circle with a given radius and
4. passing through two given points, (**a**).
5. passing through one given point and touching a given line (**a** and **b**).
6. passing through a given point and touching a given circle, (**a**).
7. touching two given lines, (**b**).
8. touching a given line and a given circle, (**a** and **b**).
9. touching two given circles. (**a**).
10. To construct a triangle of a, h_a and m_a. (**a** and **b**).
11. To a given circle draw a tangent, which a given line intersects at a given distance from the point of contact. (**a** *App. 1*).
12. To describe a circle passing through a given point and touching a given line or circle in a given point. (**c**).
13. In a given circle to find a point having a given distance from a given line. (**b**).
14. In a given line to find a point equidistant from two given points. (**c**).
15. Describe a circle touching two parallel lines and passing through a given point. (**d** and **a**).
16. To draw a tangent from a given point to a circle (**e**).
17. Construct a triangle of A, a and h_a (**e** and **b**).
18. Construct a triangle of A, a and m_a. (**e** and **a**).
19. Find a point from which two given lines are seen under given angles (Pothenot's Problem). (**e**).
20. To construct an inscribable quadrilateral of one angle, an adjacent side and both diagonals. (**e** and **a**).

21. To find a point, the distances of which from three given lines have given ratios. (**g**).

22. In a triangle to find a point, the distances of which from the three vertices have given ratios. (**f**).

23. Through a given point to draw a line intersecting a given circle so that the distances from the points of intersection to a given line have a given sum.

Determine the middle point of the chord. (**e** *App. 1* and **b**).

24. Find a point, from which tangents to two given circles have given lengths. (**a** *App. 1*).

25. Find a point, from which two given circles are seen under given angles. (**a** *App. 2*).

26. In a given triangle to inscribe an isosceles triangle having a given altitude and having its base parallel to one side of the given triangle. (**b** and **c**).

27. Describe a circle having its centre in a given line and its periphery being at given distances from two given lines. (**k**).

28. Construct a triangle of A, v_A and r. (**d**, **b** and 16).

29. Construct an inscribable quadrilateral of AB, BC, AC and the angles between the diagonals. (3 and 1).

30. To find a point, from which the tangents to 3 given circles are of equal length. (**h** *App. 1*).

31. To construct a triangle of A, a and $b^2 + c^2$. (**e** and **i**).

32. In a given triangle to find a point, from which lines drawn to the three vertices divide the triangle in three equal parts.

Be the triangle ABC, the sought point O. The condition $\triangle AOB = \triangle AOC$ determines the locus of O as a straight line through A. As the median bisects the triangle, the middle point of BC must be one point of the locus, which consequently must be the median itself. The sought point is thus the common point of intersection of the three medians

33. In a given triangle to inscribe another with two given sides and having one vertex in a given point. (**a**).

34. Describe a circle touching three given equal circles and encircling them. (1).

35. Construct a triangle of a, h_b and h_c. (e and a).

36. Find a point having a given distance from the vertex of a given angle, the distances from the legs of the angle having a given ratio. (a and g).

37. Construct a triangle of a, A and $b^2 - c^2$. (e and h).

38. Construct a triangle of a, h_a and $b^2 + c^2$. (b and i).

39. Construct a right-angled triangle; the height on the hypothenuse, two points of the hypothenuse and one in each of the other sides are given. (b and e).

40. Circumscribe an equilateral triangle with a square, having one angular point the same as the triangle.

Find the opposite angular point of the square. (e and c).

41. Construct a triangle of a, A and r. (e $App.$ 2).

42. Divide a given line in two parts having a given line as a mean proportional. (e and b).

43. Given a right-angled triangle; describe a circle touching the hypothenuse, passing through the opposite vertex and having its centre in one of the sides. (d).

44. Given two parallel lines, a point, A, in one of them, and a point O outside. Draw a line through O, intersecting the line through A in X, the other parallel in Y, so that $AX = AY$.

Find the middle point of XY.

45. Find a point, from which three parts of a given line AB, BC and CD, are seen under equal angles. (f).

46. To find a point in a triangle, from which the three sides appear to be equal (are seen under equal angles). (e).

47. To find a point from which three circles appear to be equal.

The distances of the point from the centres must have the same ratios as the radii; the point is therefore found by f.

48. Construct a triangle of a, h_a and $b : c$. (b and f).

49. In a given quadrilateral to find a point, from which the distances to a pair of opposite sides have a given

sum, the distances to the other pair have a givne ratio. (**g** and **k**).

50. In the circumference of a circle to find a point, from which the sum of the distances to two given lines is a minimum. (**k**).

51. Describe a circle intersecting three given circles orthogonally. (**h** *App. 3*).

52. Describe a circle, intersecting three given circles in points diametrically opposite. (**h** *App. 2*).

53. In a given circle to inscribe a right-angled triangle, each cathetus of which contains one of two given points. (**e**).

54. Inscribe a right-angled triangle in a given circle; one of the acute angles and a point of one cathetus is given. (**e**).

55. On a circular billard table, two balls are placed in the same diameter; how must one ball be played in order to hit the other after its recoil from the circumference? (**f**).

In the above examples loci could immediately be applied; a point was either sought directly, or the problem proved to be solved by the determination of such point. Where this is not the case, the following rules are to be applied:

The given elements are introduced in the figure; if thus the sum of two lines are given, it is not enough that these lines are to be found, but the given sum itself must be introduced; generally it is done in such a way, that one end falls in a given point.

The figure is subjected to a careful examination in order to find the lines and angles, which, though not given, can be easily found by means of the given elements.

After this we try to find such part of the figure, which in itself is determined by the given elements, and which, being drawn right off, may serve as a starting point for the determination of the other parts of the figure. If there is a choice between several parts, it is ordinarily best to select the one determining the greatest part of the sought figure.

The principle most generally applied is *to look for triangles* with three given elements.

To introduce the sides of a triangle or the sums or differences of these, the four circles touching the sides are often used. Each side contains two vertices and four points of contact, and the distance between any two of these six points is simply expressed by the sides of the triangle. Especially, s being half the perimeter,

   a) The inscribed circle divides the sides in parts equal to $s-a$, $s-b$ and $s-c$.

   b) The distance from A to the points of b and c, in which these lines touch the circle with radius r_a, is equal to s. The distance from these points of contact to the points of contact of the inscribed circle is a.

   c) The inscribed and the exscribed circle touch a in points, which are equally distant from B and C, the distance between the points of contact being $b-c$ or $c-b$.

EXAMPLES.

56. Construct a quadrilateral $ABCD$ of AB, BC, AC, BD and $\angle D$.

   $\triangle ABC$ may be drawn; next point D is determined. (**a** and **e**).

57. To construct an inscribable quadrilateral $ABCD$ of $\angle A$, $\angle ABD$, AC and BD.

   Draw $\triangle ABD$; thereby the circumscribed circle is determined, and C is now found by **a**.

58. Construct a parallelogram of AB, AC and AD.

59. Construct a triangle of A, h_a and v_A.

   The triangle with the two sides h_a and v_A is drawn first.

60. To construct a triangle of h_a, m_a and R.

   The triangle with the two sides h_a and m_a is drawn, and then the centre of the circumscribed circle is determined by **a** and **c**.

61. Construct a triangle of a, R and h_b.

   Draw the triangle, in which a and h_b are sides; then find the centre of the circumscribed circle by **a**.

62. Construct a triangle of B, a and r.
63. Construct a triangle of a, $b + c$ and h_b.
64. Construct a parallelogram of one side and both diagonals.
65. Construct a triangle of h_a and m_a having also $a = 2b$.
66. Construct a quadrilateral of AC, $\angle CAB$, $\angle ACD$, CD and DB.

   $\triangle ADC$ is drawn, then B is determined.

67. Through a given point to draw a line intersecting two sides of a triangle in points contained in the periphery of a circle, which passes through the ends of the third side.

68. Construct a triangle of a, h_b and m_a.
69. Construct a triangle of h_a, m_a and b.
70. Construct a triangle of h_a, h_b and B.
71. Construct a triangle of h_a, m_a and $a : b$.
72. Construct a triangle of h_a, B and C.
73. Construct a triangle of a, A and $b + c$.

   Introduce $b + c$ in the figure by prolonging AC beyond A to D, making $AD = c$ and draw BD; it is then easily seen, that $\triangle CDB$ can be constructed, $\angle D$ being equal to $\frac{1}{2} A$. A is found by c.

   From the above it is also evident, that if BC be a given chord, and a chord BA is prolonged to D, making $AD = DC$, the locus of D will be a circle having its centre in the middle point of $\frown BC$.

74 Construct a triangle of A, b and $a - c$.

   Prolong c beyond A the distance $a - c$.

75. To divide a given arc in two others, so that the sum of their chords is a maximum.

76. Construct a triangle of A, $b + c$ and $h_b + DC$, D being one end of h_b.

77. Construct a triangle of a, $b + c$ and $B - C$.
78. Construct a triangle of a, A and $b - c$.
79. To circumscribe a given square with another given square. (73).
80. To circumscribe a given regular polygon of n sides with another given regular polygon of n sides.

81. Construct a quadrilateral of AB, BC, BD, $\angle A$ and $\angle B$.
82. Construct a quadrilateral of AB, AC, $\angle A$, $\angle D$ and $\angle C$.
83. Construct an inscribable quadrilateral of R, AC, BD and $AB \pm BC$.

    Draw the circle; then AC; find B (73); then find D.
84. Construct an inscribable quadrilateral of AB, BC, AC and $CD \pm DA$.
85. Construct a quadrilateral of AB, CD, AC, $\angle BAC$ and $\angle ABD$.
86. Construct an inscribable quadrilateral of $AB \pm BC$, DA, BD and $\angle A$.
87. Construct a triangle of a, $b - c$ and $B - C$.

    Draw BD so that $AD = AB$, consequently $DC = b - c$; it is then easily seen, that $\angle DBC = \frac{1}{2}(B - C)$. $\triangle BDC$ is thus determined, and A is then found by **c**.
88. Construct a triangle of c, v_A and $B - C$.

    The triangle in which c and v_A are sides is easily drawn, having $\angle (v_A, a) = 90° - \frac{1}{2}(B - C)$.
89. Construct a trapezium of its diagonals, one of the parallel sides and an angle.
90. Given a line, in which a point A, and outside the line the point, P. Find a point X in the given line, for which $AX + XP$ is equal to a given line m. (AX taken with its sign).

    Apply m to the given line from point A; X is found by **c**.
91. Given two points A and B and a line through B; in this line find two points, X and Y, equidistant from B, XY being seen under a given angle from A.

    Prolong AB to C, making $BC = AB$.
92. Given two parallel lines, in one of them a point A, in the other a point B and between the parallels a point O. Draw a line through O intersecting the parallels in X and Y, so that AX and BY (taken with their signs) have a given sum.

    The line bisects AC, YC being equal to AX.

93. Construct a triangle of a, A and $CD \times b$, D being one end of h_b.

The point, in which h_a intersects a, is easily determined

94. Construct a triangle of B, $c - a$ and the difference of the parts, in which b is divided by h_b.

Apply the given lenghts AD and AE to AB and AC; $\angle AED$ is known. $(BE = BD = BC)$.

95. Given three points A, B, C and a line through A; draw a circle through A and B, which intersects the given line in another point D thus situated, that line CD will be a tangent touching the circle in point D.

$\angle BDC = BAD$, hence easily D.

96. Construct a triangle of R, h_a and $B - C$.

The angle between radius to A and h_a is known.

97. In $\triangle ABC$ draw a line $XY \neq BC$, so that $XY = XB + YC$.

The sought line contains the centre of the inscribed circle.

98. Construct a triangle of $B - C$ and v_A, the ratio $\dfrac{b + c}{a}$ being also known.

99. In a parallelogram $ABCD$ draw a line AX through a point X of CD, so that $AX = AB + XD$.

A point E of AX, for which $AE = AB$, will also be a point of BD.

100. Circumscribe a triangle with a circle; AB is drawn and $\angle A$ is given as well as the point, in which a diameter through C intersects AB.

DB is seen from the centre under a known angle.

101. In a triangle line AD bisects $\angle A$; given AD, $AB - BD$ and $AC - CD$. Construct the triangle.

Lay down BA and CA on BC, so that DA_1 and DA_2 be the given differences. Circle $A A_1 A_2$ is concentric with the inscribed circle and has a known diameter.

102. Construct a quadrilateral having the four points given, in which perpendiculars from the intersection of the diagonals, meet the four sides.

The angle between the perpendiculars to opposite sides is known.

103. In one leg of a right angle two points, A and B, are given. Find a point X in the other leg making $\angle AXB = 2 \angle ABX$.

One of the angle is known.

Find the middle point of XY, Y being a point in XB for which $AX = AY$.

104. Through a given point to draw a line, which, intersecting an angle, cuts off from this a triangle with a given perimeter.

One of the exscribed circles can be drawn.

105. Construct a triangle of A, v_A and $a + b + c$.

106. Construct a triangle of A, r and $a + b + c$.

107. Construct a triangle of A, R and $a + b + c$.

a being known the problem is reduced to 73 or 137.

108. Construct a triangle of r, r_a and v_A.

r and r_a determine h_a.

109. Construct a triangle of r, r_a and $b - c$.

$b - c$ is the distance between two points of contact.

110. Construct a triangle of a, r and $b + c$.

s and a are known and determine two points of contact as well as one vertex.

111. Construct a triangle of a, r and $b - c$.

112. Construct a triangle of h_a, r and $a + b + c$.

a is known.

113. Construct a triangle of a, r_b and r_c.

The distance between the two points of contact is known.

114. Construct a triangle of r_a, r_b and $a + b$.

The distance between the two points of contact is known.

115. Construct a triangle of r_b, r_c and $B - C$.

The angle between BC and the centerline (the line joining the centres) of the two circles is known.

116. Construct a triangle of a, $b + c$ and v_A.

As the centres of the inscribed and the exscribed circle,

and the intersections of their common tangents are situated harmonically, their projections on AB must also be harmonically situated. Of these four points three are known and the fourth is easily found.

A simpler solution of the problem is to draw v_A and to determine B and C, the distances of these points from the ends of v_A having a known ratio $(b + c) : a$.

MULTIPLICATION OF CURVES.

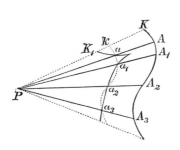

If a line be drawn from a point P to any point A of a given curve K and this line divided by point a so that $Pa : PA = m : n$, then the locus of a will be a curve k, similar to the given.

The two curves are said to be similarly situated. P is called their centre of similitude. Similarly situated points in the curves are those contained in the same line through the centre of similitude; similarly situated lines those connecting similarly situated points. The idea may be extended, considering any point in the plane of the curve as belonging to one system, having its simularly situated point in the other system. If the centre of similitude be considered as belonging to one system, it will coincide with its similarly situated point of the other system. The theory of similarity being treated of in most geometrical schoolbooks, it is only necessary here to mention the following:

To a straight line or a circle corresponds a straight line or a circle.

All similarly situated lines are parallel.

All similarly situated angles are equal.

All similarly situated lines are proportionate in the ratio $m : n$. The figures are therefore said to be similar in this ratio.

If Pa be produced beyond P on PA, the above theorems

are yet true. The systems are then said to be inversely similarly situated.

Any two circles may be considered directly or inversely similarly situated. The two centres of similitude are called the external and the internal centres of similitude.

By the aid of the above may be solved a problem, which is largely applied:

Through a point P to draw a line, intersecting two given curves K and K' in points A and a, so that PA and Pa have a given ratio m : n.

Make the given point, P, centre of similitude and draw a curve k, similar to K in the ratio $m : n$; this curve will intersect K' in the sought point. The number of solutions is equal to the number of points of intersection of K' and k. The problem can always be solved by straight edge and compasses, if the given curves are compounded of straight lines and arcs of circles.

If A and a shall be situated on the same side of the given point ($m : n$ positiv), k is drawn directly similarly situated to K; if on opposite sides, k is drawn inversely similarly situated to K.

To draw a curve similar and similarly situated to a given in the ratio $m : n$, I will call to multiply this in regard to the centre of similitude by $\pm \frac{m}{n}$; + or — as the similar situation is direct or inverse.

To multiply a straight line it is sufficient to multiply one of its points, the direction of the line being unaltered.

To multiply a circle, multiply the centre and radius or the centre and a point of the circumference.

EXAMPLES.

117. Through a given point O to draw a line, intersecting two given lines in distances from O having the ratio $m : n$.

Multiply one of the given lines by $\pm \frac{m}{n}$, O taken as centre of similitude and draw the line to the found point of intersection.

118. Through a point O within a circle to draw a chord, which by the point O is divided in the ratio $m:n$.

Take O as centre of similitude and multiply the circle by $-\dfrac{m}{n}$; the sought lines go through the points, in which the new circle intersects the given. If the given point is outside the circle multiply by $\dfrac{m}{n}$ or by $\dfrac{n}{m}$.

If the ratio between the chord and the portion cut off outside the circle shall be $\dfrac{m}{n}$, multiply by $\dfrac{m}{m+n}$ or by $\dfrac{m+n}{m}$.

119. Through O one of the points of intersection of two circles to draw a line, of which the two circles cut off equal chords.

One circle is multiplied by -1, O being the centre of similitude.

120. In a given quadrilateral to inscribe a parallelogram, the centre of which is a given point.

121. Construct a triangle of a, b and m_c.

Draw $CE = m_c$. From C as centre describe circles having radii a and b; multiply one of these circles by -1, E being the centre of similitude.

If one of the given sides be drawn first, the solution would be to multiply one arc by $\frac{1}{2}$ or the other by 2. The latter is the easiest to draw but requires more room.

122. Construct a triangle of a, A and m_b.

On a describe the arc containing A. From B describe an arc with radius m_b; multiply this arc by 2 or the first by $\frac{1}{2}$, C being the centre of similitude.

123. Through a given point of the periphery of a circle to draw a chord, which is bisected by another given chord.

The given point being centre of similitude, multiply the given chord by 2 or the circle by $\frac{1}{2}$.

124. Through two concentric circles to draw a line, so that the smaller of the chords shall be one half of the larger.

125. Construct a triangle of a, $\dfrac{b}{c}$ and m_c.

126. Construct a triangle of an angle and two medians.

127. Construct a triangle the three medians being given.

 Reduced to 121, the medians being divided by their point of intersection in the ratio 1 : 2.

128. To draw a triangle knowing its centre of gravity (the intersection of the medians), one vertex and two curves (straight lines or circles) containing the other two vertices.

129. Construct a triangle of a, m_b and $\angle\,(m_a,\ b)$.

130. Construct a triangle of b, m_b and $\angle\,(m_a,\ a)$.

131. Construct an inscribable quadrilateral of $\angle A$, DB, $\angle ACB$ and the ratio between the parts of AC.

132. Construct a parallelogram having two opposite angular points in two given points, its other two angular points on a given circle.

133. In a triangle draw from A to BC a line AD, which shall be a mean proportional between BD and DC.

 Use the circumscribed circle.

134. Construct a triangle of a, b and v_c.

135. Construct a triangle of A, b and $\angle\,(m_a,\ a)$.

136. In a given triangle to draw such a line through A, that AY and AX have a given ratio, BX and CY being perpendiculars to AX.

137. Draw the common tangents to two given circles.

 Two circles, considered as similar figures, have two centres of similitude. These are situated in the centerline, and a line through the ends of parallel radii goes to the external or internal center of similitude, according to the radii having the same or opposite direction. A tangent from the center of similitude to one circle will also be a tangent to the other circle.

138. Given a point O and two circles; to these draw parallel tangents having their distances from O in a given ratio.

 By a multiplication of one of the given circles in regard to O, the problem is reduced to 137.

139. Construct a triangle of A, m_b and $\angle\,(a,\ m_c)$.

140. *A* and *B* are given points in the circumference of a circle; find a point *X* in the circumference, so that *XA* and *XB* intersect a given diameter in points *Y* and *Z*, the distances of which from the centre have a given ratio.

Multiply *AX* in regard to the centre, *Y* falling in *Z*; *A* will then fall in a known point A_1, and $\angle\ A_1ZB$ is known.

141. Draw a triangle when given the situation of three points, which divide the three sides in given ratios.

ABC be the given triangle, *D*, *E* and *F* the given points and $BD:DA = m:n$; $AF:FC = p:q$; $CE:EB = r:s$. Multiply *BD* by $-\dfrac{n}{m}$, *D* being the centre of similitude; *D* will not move and *B* will fall in the unknown point *A*; multiply next *DA* by $-\dfrac{q}{p}$ in regard to *F*, and *A* will fall in *C*, *D* in a known point D_1; multiply again $D_1 C$ by $-\dfrac{s}{r}$ in regard to *E*, and *C* will fall in *B*, D_1 in a new known point D_2.

The direction of a line being unchanged by multiplication, we must have $BD_2 \gtrless DB_1$ and DD_2 falling in the line *AB*. To obtain line *BC* the same operations are repeated inversely, starting from *E*.

The same construction can be applied to any polygon.

In the special case, where all the middle points of the sides are given, and the number of the sides is even, the problem is either indeterminate or impossible.

142. Given four concentric circles; draw a line intersecting the circles respectively in *A*, *B*, *C* and *D*, making *AB = CD*.

Be (*AB*) the power of a point of circle *A* in regard to circle *B*, and be the other set of points of intersection A_1, B_1, C_1 and D_1 we must have $(AD) = AD \times AD_1$; $(BC) = BC \times BC_1$; AD_1 being equal to BC_1 we have
$$AD : BC = (AD) : (BC).$$

This ratio is easily constructed by drawing two lines in such a manner, that the part of one of the lines intercepted between circles A and D is equal to that intercepted by B and C of the other line. The ratio $AB : AC$ being also known, the sought line can be drawn, A being chosen anywhere.

143. In a quadrilateral $ABCD$ are given AB, BC, CD and AC; the first line being fixed, what will be the locus of
    α) the angular point D,
    β) the middle point of the diagonal BD,
    γ) the middle point of the line connecting the middle points of both diagonals?

144. In a circle with O as centre, draw the fixed diameter AOB and a chord BC produced to D, making $CD = BC$. Find the locus of the point of intersection of OD and AC.

145. Find the locus of the point, which is symmetrical to a fixed point A in regard to a line, which revolves around another fixed point B.

THE METHOD OF SIMILITUDE.

The method used in the multiplication of curves is included in a more general, the method of similitude. *It is applied, when we obtain a system of similar (and similarly situated) figures by the removal of one of the given conditions.* While formerly we have looked for parts of the figure, which were completely determined, *we now try to find such parts of the figure, the form of which we know.*

The most important cases are the following:

a) *Given one length, otherwise only angles and ratios.* Looking aside from the given length we try to construct a figure having the given angles and ratios, one of the lines of the figure being chosen at will. The figure thus constructed is similar to the sought, which can be found by introducing the given line.

146. Construct a triangle of two angles and one line (median, altitude, perimeter etc.).

Construct any triangle containing the given angles,

and draw another similar to the first and containing the given line.

147. Construct a triangle of A, a and $b:c$.

Any triangle containing the angle A, the adjoining sides having the given ratio, must be similar to the sought.

148. Construct a square, in which the difference of the diagonal and the side is known.

149. To construct a triangle of A, b and $a:c$.

150. Given an angle at the centre ACB; to draw a tangent, which is divided in a given ratio by the point of contact and the points, in which the legs of the angle at the centre intersect the tangent.

The tangent is drawn first in any size; then the centre is determined. The figure thus obtained will have the demanded form and is easily given the demanded size by taking the centre of the circle as the centre of similitude.

151. Construct a triangle of A, h_a and the ratio between the parts of a.

152. Construct a triangle of the three altitudes.

The ratios of the sides are known. Draw from a point outside a circle three secants, of which the external parts are equal to the given altitudes and we have the secants proportionate to the sides of the triangle.

153. In a semicircle to inscribe a quadrilateral, similar to a given, and having two of its angular points in the diameter, the other two in the periphery.

Describe a semicircle round the given quadrilateral, and the figure will be similar to the one demanded.

b) In the above examples the place of the sought figure was indifferent; *if the figure must have a certain position in regard to certain given lines or points, we must try to remove one condition, of such sort, that we obtain a system of similarly situated figures.* The loci of all the points of the figure will thus be straight lines through the centre of similitude, and the sought figure is found by drawing any one of the figures, then the figure similarly situated to this and satisfying also the condition, which is removed. This condition is generally either that, *a line shall have a certain length* or that *a point shall be situated in a given line* or that *a line shall pass through a given point.*

154. In a given triangle ABC to inscribe another, abc, which shall have its sides parallel to given lines.

Remove the condition, that a shall fall in BC, and the other conditions will be satisfied by a system of similarly situaled triangles having A as their centre of similitude. Draw any one of these $a_1b_1c_1$ and Aa_1, will interseet BC in a.

155. To inscribe a square in a given triangle, sector or segment.

156. To inscribe a parallelogram, similar to a given, in a given triangle.

157. Through a given point to draw a line forming equal angles with two given lines.

158. Through a given point to draw a line, of which three given lines, meeting at the same point, cut off two parts having a given ratio.

Instead of the given point take any point in one of the given lines (117).

159. Through a given point to draw a line cutting off the legs of a given angle in a given ratio.

160. In a triangle to draw a line parallel to one of the sides and having a given ratio to one of the parts, in which it divides one of the other sides.

161. Draw a line in a given direction and intersecting the legs of two given angles, so that the parts intercepted have a given ratio.

Be the angles BAC and DEF, X the sought point in EF; if EF be removed, X will describe a straight line through that point of DE, in which a line through A in the given direction intersects DE.

162. Construct an isosceles triangle of the altitude and the median to one of the equal sides.

The triangle in which the given lines are sides can be drawn at once; then we know the form of the triangle, of which the median is one side and the vertex of the isosceles triangle the opposite angular point.

163. Given a point A in the circumference of a circle and the chord BC. Draw a chord AD intersecting BC in E, the ratio $DE : DC$ being given.

The form of $\triangle CED$ being known, draw another similar to it, taking C as centre of similitude.

164. In a circle two radii are drawn; draw a chord, which will be trisected by the radii.

165. In a quadrilateral to inscribe a rhombus having its sides parallel to the diagonals of the quadrilateral.

166. In a given triangle to inscribe another XYZ, of which we know the direction of YZ, the point of BC in which X shall fall and the ratio $XY : XZ$.

Remove BC (but not the line from A through the given point of BC) and take A as centre of similitude.

167. Draw a line in a given direction and dividing one pair of opposite sides of a quadrilateral in proportional parts (154).

168. In a triangle to draw a line parallel to one of the sides and which shall be a mean proportional to the parts, in which it divides one of the other sides.

169. Given a point, B, and two parallel lines, one of these passing through A. Draw through A and B two new parallel lines, which in connection with the given parallels form 1) a rhombus, 2) a parallelogram with a given perimeter, 3) a parallelogram of which the sides have a given ratio.

170. In a triangle to inscribe a rhombus, one vertex of which coincides with one of the vertices of the triangle.

171. In a circle to inscribe an isosceles triangle, of which the base and altitude have a given sum.

Be $\triangle ABC$ the one in quest of, and do we introduce the given sum in the figure by producing the altitude BD to E, we must have $DE = 2\,AD$, consequently the form of $\triangle ADE$ is known. The problem is now easily solved by taking E as centre of similitude.

172. In a triangle to inscribe a rectangle with a given perimeter.

Introduce half the perimeter in the figure.

173. In a triangle to inscribe another, having one vertex, A, in a given point of a side of the former, angle A being given and the opposite side being parallel to a given line.

174. In a given triangle to inscribe a parallelogram, of which the sides have a given ratio. One side shall fall in BC, and one extremity of this side in a given point of BC.

175. In one side of a given triangle to find a point, from which lines, drawn in given directions to the other sides, have a given sum.

176. Given a point B and two parallels AX and CY. Through B draw a line, intersecting the parallels in two points, X and Y, the lines AX and AY having a given ratio.

Remove B; choose X_1 for X anywhere in AX and determine Y_1 corresponding to Y in AY.

177. Given an angle and a point. Through this draw a line XY, which intersects the legs of the angle in X and Y, the distance of XY from the vertex of the angle having a given ratio to XZ, which connecting X with a point, Z, in the other leg of the angle, has also a given direction.

Remove P and choose X_1 for X anywhere in AX.

178. In a triangle ABC to draw a line, having a given direction and intersecting AB in X, BC in Y, AX and CY having a given ratio.

The form of $AXYC$ is known; take A as centre of similitude and choose B for X.

179. In triangle ABC to draw a line, XY, from a point X of AB to a point Y of AC so that $BX = XY = YC$.

The form of $BXYC$ is known.

The problem, to construct a triangle of A, $a + b$ and $a + c$, may be reduced to 179.

180. In a triangle ABC to draw a line $XY \neq BC$ so that a given homogeneous relation shall exist between XY, XB and YC (for instance $\overline{XY}^2 = XB \times YC$; $\overline{XY}^2 = \overline{XB}^2 + \overline{YC}^2$ etc.).

181. To describe a circle, which shall pass through a given point and touch two given lines, which meet at a point O.

Any circle touching the two straight lines must be similarly situated to the sought, O being the centre of similitude. Line OA must intersect the described circle in a point similarly situated to A in the sought circle. The two points of intersection will therefore determine two solutions. The centre of the sought circle is now easily determined by the line from A parallel to one of the radii through the points of intersection in the described circle.

182. In a given line to find a point, having equal distances from a given point and a given line (intersection of a straight line and a parabola).

Remove the point and take the intersection of the given line for the centre of similitude. In reality this problem is the same as the preceding.

183. In a given line to find a point, the distance of which from a given point has a given ratio to the distance from a given line. (Intersection of a straight line and a conic section, determined by focus, directrix and excentricity).

For the perpendicular from the sought point to the given line may be substituted a line forming a given angle with the given line without altering the solution essentially.

184. Describe a circle passing through a given point, having its centre in a given line, and of which a given line cuts off an arc corresponding to a given angle at the centre.

185. Describe a circle passing through two given points and touching a given line.

186. In the triangle ABC to draw a line with a given direction and intersecting AB in X, BC in Y, $XY + YA$ being given.

187. Construct a triangle of a, B and b—h_a.

Produce h_a beyond a the given length b—h_a. (182).

188. Construct a triangle of A, $a - c$ and $h_b + CD$, D being one extremity of h_b.

Produce CD to E, $ED = h_b$. Produce BA to F, AF $= a - c$. CE and $\angle CEB = 45°$ may be drawn as well as a line through $F \not\perp CE$. B is then determined by 183.

189. Construct a triangle of a, A and $b + nc$, n being a given number.

190. Construct a triangle of A, $b + c$ and $a + c$.

Produce b beyond A to D the length c, and c beyond B the length a; draw CD, DB and determine B.

191. In a given triangle ABC to inscribe a semicircle, touching BC in a given point P, while the extremities of the diameter fall in the other two sides.

Multiply AB or AC by -1 in regard to P, and the problem is reduced to 173.

INVERSE FIGURES.

Let a line revolve around a fixed point P (centre of inversion), and a moveable point A of the line follow a given curve K. A point A_1 is determined in the line in such a manner, that $PA \times PA_1 = I$, where I, (the power of inversion) is a constant (positiv or negativ). A curve K_1 will thus be described by A_1. The curves K and K_1 are each others *inverse* curves. (Transformed by reciprocal radii). A and A_1 are *corresponding* points.

The inverse curve of a straight line is a circle through the centre of inversion.

Be PB perpendicular to AB and B_1 the point corresponding to B, while A and A_1 are another pair of corresponding points. It follows from

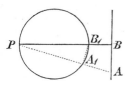

$$PA \times PA_1 = PB \times PB_1$$

that the triangles BPA and A_1PB_1 are similar, consequently $\angle PA_1B_1 = R$. The locus of A_1 is therefore a circle with the diameter PB_1.

If the given straight line passes through the centre of inversion, it will coincide with its inverse curve.

As A_1 describes the circle, A will describe the straight line; therefore *the inverse curve of a circle passing through the centre of inversion is a straight line.*

The inverse curve of a circle, which does not pass through the centre of inversion, is another circle, and the centre of inversion is a centre of similitude of both circles.

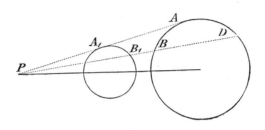

Let B and B_1 represent two corresponding points, while D is the other point in which PB intersects the circle. Both products $PB \times PB_1$ and $PB \times PD$ are constant, and therefore also the ratio $PB_1 : PD$ constant. The locus of B_1 will thus be found by multiplying the locus of D (the given circle) by a constant in regard to P. The locus is consequently a circle, similarly situated to the given, P being the centre of similitude. If the power of inversion is the power of P in regard to the given circle, this will be its own inverse curve.

We have proved, that B and B_1 simultaneously describe circles, but it must be remarked that they do not simultaneously describe similar arcs; whereas B_1 and D describe similar and similarly situated arcs.

We may now solve the problem:

Through a given point, P, to draw a line, of which two given curves K and K_1 cut off segments PX and PY, the product of which is given.

By removing K_1, the locus of Y will be the inverse curve of K taking P for centre of inversion and the given product for power of inversion. Y is thus the point of intersection of this curve and K_1. The problem can be solved by straight edge and compasses if the given curves are compounded of straight lines and arcs of circles.

192. From a given point P to draw a line, intersecting the legs of a given angle in A and B so that $PA \times PB = a^2$, a being a given line.

193. Given a circle, one of its diameters and a point, P; through P draw a line intersecting the circle in X and the diameter in Y, so that $PX \times PY = a^2$.

194. Through a point of intersection of two circles to draw a line, of which the two circles intercept chords having a given product.

195. Construct a triangle ABC; given the side of the inscribed square having two angular points in BC, $\angle A$ and the product of the parts, in which AB is divided by one angular point of the square.

196. Construct a triangle of a, A and $BD \times BA$, D being one extremity of h_c.

Inversion is often used to advantage, the inverse figure being often simpler than the given; it is well here to notice the following relations between inverse figures:

a) *If two curves intersect or touch each other in A, the inverse curves will intersect or touch each other in A_1, the point corresponding to A.*

If A is contained in both curves, A_1 must also be contained in both inverse curves, and if two points of intersection fall in A, the two corresponding points must fall in A_1.

If A coincides with the centre of inversion, the theorem will not hold, as the centre of inversion will generally have the infinitely distant straight line and not a point corresponding thereto.

b) *If two curves intersect in A forming a certain angle (the angle between the tangents) the inverse curves will intersect in A_1 forming the same angle* (having the opposite sign if the angle be measured from one curve to the other).

It is easily seen (fig. pag. 34) that the theorem will hold, if one of the curves is a circle and the other a straight line through the centre of inversion. It is also true for any two circles; for a straight line from A to the centre of inversion passes through A_1. This may again be extended to any two curves; for the angle between these at A is the same as the angle between two circles touching each curve at A.

APPLICATIONS.

197. Construct a circle passing through a given point P and touching two given circles.

By inversion, P being the centre of inversion, the problem is reduced to drawing the common tangents to two given circles. The power of inversion may be so chosen, that one of the given circles remains unaltered.

198. Prove that any circle, passing through the points of intersection of two circles, does intersect a system of circles touching the two given circles (the system including a common tangent) under equal angles.

The conclusion is derived by inversion from the following theorem: Any straight line through the centre of similitude of a system of similarly situated circles will intersect all of the circles under equal angles.

199. Construct a circle touching three given circles, which all pass through the same point.

200. In a given circle to inscribe a quadrilateral, each side of which shall pass through one of four given points.

Let the sides be AB, BC, CD and DA, respectively passing through the points a, b, c and d. We use these points as centres of inversion, using for the power of inversion of each one its power in regard to the circle. A will by four successive inversions about a, b, c and d fall in A again. Let P be the point, which by three inversions through a, b and c will fall in d; this point is determined by inverting d, successively through c, b and a. Any circle or straight line through P, will by being inverted through a, b and c be reduced to a circle through c, and then by inverting through d, to a straight line. The straight line PA will thus by four inversions be the line $P_1 A$, P_1 being the point obtained by inverting a

successively through b, c and d. As the angle between PA and the circle does neither change its size nor its sign by the four inversions and the circle remains stationary PA and P_1A must be one straight line.

The solution will therefore be the following: Invert a through b, c and d to P_1; invert d through c, b and a to P. Line PP_1 will intersect the circle in A.

The solution is easily extended to any figure having an even number of sides.

201. In a circle to inscribe a triangle ABC, each side of which shall pass through one of three given points, a, b and c.

Proceed as in 200, only inverting three times instead of four. The consequence will be that PA and P_1A do not fall in one straight line, as their angles with the circle have opposite signs. We invert one of the points, in which line Pa intersects the circle, through a, b and c; be the point thus found Q. The lines aP and PA have by the inversions changed to QP_1 and P_1A, which lines consequently must form the same angle as the first two lines. These angles have the same sign (the reason why is easily seen by following the inversions; the lines correspond in pairs, but their points of intersection do not correspond), and the four lines forming therefore an inscribable quadrilateral, A will be determined by a circle through P, P_1 and the point, in which aP and P_1Q intersect.

This solution may easily be extended to any polygon having an odd number of sides.

LOCI IN GENERAL.

Besides the loci, which we have discussed in the preceding, a great many exist, which are frequently applied; but it would be too lengthy to mention each one separately. It is therefore necessary in each problem, where the stated loci are not applicable, to find straight lines or circles, which are loci of the points of the figure. A correct drawing may often be of practical assistance, although not very scientific.

Where a figure has to be drawn in a certain position, it is frequently possible, by removing one of the conditions, to draw the figure in any position and then by parallel translation or by revolving it round a certain point to bring it into the desired position. The loci of the points of the figure are then respectively parallel straight lines or concentric circles.

EXAMPLES.

202. Describe a circle with a given radius, having its centre in a given line and intercepting a chord of a given length of another given line.

Describe the circle intercepting the given chord any ·where of the line; it is then brought into the desired position by moving its centre on a line parallel to the given.

203. Describe a circle with a given radius, having its centre in the periphery of a given circle and intercepting an arc with a given length of chord of another given circle.

204. Describe a circle with a given radius, passing through a given point and intercepting a given chord of a given line.

205. Draw a triangle congruous to a given, having one side in a given line and the opposite vertex in another given line.

206. In a given segment of a circle to inscribe a triangle, which shall be congruous to a given triangle.

207. With a given radius to describe a circle, of which two given lines cut off given chords, or two circles cut off arcs with chords of given lengths.

208. To a given circle to draw a tangent, of which a given length is intercepted between two given parallel lines or between two concentric circles.

209. From a point to draw a line, the part of which, intercepted between two concentric circles, shall be seen from the centre under a given angle.

210. Given two circles. Find a point from which tangents to the circles form a given angle, one of the tangents having also a given length.

The tangent, of which the length is given, is drawn touching the circle in any point; at the end of the tangent the given angle is drawn; revolve the second circle round the centre of the first till it touches the leg of the angle; then return to the original position moving also the tangents.

211. To describe a circle touching two given parallel lines and passing through a given point.

212. Through a given point to draw a line, of which equal parts are intercepted between each of two given pair of parallel lines.

The line must be parallel to the diagonals of the parallelogram formed by the two pair of parallels.

313. Describe two circles with given radii; one circle shall cut off a chord of given length of one given line, the other circle a chord of given length of another given line. The circles shall also touch, and their common tangent shall have a given direction.

214. In a given circle to inscribe a triangle, of which we know one side and the median to this; the median shall also pass through a given point.

215. In a given circle to inscribe a triangle, of which we know one side and the median to one of the other sides; the point, in which the medians intersect shall also fall in a given diameter.

216. In a given circle to draw a chord of a given length and which a given diameter divides in a given ratio.

217. In a given quadrilateral to inscribe a parallelogram, the sides of which have given directions.

Remove one of the sides of the quadrilateral and the free vertex of the parallelogram will describe a straight line.

218. Through a given point to draw a line, intersecting three

given straight lines in three points, which with the given shall be harmonically situated.

Remove one of the given lines, and the free point will describe a straight line through the intersection of the other two given lines.

219. Construct a triangle of v_A, B and the distance from C to v_A.

Draw v_A and a perpendicular to v_A in A.

The problem is now reduced to the foregoing, the arc containing $\angle B$ being only substituted for one of the given lines.

B. LOCI OF LINES.

The straight line, like the point, is determined, when it shall satisfy two conditions, and also like the point partly determined by one condition, there being always one or an other curve, which all the lines, satisfying this one condition, shall touch. This curve may, through analogy, be called the locus of the line. In special cases the curve may become a point, consequently all lines satisfying the given condition will pass through this point. Except this case we here only regard the one, in which the curve becomes a circle.

If therefore it is possible to determine two loci of a line, the problem is reduced to one of the following:

1. To draw a straight line through two given points.
2. To draw a tangent from a given point to a circle. (16).
3. To draw common tangents to two given circles. (137).

We will now mention the most important loci of lines.

l. *The locus of chords of equal lengths in the same circle, is a circle concentric with the given, touching any chord of the given length.*

m. *The locus of the lines, the distances of which from two given points have a given ratio, is the point, which divides the line joining the given points in the given ratio.* The distances are taken with their signs.

n. *The locus of the lines, the distances of which from two given points have a given sum, is a circle, the centre of which is the middle point of the line connecting the two given points.*

If the *difference of the distances* be given, *the locus will be two infinitely distant points*, the lines consequently two systems of parallels. Their directions are determined by the tangents from one of the given points to the circle having its centre in the other given point and its radius equal to the given difference.

Remark. The distances are here taken with their signs. If the distance to a certain one of the given points be made the minuend, the locus will only be one of the two infinitely distant points.

o. *Draw in a circle angles at the circumference standing upon the same arc and divide all of them in the same two angles; the locus of the dividing lines will be the point of the arc determined by dividing any one of the angles in the given manner.*

p. *Describe circles passing through two given points and intersecting (or touching) a given circle; the locus of the common chords will be a point of the line joining the two given points.*

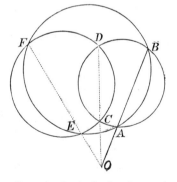

Be the given points A and B, C and D the points, in which a circle through A and B intersects the given. The line CD will intersect AB in O, which will be the locus in quest of; for if we describe another circle through the points A and B intersecting the given circle in points E and F, the lines FE, DC and AB will be the radical axes of the three circles, and as the radical axes intersect in one point, FE must pass through O.

EXAMPLES.

220. Through a given point to draw a line, of which a given circle intercepts a chord of given length.

By I the problem is reduced to 16.

221. To draw a line, of which two given circles intercept chords of given lengths.

222. To draw a line, which shall intersect a given line in X and a given circle in Y and Z in such a manner, that YX and YZ will be of given lengths.

By I the problem is reduced to 11.

223. In a given circle to inscribe a triangle similar to a given, having given a point, through which one side of the triangle shall pass.

224. In a given circle to draw a chord of a given length and having a given direction.

225. In a given circle to inscribe a triangle, one side of which is equal and parallel to a given line; the line, which bisects the opposite angle shall also pass through a given point.

One side is obtained by I; two points of the line bisecting the opposite angle are then known.

226. In a given circle to inscribe a triangle, of which is given the direction of one side, the length of the line bisecting the opposite angle as well as a point, which this line shall contain.

The given direction of the side determines the middle point of the corresponding arc; the line bisecting the opposite angle is thus determined.

227. Through a given point to draw a line having a distance from one given point equal to the sum of its distances from two other given points.

228. In the circumference of a given circle points A and B are given. Through a given point P draw a line intersecting the circle in two points X and Y, so that AX and BY form a given angle. (220).

229. To divide a given arc of a circle in two segments, the chords of which have a given ratio.

The sought chords form an angle, which is bisected by the line, which divides the chord of the given arc in the given ratio and which passes through the middle point of the remaining part of the circumference.

230. From a given point to draw a line, which produced shall pass through the point in which two given lines would intersect, if they could be sufficiently produced.

The line divides two parallels intercepted between the given lines in the same ratio; draw one of the parallels through the given point.

231. To construct a triangle of the parts, in which $\angle A$ and a are divided by a line AD.

Draw the circumscribed circle and a chord in it equal to a; two points of AD are then known. (o).

232. Construct a triangle of h_a, v_A and m_a.

The three given lines may at once be drawn; point A and the site of a are then known. Points B and C may be obtained by the construction of the circumscribed circle. If we produce v_A and draw a line perpendicular to a in the middle point of a, the point, in which these lines intersect, will be the middle point of the arc corresponding to a; this point being determined, it is easy to describe the circle.

233. To a given circle to draw a tangent, the distances of which from two given points have a given sum.

234. Given a quadrilateral $ABCD$; draw a line, which shall be equidistant from A and C as well as from B and D. (The equal distances having opposite signs).

235. In a given circle to inscribe a quadrilateral $ABCD$, of which we know the diagonal AC and the angle between the diagonals. The quadrilateral shall furthermore have the property, that a circle may be inscribed in it.

Draw the diagonal AC; the direction of BD is then known, consequently also the middle points of the arcs, which correspond to BD. The lines, which bisect angles A and C may now be drawn and must intersect in the centre of the circle inscribed in the quadrilateral. The lines, bisecting the angles B and D, must pass through this point as well as through the middle points of the arcs corresponding to AC; those lines may now be drawn and B and D thereby determined.

236. To draw a square, each side of which contains one of four given points, A, B, C and D.

Describe circles with the diameters AB and CD; these circles are loci of two angular points of the square; as the diagonal bisects the angle of the square, it must pass through the middle points of the two semicircles and may thus be drawn at once. Two angular points are thereby determined, and the other two are easily found.

237. To draw a quadrilateral, which shall be similar to a given, and of which each side shall pass through one of four given points.

The solution of this problem is similar to that of 236; we know the parts, in which the angles of the quadrilateral are divided by the diagonals.

238. Describe a circle passing through two given points and touching a given circle.

Describe a circle passing through the given points A and B and intersecting the given. The common chord will intersect AB in a point, through which the common tangent to the given and sought circles at their point of contact must also pass. The point of contact of the two circles is thus obtained, hence easily the centre of the circle.

The problem may also be expressed thus: Given a circle and two points A and B; in the circumference find a point X, so situated, that lines AX and BX intersect the circle in points, the connecting line of which shall be parallel to AB.

239. Describe a circle, which shall pass through two given points and intercept an arc with a chord of given length of a given circle.

240. Construct an inscribable quadrilateral of CA, BD, $\angle A$ and $\angle ACB$.

Draw DB and determine point A by e and o.

241. Describe a circle passing through two given points and intersecting a given circle in such a manner, that their common chord will be a tangent to another given circle.

242. Describe a circle passing through two given points and intersecting a given circle in such a manner, that the distances of their common chord from two given points have a given ratio.

243. Draw a triangle, congruous to a given; two of the sides shall pass each through one of two given points and the line, which bisects the angle enclosed, shall be a tangent to a given circle.

244. Given two parallel lines, in one of them a point A and in the other line a point B. Through a given point P to draw a line, which shall intersect the parallels in X and Y, AX and BY having a given ratio.

245. Given a circle and three points, A, B and C. Through A draw a line intersecting the circle in X and Z, through B one intersecting the circle in Y and V; the lines XY and VZ shall also pass through C.

SECOND CHAPTER.

TRANSFORMATION OF THE FIGURE.

In order to apply the methods given in the previous chapter, it is necessary that the given elements of the figure should be *adjoining* to a certain extent, as in this case it is often possible to construct a greater part of the figure at once, thus reducing the problem to the determination of a point or a line. As soon as this is not the case, loci can not be directly applied; but the preceding directs us to the principle, which must be followed, and which will form the fundament of the following discussion. *We must try of the drawn figure to form another, in which the given parts are thus gathered, that the construction may be carried out.* This figure being drawn, it is generally easy to go back to the first figure, which was wanted. The methods used in transforming are:

        A. Parallel translation,
        B. Replacing and
        C. Revolution.

A. PARALLEL TRANSLATION.

This method is applied to gather the given parts, some of the lines of the figure being translated to new positions, parallel to the original. The method will especially be applicable where two lines and the angle, which they form, are known; by translation of one line till its extremity coincides with that of the other line, we obtain a triangle, which can be drawn at once. In any polygon it is possible to gather the parts by translation of the sides, so that these shall radiate from one point. The lines may be drawn in such directions, that the angles, which thev form, are equal to the angles adjacent to those of the polygon, the sum of those adjacent angles being 4 *R*. The new polygon formed by joining the extremities of the lines by straight lines is often easier to construct than the original. The following special cases will illustrate this.

The triangle. The triangle *CDE* is found by translation of *ABC*, *AE* being equal to *AB* and *DB* = *AC*. The lines radiating from *A* are the sides in the original triangle, the angles round *A* are equal to those, adjacent to the angles of the triangle. As *DC* = 2*CO*, the sides of the new

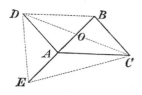

triangle are twice the medians of the original, while *A* is the centre of gravity (intersecting point of the medians) of the new triangle. *B* and *D* being equidistant from *AC*, it follows, that the altitudes of the triangles round *A* are equal to the altitudes of the original triangle. As we do not alter the angles by parallel translation, we will find in the new figure all the angles formed by the sides, the altitudes and the medians of the original triangle. △ *DAC* being equal to △ *ABC*, the area of *DEC* is three times the area of △ *ABC*.

If △ *DEC* can be drawn (or one of the small triangles around *A*) it is easy to return to △ *ABC*.

EXAMPLES.

246. Construct a triangle, the three medians being given.
    Draw *DEC*, then find *A* and *B*.
247. Construct a triangle of m_c, h_a and h_b.
    Draw *DOC* (35); then draw *OB* = *OA*.
248. Construct a triangle of h_a, m_a and m_b.

249. Construct a triangle of h_a, m_b and h_c.
250. Construct a triangle of h_a, m_b and m_c.
251. Construct a triangle of A, h_a and m_a.
252. Construct a triangle of h_a, m_a and $h_c : b$.
253. Construct a triangle of A, h_a and m_b.
254. Construct a triangle of m_a, m_c and $\angle(m_b, a)$.
255. Construct a triangle of m_a, h_a and h_b.
256. Construct a triangle of h_a, h_b and $\angle(m_a, b)$.
257. Construct a triangle of h_a, a and $\angle(m_b, c)$.
258. Construct a triangle of h_a, $b + c$ and $h_b : h_c$.

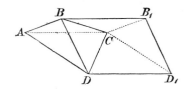

The quadrilateral. In the quadrilateral $ABCD$ we may translate AB and AD respectively to CB_1 and CD_1; in the parallelogram BD_1, thus obtained, we will find many of the parts of the quadrilateral in simple relations to each other, viz:

The lines radiating from C are the sides of the quadrilateral.

The angles around C are the angles of the quadrilateral.

The sides of the parallelogram are the diagonals of the quadrilateral, and the angles of the parallelogram are equal to those formed by the diagonals.

The angles between the lines radiating from C and the sides of the parallelogram are equal to the angles between the sides and the diagonals of the quadrilateral.

The area of the parallelogram is twice that of the quadrilateral.

The diagonals of the parallelogram are twice the length of the lines, which are drawn between the middle points of opposite sides of the quadrilateral; this is easily proved by drawing the parallelogram, which has its vertices in the middle points of the sides of the quadrilateral.

It is thus seen, that the parallelogram contains all the parts, which are mostly considered in the quadrilateral.

The translation is especially practical if the diagonals and their enclosed angle be given; in this case we are able to draw the parallelogram directly, and the problem is therefore reduced to the determination of point C. We have two loci of C, if among the above mentioned parts two are known or certain relations between some of them (for inst. the ratio of two sides, the sum or difference of their squares etc.). The large class of problems, which are thus easily solved, may be further extended, remembering the fact, that in a quadrilateral two opposite sides may be considered as diagonals and the diagonals as sides; thereby we solve those problems, in which the opposite sides and the angle, which they form, are given instead of the diagonals and their enclosed angle.

The following examples will serve to further explain the method.

EXAMPLES.

259. Construct a trapezium, the four sides of which are given.

Translate one of the sides, which are not parallel, to the extremity of the other and we obtain a triangle, of which the three sides are known.

260. In a circle two chords AB and CD are drawn. To find a point X in the circumference, from which lines XA and XB shall intercept a given length, FG, of the chord CD.

Imagine FG translated till F coincides with A; G will then fall in a point H, which can at once be determined; point G is determined by e, as we have $\angle G = \angle X = \frac{1}{2} \smile AB$.

261. To construct a quadrilateral $ABCD$ of the four sides and the line EF, which is drawn between the middle points of AB and CD.

The given parts are gathered, BC and AD being translated to EC_1 and ED_1. C_1, F and D_1 are situated in one straight line, as $\triangle C_1 CF \cong D_1 DF$. It is now possible to construct $\triangle C_1 ED_1$ (121); then C and D are determined. The construction shows, that the angle between the two opposite sides is independent of the length of the other two sides.

The construction may also be done by the above general method of translation.

262. Through one of the points of intersection of two circles to draw a line, of which the two circles cut off chords, having a given difference. (The chords taken positiv or negativ according to their situation on one or the other side of the point of intersection).

The projection of the centerline on the required line is equal to one half of the given difference. If therefore this projection be translated, so as to have one extremity in one of the centres, we obtain a right angled triangle, which can be drawn. The line demanded will be parallel to one side of this triangle.

If the *sum* of the chords be given, it is introduced in the figure by multiplying one circle by — 1 in regard to the point of intersection, substitute the new circle for the given and proceed as above.

263. To draw a rectangle having one side given and each side passing through one of four given points. (262).

264. In a given triangle ABC to draw a line from a point X in AB to a point Y in BC; XY shall have a given length and $AX : CY = p : q$.

Translate XY to AY_1; point Y_1 may be determined, as we know its distance from A and the form of $\triangle Y_1 YC$.

265. Through two given circles to draw a line in a given direction, and of which the intercepted chords shall have a given sum or difference.

Translate one circle in the given direction till it intersects the other circle in the line demanded; in this position the centre is easily determined.

266. Through a given point to draw a line, of which two given circles cut off chords of equal length.

Translate one circle till the equal chords coincide. In this position the centre is easily determined; from it we see the centreline under a right angle, and we also know its distance from the given point, as the tangent from this to the circle must be equal to the tangent from the point to the fixed circle.

267. In two given circles with the centres A and B to draw two parallel radii AX and BY, which from a given point, P, are seen under equal angles.

Translate $\triangle AXP$ along the centerline through a distance equal to this; alter the triangle in the ratio of the radii, making AX and BY cover each other. The point, P, will then have a new position P_1, which is easily determined, as we know the length and the direction of BP_1. As we have $\angle YP_1B = XPA$, the four points, P, P_1, B and Y must fall in the same circle, and Y is thereby determined.

268. To construct a parallelogram, of which the sides and the angle formed by the diagonals, are given.

Translate one diagonal till its extremity coincides with that of the other; the triangle, in which the two diagonals are sides, may now be constructed (18).

269. Construct a trapezium of the diagonals, the line drawn between the middle points of the two sides, which are not parallel, and one angle.

Proceed as in 268 and the problem is solved by 3.

270. In which case will point C, by the ordinary translation of the quadrilateral, fall in one of the diagonals of the parallelogram?

By parallel translation we may solve a general problem, which often occurs:

To place a line with its extremities in two given curves, the line being equal and parallel to a given.

Translate one curve parallel to the given line and through a distance equal to that line; it will then intersect the other curve in the point, from which the line must be drawn. It is always possible to solve this problem by straight edge and compasses, if the curves are systems of straight lines and circles.

271. To place a line with its extremities in two given circles, the line being equal and parallel to a given.

272. In a triangle to draw a transversal of a given length parallel to one side.

273. In a circle to draw a chord equal and parallel to a given line.

274. From a vessel two known points are seen under a given angle; the vessel sails a given distance in a given direction, and now the same two points are seen under another known angle. Find the position of the vessel.

Describe the arcs, which passing through the given points, contain the given angles, and the problem is reduced to 271.

———————

A certain method, which may be classed as parallel translation, is often applied to problems, where circles shall touch other circles or straight lines; it consists in diminishing the radius of a circle to naught, the circle becoming a point, while simultaneously the lines and the other circles follow; the former without changing their direction, the latter without changing their centre. Having thus substituted a point for a circle, the problem is generally reduced to a simpler one, the other given conditions remaining unaltered.

275. To draw the common tangents to two circles.

Reduce the smaller circle to a point, the tangents following, and the other circle, which still must touch the tangents, will have a radius equal to either the sum or the difference of the given, the sum if the internal and the difference if the external tangents are considered. The problem is thereby reduced to 16.

276. To construct a circle, which shall touch two given lines and a given circle.

The reduction of the given circle to a point reduces the problem to 181. The circle demanded can touch the given in two ways, to which corresponds translation of the given tangents in opposite directions.

277. Construct a circle, which shall touch a given line in a given point and shall also touch a given circle.

278. Construct a circle, which shall touch two given circles, one of these in a given point.

MIXED EXAMPLES IN PARALLEL TRANSLATION.

279. Construct a quadrilateral, the four sides and the angle between two opposite sides being given.

280. Construct a quadrilateral of the diagonals, their enclosed angles and two opposite angles.

281. Construct a trapezium of the diagonals, their enclosed angle and the sum or difference of two adjacent sides.

282. Construct a triangle of $m_a \angle (m_b, m_c)$ and the area.

283. In a triangle ABC, in which $\angle B = R$, to draw a line XY of given length and satisfying the condition, that $\overline{AX}^2 + \overline{XY}^2 + \overline{YC}^2$ shall be equal to a given square.

Point Y_1 (see 264) is determined by **a**.

284. Construct an inscribable quadrilateral of the diagonals, their enclosed angle and the angle, which one diagonal forms with one side.

285. Construct a quadrilateral of the diagonals, their enclosed angle, the ratio between a pair of adjacent sides and the angle between the other pair of sides.

286. To circumscribe a given triangle with the largest possible equilateral triangle.

287. To construct a quadrilateral of two opposite angles, the area and the lines, which are drawn between the middle points of opposite sides.

The angle between the given lines is determined by these lines and the area. The ordinary translation of the quadrilateral may now be applied.

288. Construct a quadrilateral, $ABCD$, of AB, CD, $\angle BAC$, $\angle ACD$ and $\angle BDA$.

289. Construct a quadrilateral of two opposite sides and all the angles.

290. Construct a trapezium of the diagonals, their enclosed angle and one side.

291. Construct a quadrilateral of three of the sides and the angles at the fourth.

292. Construct a quadrilateral, $ABCD$, of AB, CD, AC, $\angle ABD$ and $\angle BDC$.

293. Construct the quadrilateral of $\angle BCA$, $\angle CAD$, the diagonals and their enclosed angle.

294. Given two parallel lines L and M, a third line N and a point P. To draw a line through P, which shall intersect the given lines respectively in A, B and C, so that AB and CP have a given ratio.

    Translate AB and CP to $A_1 Q$ and QP_1, Q being the point, in which M and N intersect, and determine P_1.

295. In a triangle $AXBYC$ to draw XY in a given direction, so that AX and YC have a given sum.

296. Construct a trapezium of the diagonals and the sides, which are not parallel (142).

297. Solve the problems 169, A being any point.

298. Construct a quadrilateral of the diagonals, two opposite sides and the angle, which they form.

299. Construct a quadrilateral of the line, which connects the middle points of two opposite sides, the diagonals, the ratio between one pair of opposite sides and the sum of the squares of the other pair.

    The usual parallelogram may be constructed, as we know the sides and one diagonal.

300. Construct a quadrilateral of the four sides and the line which connects the middle points of the diagonals.

    Analogous to 299 or 261.

301. Construct a triangle of the two medians and the angle, which the third median forms with its corresponding side.

302. To construct a trapezium of the parallel sides and the diagonals.

303. In a given circle to inscribe a trapezium, of which we know the altitude and the difference of the parallel sides.

304. To construct a quadrilateral of a pair of opposite sides, the line, which divides the other pair in a given ratio, the angle between these sides and their ratio.

Analogous to 261.

305. Construct a trapezium of the diagonals, the line, which joins the middle points of the diagonals, and the line, which joins the middle points of two opposite sides.

306. In a circle to inscribe a trapezium, of which we know the altitude and the sum of the parallel sides.

The trapezium may be placed in such a manner, that it is divided symetrically by a diameter. The middle point of one of the sides, which are not parallel, must fall in a known line parallel to the diameter. The extremity of the altitude drawn from the end of one of the sides, which are not parallel, may now be determined. (271 and 336).

307. On a given line AB to place a line CD of given length in such a manner, that C and D shall divide AB harmonically.

Describe any circle, in which AB is a chord; while imagining the problem solved, draw from C and D the lines CE and DF to the middle points of the two arcs AB. These lines are perpendicular to each other and intersect in the circumference. Translate CD parallel to itself to EG, and FG will then be seen from D under a right angle.

Be M the middle point of AB, the product and the difference of MC and MD are known; this leads also to an easy solution. (220).

308. Given two points A and B, and between these points two parallel lines. To place a line, MN, in a given direction on these parallels so that $AMNB$ shall be a minimum.

309. Through a given point, P, to draw a line, the distances

of which, AX and BY, from two given points, A and B, have a given product.

Translate YB to $Y_1 A$ and the locus of Y_1 will be a straight line, the locus of X being a circle, in which AP is a diameter. Translate the straight line a distance AB and we obtain a straight line and a circle as loci of Y.

310. From a given point P draw a line PA to a given point A of a given curve, and from another given point L draw the line $LB \neq PA$; if we shall have $LB : PA = m : n$, what will be the locus of B?

B. REPLACING.

This method is applied as the former to arrange the position of the given parts in one more convenient to the construction. By this method we place a part of the figure in a new position, thereby endeavouring:

1) *To gather the given parts.*

311. In a given circle to inscribe a quadrilateral $ABCD$, of which we know the size of one pair of opposite sides, AB and CD, and the ratio of the other pair.

Replace $\triangle ABC$ with A in C and C in A; B will continue to be a point of the circumference. We have now obtained a more convenient position of the given parts, knowing now two adjacent sides and the ratio of the other two; the two sides may at once be drawn and then the fourth vertex determined. (229).

The figure being constructed it only remains to replace $\triangle ABC$ in its original position.

312. To construct a quadrilateral $ABCD$, in which a circle may be inscribed; given AD, AB, $\angle D$ and $\angle B$.

Revolve ADC round the line, which bisects $\angle A$; D and C will take the positions D_1 and C_1, $D_1 C_1$ remaining a tangent. The triangle, in which BD_1 is a side, may now be constructed, as we know this side and the two angles at its extremities; then the circle is easily drawn, as it shall touch the three sides of this triangle·

2) *To introduce the given parts in the figure.*

313. To construct a triangle of a, b and $A - B$.

Replace the triangle with A in B and B in A; then the triangle, in which a and b are sides and $A - B$ their enclosed angle, may be constructed.

314. Construct a triangle of a, h_a and $B - C$.

Introduce $B - C$ by replacing the triangle with B in C, C in B and A in a point A_1. The parallelogram, of which AA_1 is a diagonal, B the third vertex, may now be drawn, as the diagonal through B is seen from A under a known angle.

315. Construct a triangle of $b \times c$, m_a and $B - C$.

Replace the triangle in the position $BA_1 C$; the known area $A_1 BA$ will be equal to the area of the isosceles triangle, the equal sides of which are m_a.

3) *To make equal lines or angles cover each other*; this is most frequently done, where the equal parts are unknown, the method thus serving to eliminate such a part. A similar method may be applied, where the ratio of two lines is given; to make one of these cover the other, we must, in replacing, increase one part of the figure in the given ratio.

316. Construct an inscribable quadrilateral $ABCD$, of which the four sides are given.

Replace ABC to the position ADC_1, having first mnltiplied the sides by $AD : AB$; DC_1 and DC fall in one straight line. The triangle CAC_1 may now be constructed, as we know CD, DC_1, DA and the ratio $CA : C_1 A$.

317. In a circle to inscribe a triangle, the middle points of the three arcs being given.

Be the triangle ABC, γ the middle point of AB, β of AC and α of BC. Revolve A around γ, then around α and β, and it will return to its original place in A, while a point of the circumference, at a certain distance from A, will fall on the opposite side of A but at the same distance from A, which it had previous to the operation. A is thus determined by revolving any point of the arc $\gamma\beta$ successively around γ, α and β taking the middle point of the two positions. The problem may be extended to a polygon of n sides; if n is an even number the problem is indeterminate or impossible; if n is an odd number the problem will be determinate.

318. Given a line and a point A in this line. From the centre, O, of a given circle draw a line, which shall intersect the circumference in Y, the given line in X, XY and XA having a given ratio.

If XY (increasing) be made to cover XA, O will fall in a known point O_1, and $AY \neq O_1 O$.

319. Construct a quadrilateral $ABCD$ of AB, AD, $\angle B$, $\angle D$ and the ratio $BC : CD$.

Proceed as in 316.

4) *To produce a symmetrical figure, the axis of symmetry containing a point demanded.*

320. In a given line to find a point, the distances of which from a given point in the same line and from another given line shall be equal.

Draw a perpendicular through the given point and bisect the angle between this and the other given line.

321. Describe a circle, which shall touch a given line in a given point and shall intersect a given circle under a certain angle.

Replace the given circle in such a manner, that it intersects the given line in the given point under the given angle; the axis of symmetry of the two circles must then contain the centre of the circle demanded.

5) *To place a part of the figure in such a position, that two unknown points coincide, while two lines through this point of coincidence form a known angle, each line containing a known point.*

322. Given two circles and in the circumference of one the two points A and B. In the circumference of the same circle find a point X, through which we imagine lines AX and BX drawn. Be M and N points, in which AX

and BX intersect the other circle, it is demanded, that the chord MN shall have a given length.

We know $\angle MON$, O being the centre of the other circle. Revolve MA around O through this angle and M will fall in N, A in a point A_1, which we know. As MA and NB form a known angle, the angle A_1NB is also known and N thereby determined.

MIXED EXAMPLES OF REPLACING.

323. In a given circle to inscribe a quadrilateral, of which one pair of opposite sides and the sum of the other pair of sides are given.

324. To construct a triangle of A, h_a and m_a.

Replace the triangle with B in C and C in B, A falling in A_1 on the opposite side of BC. AA_1 may now be drawn and B then determined.

325. To circumscribe a circle with a triangle, the three vertices of which shall fall in three given lines radiating from the centre.

Analoguous to 317.

326. Construct a rhombus, of which two sides fall in two given parallel lines, the two other sides passing through points A and B respectively.

Replace the rhombus with the other two sides on the parallel lines; AB will then have a new position, the direction of which we know. The angle between this and AB determines the angle of the rhombus.

327. Construct a triangle, which shall have its vertex in a given line, having a given base and a given difference of the angles at the base.

Replace the triangle as in 313 and apply the method of similitude.

328. In a triangle a line has been drawn from the vertex to a given point of the base; find a point in this line from which the two parts of the base are seen under equal angles.

329. In a triangle ABC, AC has been divided in AD and DC. Find a point X in AB, from which AD and DC are seen under equal angles.

The point in AB, which is situated symmetrically to C, DX being the axis of symmetry, can be determined.

330. Through the vertex B of a triangle to draw a line and perpendicular to this the lines AP and CQ; the areas of the triangles ABP and CBQ, thus determined, shall have a given ratio.

Replace ABP altering its size to CBP_1. Describe a circle with the diameter BC; the chord P_1Q has a known length and is divided by BC in a known ratio.

331. Construct a triangle of m_a, $b^2 - c^2$ and $\angle (a, m_a)$.

332. Construct a quadrilateral having four given sides, and of which one diagonal shall bisect one of the angles.

333. Given two circles with centres A and B. Describe a circle passing through A and B and intersecting the two circles respectively in X and Y (on opposite sides of AB); the sum of the angles ABY and BAX shall be equal to a given angle.

Replace $\triangle ABY$ to the position BAY_1 making $\angle XAY_1$ equal to the given angle.

334. Construct a triangle of A, r and $c - b$.

Be the centre of the inscribed circle K, then we know three elements of $\triangle BKC$, viz: $\angle K$, the altitude KF and the distance from F to the middle point of BC.

335. Construct a triangle of r, $c - b$ and $C - B$.

Draw the same triangle as in 334.

REVOLUTION AROUND AN AXIS

is only a special case of replacing, but it is so frequently applied, that it must be specially discussed. We endeavour to obtain the same advantages as above mentioned by revolving a part of the figure around a straight line, which will be the axis of symmetry of the two positions. The following problem, which frequently occurs, is thereby easily solved:

336. *To a given line to draw a perpendicular, of which two given curves shall cut off equal parts.*

Revolve one curve around the given line as axis; it will then intersect the other curve in the points sought.

337. To place a square with two opposite vertices in a given straight line and the two other vertices in the circumference of two given circles. (336).

338. In a given line to find a point X, from which lines drawn to the given points A and B (situated on the same side of the given line) shall form equal angles with the given line.

Revolve one of the given points, A, around the given line to A_1, and the line BXA_1 will be a straight line.

Remark. This problem is often met with in nature; an elastic body striking a plane, a ray of light meeting a mirror, etc. are reflected at an angle, which is equal to the angle of incidence. A may thus be a luminous point, the line a cross section of a mirror. The problem is therefore to find the path of a ray of light from A, which shall meet B after being reflected. The length of the path travelled by the ray of light is equal to the straight line BA_1, while any other point than X would give a broken line between the same two points, hence *the distance travelled is a minimum.*

If the ray met any other point than X, it would still be reflected as if it emanated from A_1; in this class of problems we may thus imagine the line removed, substituting only A_1 for A.

339. Two balls M and N are placed on a billard-table, which has the form of a polygon with n sides. M shall be rolled against the side AB then recoiling it shall strike all the sides successively and from the last side recoil to N.

Revolve M around AB to M_1. Imagine AB removed, M_1 being substituted for M. Continue this proceeding till the problem has been reduced to 338. The sought point in the last side is therefore first determined, and from this it is easy to return to the others. The problem can not be solved, if one of the sought points falls in the prolongation of a side.

340. In a given polygon to inscribe another, the perimeter of which shall be a minimum.

Two adjacent sides must form equal angles with the side of the polygon, which contains their point of intersection; if this was not the case for one of the points, we would obtain a smaller perimeter by placing the point where the above condition would be satisfied. The problem is related to the former and is solved analoguously.

We may commence with the sought point in one of the sides, but as we do not know its place, we must revolve the whole side successively around all the other sides of the polygon. In this way the perimeter of the sought polygon is straightened out into one line, the extreme parts of which are the two sides, which intersect in the line, which has been revolved. As one of these has followed the side during the revolutions, the angle, which it forms with the side, has not been altered, and the problem will thus be reduced to the following:

Through two lines of equal length to draw a third line, which shall form equal angles with the former and cut off equal parts, these parts to be reckoned from a certain extremity.

If the equal angles become alternates the problem will be indeterminate if the lines are also parallel, impossible if this be not the case. The last case occurs, where the given polygon has an even number of sides; when the number of sides is odd, the solution is always possible if we also call those polygons inscribed, which have their angular points in the prolongation of the sides of the given polygon.

341. To construct a polygon, in which we know the situation of the perpendiculars bisecting the sides.

Be A one of the sought angular points, B any other point; revolving the line AB successively around all of the perpendiculars, A must return to A, while B takes the position B_1; as the line AB does not alter its size during the operation, we must have $AB = AB_1$. The problem will therefore be solved by commencing with any point B thereby determining B_1. The locus of A is the line perpendicular to and bisecting BB_1. Choose another situation of B and repeat the operation; the location of A will then be determined. The discussion is similar to that of 340.

342. To construct a polygon, in which we know the situation of the lines, which bisect the angles.

The solution is analoguous to that of 341.

343. Given two circles; draw tangents to these, which shall intersect in and form equal angles with a given line.

Analoguous to 338. The problem is reduced to 137.

344. In a given line to find a point, X, the distances of which from two given points A and B have a given sum.

Introduce the given sum by prolonging AX to B_1, XB_1 being equal to BX. X will be the centre of a circle, which shall pass through B and touch the circle described from A as centre with radius AB_1. As the sought circle shall also pass through the point, which is symmetrically situated to B in regard to the given line, we have the problem reduced to 238.

345. In a given line to find a point, the distances of which from two given points have a given difference.

Analoguous to 344.

Remark. The last two problems may also be expressed thus:

To find the intersection of a given straight line and a conic section of which the focal axis and the foci are given. This problem can always be solved by straight edge and compasses. If we substitute a circle for the straight line, the problem can generally not be solved by straight edge and compasses.

346. Line AD bisects the angle, A, of a triangle ABC. From a point M in AD draw the lines MB and MC; the diffe-

rence of the angles DMC and DMB shall be a maximum; determine point M.

The problem is reduced to 185 by revolving AB around the line AD.

347. Two circles pass respectively through A and B. In their radical axis to determine a point P, which shall be so situated, that the line QR (Q and R being the points, in which the lines PA and PB intersect the circles) shall be perpendicular to the radical axis.

Revolve the circle through A around the radical axis; be A_1 the new position of A, Q_1 that of Q, it will be seen, that the quadrilaterals $QABR$ and Q_1A_1BR are inscribable, consequently the circle AA_1B must pass through P.

348. Given two points A and B on the same side of the given line PQ. In this line find a point X for which $\angle BXQ = 2 \angle AXP$.

Revolve AX around PQ to A_1X and determine the projection of B on A_1X.

THIRD CHAPTER.

THE THEORY OF REVOLUTION.

I. From a given point, O, lines are drawn to the points of a given curve k; revolve these lines around O a given angle, v, increasing them at the same time in a given ratio, f, and the locus of the extremities of the lines will be a new curve, K. This curve must be similar to k; for we may imagine the operation performed by two separate ones, namely revolving the curve, thereby only changing the position, and then multiplying the curve by f in regard to O. A point a in the curve k will determine another, A, in K. a and A are called similarly situated points.

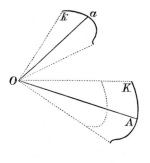

Similarly situated lines are those joining similarly situated points, similarly situated angles are those formed of similarly situated lines. I will call point O the *pivot point*, v *the angle of revolution*, f *the ratio of revolution*. For any two similarly situated points, A and a, the $\triangle AOa$ must have the same form, $\angle aOA$ being equal to v and $\dfrac{AO}{aO} = f$ being constant. The curve K may also be said to be described by one vertex, A, of a triangle AOa, which revolves around its other vertex O, while the third vertex, a, follows a given curve k, the triangle meanwhile preserving its form. To revolve a curve around O, v being the angle of revolution and f the ratio of revolution, we will call to multiply the curve by f_v in regard to O.

2. Every point in the plane may be considered as belonging to one system and will have its similarly situated point in the other system. The pivot point, being regarded in this way, will become its own similarly situated point, and might for this reason be called the common point of the systems. We may likewise regard the whole plane as revolving around O, while one of its points describes a given curve: if the whole system of points preserves its form while revolving, every point of the system will describe a curve, which is similar to the given.

3. The pivot point, the angle of revolution and the ratio of revolution being known, any system of straight lines and circles may be revolved by means of straight edge and compasses. A point a is revolved around O by drawing $\angle aOA = v$, making $OA = f \times Oa$. A straight line is revolved by revolving a point in the line, the angle between this and the line, which connects the chosen point with the pivot point, remaining unaltered.

A Circle is revolved by revolving the centre and a point of the circumference.

4. By the aid of the above the following common problem may be solved:

To place a triangle, which shall be similar to a given, with one vertex in a given point and the two other vertices in two given curves.

Make the given point O the pivot point and revolve one curve around this, the angle of revolution being the angle of the triangle, of which the vertex is O, and the ratio of revolution being the ratio of the sides of the triangle, which enclose this angle; the curve will, after being revolved, intersect the other given curve in the points, which may be the second vertex of the triangle; the third vertex is then obtained by drawing the given angle at O.

If, instead of the form of the triangle, we know the angle, the vertex of which is the given point, and the product of the sides enclosing this angle, the problem is solved in a similar manner; instead of revolving a curve similar to one of the given, we must revolve the inverse curve.

EXAMPLES.

349. To place an equilateral triangle with its vertices in three parallel lines.

Take any point in one of the parallels as one vertex; this point will be the pivot point; $v = 60°$, $f = 1$.

350. To place an equilateral triangle with its vertices in three concentric circles.

351. In a parallelogram to inscribe an isosceles triangle the angle of which is given; the vertex shall coincide with one vertex of the parallelogram.

352. In a given triangle to inscribe another, which shall be similar to a given and have its vertex in a given point of one side.

353. In a given segment of a circle to inscribe a triangle, which shall be similar to a given and have one vertex in a given point of the chord.

354. In a given circle to draw a chord, the length of which shall have given ratios to the distances of its extremities from a given point.

355. In a parallelogram to inscribe a rectangle, the diagonals of which shall form a given angle.

The two figures must have the same centre.

356. In a parallelogram to inscribe a rhombus, the diagonals of which shall have a given ratio.

357. In a square to inscribe an equilateral triangle.

358. Given a circle and two points, A and B. To this circle draw a tangent, and from B draw a perpendicular to this tangent; the distances of the tangent and its perpendicular from A shall have a given ratio.

By revolution around A make B fall in the tangent.

359. In a given parallelogram to inscribe a rhombus, which shall have a given area.

360. Two points A and B and two lines, intersecting in C, are given; through A and B draw two lines enclosing a given angle and intersecting the given lines in X and Y respectively; AX and BY shall have a given ratio.

Translate AX and BY to the parallel positions $A_1 C$ and $B_1 C$.

361. Construct a triangle of h_a, $B — C$ and $b \times c$.

362. Describe two circles, which shall pass through a given point A and intersect under a given angle v; the ratio of the radii is given equal to f, and each of the circles shall touch one of two given lines.

To multiply one given line by f_v in regard to A reduces the problem to 181.

5. We are always able to find a pivot point, around which one of two similar figures may be revolved and brought to cover the other, it being supposed, that the parts run in the same direction of revolution (this will commonly be supposed to be the case in the subsequent treatment of similar figures); we know the ratio of revolution, which is the ratio of two similarly situated lines, and the angle of revolution is the angle between two such lines. To find the pivot point

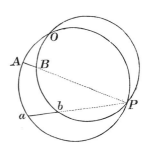

we might use the known ratio of its distances from two similarly situated points, but we have a still easier construction. Let A and a, B and b represent two pair of similarly situated points; the similarly situated lines AB and ab must form the angle of revolution; this angle is also enclosed between the lines from a pair of similarly situated points to the pivot point, *which consequently lies on a circle passing through the point of intersection of two similarly situated lines and through two similarly situated points in these lines.*

The pivot point of two similarly situated lines in two similar figures is the pivot point of the figures; for if one line be revolved so as to cover the other, the whole figure must also cover the other figure.

The pivot point of two infinite straight lines, considered as similar figures, is indeterminate; are two points, one in each line, regarded as similarly situated, a circle will be the locus of the pivot point; take two more points as similarly situated, or in other words decide upon the ratio of revolution, and the pivot point will be determinate; there will only be one such point, as the other point of intersection of the circles is the intersection of the lines.

For two circles the pivot point is indeterminate, as any two points of the circumferences may be considered as similarly situated; as the distances of the pivot point from the centres must have the same ratio as the radii, the locus must be a circle, which divides the centerline harmonically in this ratio (the circle having its centre in the centerline of the given circles and passing through the two points of similitude). Decide upon two points of the circles, which shall be similarly situated, and the pivot point will be determinate; it is most coveniently found by the two similarly situated radii, the centres being always similarly situated points.

6. *The pivot point of two opposite sides in a quadrilateral is also the pivot point of the two other sides.*

Be O the pivot point of BA and CD; we have then $\triangle\ AOB \backsim \triangle\ DOC$ and therefore also $\triangle\ AOD \backsim BOC$; hence, O must be the pivot point of AD and BC. In the first case B is similarly situated to C and A to D; in the second B is similarly situated to A and C to D.

In the same way we see, that the pivot point of AB and CD is also the pivot point of AC and BD.

If the opposite sides be prolonged, till they intersect, the circles, by which the pivot point is determined, are described about the four triangles, which are formed in the figure; the same circles would be employed to determine the pivot point of any two parts of the figure, which do not intersect in one of their extreme points; we have thus the following theorem:

By removing successively one of the four sides of a quadrilateral, we obtain four triangles, of which the circumscribed circles pass through the same point; this point is the pivot point of any two parts of the figure, which do not meet in one of their extremities.

7. *Be the lines, joining similarly situated points of two similar curves, divided in proportionate parts, the locus of the points of division will be a curve similar to the given, and any two such curves have the same pivot point as the given.*

Be A and a two similarly situated points and the line Aa divided by the point P in a given ratio. O being the pivot point, the form of $\triangle AOa$ must be constant, which must also be the case for $\triangle AOP$, consequently P must describe a curve similar to the given, while the triangle revolves around O.

App. The lines, which divide both pair of opposite sides of a quadrilateral in proportionate parts, divide each other in proportionate parts.

EXAMPLES.

363. Given two lines, in each of them a point, A and B, and a point P. Through P draw a line, which shall intersect the given lines in X and Y, so that AX and BY have a given ratio.

We determine the pivot point, O, of the given lines, considering A and B as well as X and Y as similarly situated, the given ratio being the ratio of revolution; as $\triangle OXY \backsim \triangle OAB$ the line OP is seen under a known angle from X, which is thus easily determined.

Remark. Apollonius originated this problem and treated it in his work, „de sectione rationis". The work has been lost, but reproduced by Halley from an arabic translation.

364. Through a given point to draw a line, which shall intersect two given similar curves in two similarly situated points.

The problem is simply an extension of the preceding and is solved in the same way.

365. Given two lines, in each of them a point, A and B, and a point P. Through P draw a line, which shall intersect the given lines in X and Y, so that AX and BY have a given sum.

On one of the lines make BD equal to the given sum; we must then have $AX = YD$, whereby the problem is reduced to 363.

366. Through a given point, P, to draw a line, which shall form a triangle of a given area with two given lines.

Let A be the point, in which the given lines intersect; construct a triangle, which has the given area, AP being one side, and the other side falling in one of the given lines; the required line must now be drawn so, that the area, which is added to the above, equals that, which is subtracted. As the areas are triangles, of which the altitudes are known, namely the distances from P to the given lines, it follows, that we know the ratio of the bases of these triangles, consequently the problem is reduced to 363.

Remark. This problem also originated with Apollonius; the work treating of it „de sectione spatii“ has been lost and only partly restored by Halley.

367. Given two circles passing respectively through A and B. Determine in the circumferences two points, X and Y, so that the arcs AX and BY shall be similar and line XY have a given length.

Find the pivot point of the circles, A and B taken as similarly situated points. X and Y then also becomes similarly situated and the triangles ABO and XYO therefore similar to each other.

In this problem is included 262, the second point, in which the circles intersect being the pivot point.

368. Construct a rectangle, each side of which shall contain one of four given points, the length of the diagonal being also given.

Draw the two circles, which are the loci of two opposite angular points, whereby the problem is reduced to 367.

369. Given two lines AB and CD; through their point of intersection describe a circle, which shall intersect AB in X, CD in Y, so that $AX : CY$ and $XB : YD$ shall be equal to given ratios. —

The circle passes through the pivot point of AX and CY and also through the pivot point of XB and YD.

370. Through two given points, A and B, draw two lines, which form a given angle and intersect a given line and a given circle in X and Y respectively, so that $AX : BY$ shall be equal to a given ratio $1 : k$.

Multiply the given line by k, in regard to the pivot point of AX and BY.

371. Given a point, A, and two lines, BC and DE. We shall find a point X in BC and another Y in DE, the ratio of BX and DY being given as well as the angle XAY.

Revolve BX to DY; A will then fall in a known point A_1 and $\angle AYA_1$ is known.

372. Place a quadrilateral $ABCD$ with B and C in given points, A and D in given lines, $B - C$ being given as well as the ratio $BA : CD$.

Reduce by replacing. (**4**).

373. Through a point, S, in which two given circles intersect, we shall draw two lines ASa and BSb (A and B in one, a and b in the other periphery) forming a given angle, and in such a manner, that the triangles ASB and aSb shall have equal areas.

The other point of intersection of the circles is the pivot point of Aa and Bb and consequently of AB and ab. Revolve AB to ab, and S will fall in a known point S_1. ab has a known length, and its distances from S and S_1 have a known ratio.

We obtain a simpler solution, remarking that the lines through S, perpendicular to the chords, must intersect the centerline in points, equidistant from the middle point of this line.

374. Given two circles, in one a point A, in the other a point B. Describe a circle, which shall pass through A and B and intersect the two given circles in X and Y, so that the arcs AX and BY shall be similar.

Determine the pivot point, O, of the two circles, in which A and B are similarly situated. AX and BY, being similarly situated lines, must intersect in the circumference of the circle ABO; they also intersect in the radical axis of the given circles.

375. The middle points of the sides of a triangle being joined, another triangle is formed, which is similar to the given; it is easily seen, that the angle of revolution of the two triangles is 180° and the ratio of revolution $\frac{1}{2}$. The pivot point must divide any line, which joins two similarly situated points, in two parts, having the ratio $\frac{1}{2}$, and as the medians are such lines, the pivot point must be the point, in which the medians intersect. As the points in which the altitudes intersect, are similarly situated, and as that point of the small triangle is the centre of the large triangles circumscribed circle, it follows, that in any triangle the two points, in which the medians and the altitudes intersect and the centre of the circumscribed circle are situated in a straight line, the parts of which line have the ratio 1 : 2.

376. Given a circle, point O and P, and an angle v. A line through P intersects the circle in A and B; find the locus of a point X, for which $\angle\ OBX = OAX = v$.

The circle $AOXB$ intersects OB in two fixed points, has consequently the pivot point O, while the centre describes a straight line; X will therefore describe a straight line. If O is the centre of the given circle and $v = 90°$, X will describe the polar to P.

8. If we have three similar systems, *A*, *B* and *C*, and a point *O* be the pivot point of *A* and *B* as well as of *B* and *C*, *O* must also be the pivot point of *A* and *C*; *O* is then the common pivot point of the three systems; this may be extended to any number of systems.

Join three similarly situated points, *a*, *b* and *c* of the three systems, with the pivot point, and the ratio of these lines as well as the angles, which they form, must be constant; hence the form of △ *abc* will be constant, and I will therefore call it the *fundamental triangle*. Similarly it is seen, that to a greater number of similar figures, having a common pivot point, we will have a corresponding fundamental polygon of a constant form; while this revolves around the pivot point, one angular point describing one of the figures, the other angular points will simultaneously describe the other figures; any other point in the plane, regarded as belonging to the fundamental polygon will describe a figure similar to the others. The pivot point of the given figures will also be the pivot point of the fundamental polygon during its motion.

9. We have seen, that the pivot point of two straight lines, in which we have given two similarly situated points, must fall in a circle, passing through the two points and the point, in which the lines intersect; for three lines, in which three similarly situated points are given, the pivot point will be the intersection of two such circles; the third circle must pass through the same point. Joining the three points, we have the fundamental triangle; as we may decide upon any three points in the lines, this triangle may have any form, but to different fundamental triangles correspond different pivot points. Having given the fundamental triangle, the pivot point is easily determined; we place a triangle similar to the given on the three lines (f. inst. by 154) and in this way determine three similarly situated points.

Do the three lines pass through one point, *O*, this will be the pivot point for any fundamental triangle; thus all triangles, which are similar to a given fundamental triangle, will be similarly situated, *O* being the centre of similitude. In one special case the pivot point will be indeterminate; if the vertices A and B describe AO and BO and $\angle C = \angle AOB$, then C will describe a straight line through O.

10. The pivot point of two circles is according to **5** indeterminate; a common pivot point may be determined for three circles; as the point is found by the intersection of two circles (see **6**), we will have two solutions, namely the two points, the distances of which from the centres have the same ratios as the radii.

Decide upon one of these points as the pivot point of the circles and the angles of revolution are easily determined, the lines joining the centres with the pivot point being similarly situated; the triangle, having its vertices in the centres, becomes the fundamental triangle, and any other triangle, formed by joining three similarly situated points, will be similar to this.

11. *If a polygon, similar to a given, moves in such a way, that three of its points describe straight lines, (which do not meet in the same point), then every point of the figure must describe a straight line.*

The triangle, which is formed by joining the three points, has a constant form, and if we consider it the fundamental triangle, the pivot point of the three lines, in which the points move, may be determined. According to 8 this point is also the pivot point of all the positions of the fundamental triangle, and consequently for all positions of the given polygon, to which the triangle belongs; the movement of the polygon being a revolution around a fixed pivot point, we see, that all points of the polygon will describe similar curves, which in this case are straight lines. In one case the theorem may not hold, viz: when the three lines meet in one point (see **9**).

We may in **11** substitute three similar curves, having a common pivot point, for the three straight lines, and extend the theorem to include this case. The three points must always, while moving, coincide with three similar points of the curves, and the triangle which these points determine, must therefore be the fundamental triangle of the curves; be this the case, we see as above, that any other point of the polygon must describe a curve, similar to the given. It is evident, that the conditions named are more, than we need to determine the movement, and we will therefore try to remove the superfluous conditions; we will confine ourselves to examine the case, where the three curves are circles, as the only one of importance at present. What we particularly want to investigate is: Does the fundamental triangle move on the three curves by following similarly situated points only? which we know to be the case with three straight lines.

We have seen, that to three circles correspond two common pivot points; the fundamental triangle must be the same for either of the two points, as the three centres are similarly situated points, and we obtain the fundamental triangle by joining three such points. To a point A of one circle will correspond the similarly situated points B and C of the other two circles, if one pivot point be used, b and c if the other pivot point be used. We have therefore the two positions, ABC and Abc, of the fundamental triangle, one vertex of which is A, and it is easy to prove, that we can have no others. Generally, if we solve the problem, to place the fundamental triangle with one vertex in A and the other vertices on the other two circles, according to the rules given in the preceding, we obtain only two solutions, which must be identical with those, we have obtained above in a different way.

The fundamental triangle can thus only move on the three circles by following similarly situated points, but this can be done in two ways.

12. *When a polygon, similar to a given, revolves in such a manner, that three lines of the figure* (which do not meet in the same point) *each contain a fixed point, any other line, belonging to the figure, shall pass through a fixed point.*

Let the three lines AB, BC and CD each contain one of the fixed points M, N and P; we will have to prove, that any fourth line DA must contain a fixed point. First we see, that all positions of the polygon must have a common pivot point. For the two positions, $ABCD$ and $A_1B_1C_1D_1$, we obtain this point by the construction of a circle through the similarly situated points, B and B_1, and through the point of intersection of the similarly situated lines, M (see **5**); this circle must also pass through N and may thus be drawn at once, as it shall pass through the fixed points, M and N, and contain the angle B. The pivot point, O, is therefore fixed,

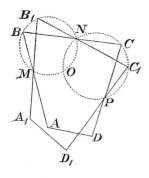

being the point, in which this circle intersects another circle, constructed in the same way through the points N and P. A circle through O, P and D must also pass through D_1 as well as through the point, in which the similarly situated lines, AD and A_1D_1, intersect for any position of the latter line; this point of intersection is consequently a fixed point.

There is also a natural extension of this theorem, which however we will prove in a different way.

13. In revolving a polygon, similar to a given, around a fixed pivot point, we have hitherto thought the motion determined by one of the points of the polygons following a certain curve; it may however be determined by one of the sides touching a given curve during the motion. In this case any line of the polygon will during the motion touch a curve, similar to the given. If AB successively takes the positions A_1B_1, A_2B_2 etc., while touching the given curve, and another line BC the corresponding positions B_1C_1, B_2C_2 etc., then we may, by a revolution around the fixed point, cause the two systems to cover each other, taking as the angle of revolution the constant angle between two such lines, and as the ratio of revolution the constant ratio between the distances of the two lines from the pivot point. The figures, which are formed by the two systems of lines, are consequently similar, and as this is independent of the number of positions, it will hold for an infinite number of positions, in which case the figures are the curves, touched by the moving lines.

It is evident, that the given point will be the common pivot point of the touched curves, the angle of revolution being the angle between the moving lines, and the ratio of revolution the ratio of the distances of these lines from the pivot point. The sides must touch the generated curves in similarly situated points and will therefore become similarly situated lines in the curves. A system of any other similarly situated lines in the curves will of course form a polygon, similar to the given; I will call this polygon the *secondary fundamental polygon*. There is a close relation between the two fundamental polygons; the primary is inscribable in the secondary and remains inscribed during a revolution around the fixed point, if one angular point of the inscribed polygon remains in one side of the circumscribed polygon.

The movement, which we have discussed in the above, can be determined in other ways; I will here only consider the case, in which it is determined by the rolling of three of the sides of the polygon on similar curves; in order that this movement shall be the same as the above described, the three curves must have a common pivot point and the three sides must always touch the curves in similarly situated points; this is sufficient to determine the movement, which will be the same as above, and consequently be a revolution of the polygon around the pivot point of the curves, each one of its lines touching a curve similar to the given; the triangle formed by the three sides, which roll on the given curves, will be the secondary fundamental triangle of these curves. The theorem in 12 is a special case of this, the curves being reduced to points.

14. Having determined the pivot point of two circles, two points A and a being decided upon as similarly situated, the tangents to these points will form a certain angle, which remains unaltered while A and a describe similar arcs. Inversely, be the angle given, we may determine a pair of similarly situated points and the corresponding pivot point. Any two tangents, forming the given angle, will touch the circles in similarly situated points (two solutions).

15. *For a revolution around a given point we may al-*
ways substitute a revolution around any point and a parallel
translation, the ratio of revolution and the angle of revolution
remaining unaltered, and the parallel translation being only
dependent upon these elements and the situation of the pivot
points.

By the new revolution the figure will obtain the right
size, the ratio of revolution being unaltered, and the lines of
the figure will fall in the right directions, the angle of revolution being unaltered. The parallel translation is thus determined in size and direction by the line, that joins the two
positions, which any point of the curve takes by the two
revolutions.

Be O the given pivot point, O_1 the new. O_1, considered
as belonging to the given curve, will by the revolution around
O, fall in a new point O_2, while by the revolution around O_1
it remains stationary. The line $O_1 O_2$ will therefore determine
the parallel translation. *The parallel translation is deter-*
mined by the line, which the new pivot point describes by
being revolved around the given pivot point.

Inversely we may for a parallel translation and a revolution substitute a revolution around a new point, which is
easily found by the above.

16. *The order, in which two successive revolutions should*
be made, may be reversed by adding a parallel translation.

Whatever order we choose, every line in the system will
be revolved through an angle, which is the sum of the given
angles of revolution, and will be multiplied by the product
of the given ratios of revolution. The two figures, which we
obtain, will have the same size, and their similarly situated
lines will have the same direction; a parallel translation will
therefore cause one to cover the other.

The two pivot points being A and B, A will by the revolution around A remain in its place, by the revolution around
B fall in a point C. If we on the contrary commence by revolving A around B, A will fall in C and will then by the
revolution around A fall in a point D. CD or DC will thus

represent the parallel translation, which must be added in order to reverse the order of the two revolutions.

17. *Two revolutions may be compounded into one.*

Let the two pivot points be A and B. In the revolution, which shall take the place of the two, the pivot point C is only unknown. The point A will by the revolution around A remain in its place, and will by the revolution around B fall in a point A_1. C must now be determined, so that $\angle ACA_1$ shall be equal to the sum of the given angles of revolution, while the ratio $CA_1 : CA$ shall be equal to the product of the given ratios of revolution. The given angles and ratios of revolution determine also the angles and the ratios between the sides of the triangle, the vertices of which are the three pivot points. If two of these points fall in one point, all three points must fall in the same point, as formerly shown; if the given angles of revolution are 0, the three pivot points will fall in one straight line. In this case the pivot points become centres of similitude of the figures, which, taken in pairs, are similarly situated. This theorem will be proved in a different way in the following.

18. We have seen, how by revolution and inversion we regard such systems of points, in which a point of one system has a corresponding point in the other, and every circle of one system has a corresponding circle in the other (the term circle including also the straight line); and we have seen, that the significance of these transformations for the elementary geometry depends upon the above mentioned relations. It is therefore reasonable to investigate, if there are no other transformations, by which point will correspond to point, circle to circle, all points in the plane being included in both systems.

Let A, B and C be three points of one system, a, b and c the corresponding points of the other system. Be M a point of the first system, which does not lie in the circumference of the circle ABC. To the circles ABM and BCM must correspond two circles abm and bcm in the other system, consequently m must correspond to M. The dependancy of the two systems is therefore completely determined by three pair of points. We will now in the circle ABC inscribe a triangle $a_1 b_1 c_1 \backsim abc$, Aa_1, Bb_1 and Cc_1 meeting in one point, O. This problem is easily solved, as we know the angles at O. We have thus seen, that by inversion of the system ABC we may form a system similar to abc, and that system may again by a revolution (and if necessary a revolution around an axis) be transformed to the system abc.

We have thus proved, that *two systems, of which point corresponds to point and circle to circle, may always be transformed one into the other by revolution and inversion.*

19. From the theorems proved in the theory of revolution we may deduct new and more general theorems by the aid of the modern geometry. As their application is not intended for this book, we will only give one example: In **11** we proved, that a straight line, which moves in such a way, that the ratio of the two parts, ab and bc, intercepted by three fixed lines, is a constant, does revolve around a fixed pivot point; consequently any point of the line, determined by the ratio, in which it divides ab f. inst., will also describe a straight line. The ratios named, may be expressed as anharmonic ratios, when the point of intersection of the moveable line and the infinitely distant straight line is taken into consideration. In that form of the theorem it expresses a projective property viz:

When a moveable straight line intersects four fixed lines in points with constant anharmonic ratio, every point of the line (determined by anharmonic ratio) *will describe a straight line.*

Let two of the fixed lines pass through the two imaginary infinitely distant points of any circle, then we deduct the following theorem:

When a given angle ABC has a fixed vertex, A, and B and C describe fixed straight lines, every point, D, of the line BC (determined by the angle BAD) *will describe a straight line.*

APPLICATIONS.

377. In a given triangle, *ABC*, to inscribe another triangle congruous to a given.

According to **9** a system of similar triangles, inscribed in a given triangle, have a common pivot point; we inscribe therefore in the given triangle another, which has the demanded form, and determine the pivot point, the latter triangle being considered the fundamental triangle; the triangle, which we seek, is obtained by a revolution of the fundamental triangle, this operation being most conveniently done by multiplying the drawn fundamental triangle in regard to the pivot point, thereby giving it the demanded size, and then revolve it around the same point, till the vertices fall in the sides of the given triangle.

378. In a given quadrilateral to inscribe another, similar to a given.

A quadrilateral, similar to the given, is placed with three vertices in the three lines, and the pivot point is determined as in the preceding problem; it is now the question, how to revolve the quadrilateral around this point, that the fourth vertex shall fall in the fourth line; during the revolution the vertex will describe a straight line (**II**), which is easily drawn, either by repeating the above construction, thus determining another point of the line, or by a revolution of the sides of the given quadrilateral around the found pivot point. If we use the first method, it is unnecessary to find the pivot point.

379. On four given lines to place a fifth line, so that the three parts intercepted shall have given ratios.

The problem is a special case of the preceding, as the sought line may be considered a quadrilateral of a known form.

Remark. We find these three problems in the first volume of Newtons „principia mathematica philosophiae naturalis".

380. In a given triangle to inscribe another, similar to a given and having an area, which shall be a minimum.

381. Construct a parallelogram with given angles and a given perimeter, each side passing through one of four given points.

Let the sides AB, BC, CD and DA contain respectively the given points, P, Q, R and S. Let T be the point, in which the circles SAP and PBQ intersect. T is then the pivot point of AB and a line A_1PB_1 between the circumferences, consequently
$$AT : AB = A_1T : A_1B_1.$$
V being the point, in which the circles PAS and SDR intersect, the ratio $AV : AD$ is determined in a similar manner, and A may now be determined (189).

382. On the circumferences of three given circles to place a triangle, which shall be congruous to the triangle, the vertices of which are the three centres.

Find the common pivot point of the three circles; the three centres being similarly situated points, the given triangle becomes the fundamental triangle; this triangle and the demanded will therefore have their pivot point in that of the three circles; revolve the first triangle around this point till one of the vertices falls in the circumference, and we have the demanded triangle. The given ratio of revolution is equal to 1 in this case, but we solve the problem in a similar manner for any other ratio.

383. To draw a triangle, congruous to a given, each side containing one of three given points.

One triangle, the sides of which pass through the three points, and which is similar to the given, is easily drawn; the given points are now considered similar curves, and the drawn triangle the secondary fundamental triangle; determine the pivot point and multiply the drawn triangle, thereby giving it the demanded size. As the ratio of revolution of the triangle, thus obtained, and the demanded is equal to 1, two similarly situated sides must have the same distance from the pivot point, and one of the sought lines is consequently determined as a line, which shall touch a known circle and pass through a given point.

384. To draw a quadrilateral, similar to a given, each side passing through one of four given points.

Draw any quadrilateral, similar to the given, so that three sides pass through three of the given points, and determine the pivot point as in 383. This quadrilateral must now be revolved so that the fourth side passes through the fourth point; this is easily done as the side shall also contain a fixed point, which may be determined in two ways (analoguous to 378).

385. The triangle ABC and the circumscribed circle are drawn; from a point, O, of the circumference draw lines, which form a given angle with the sides. Prove that the points, in which these lines meet the sides, fall in one straight line.

Choose A, B and a suitable point of AB as similarly situated points in the three sides, and O will be the pivot point; the three points of intersection will be similarly situated points, which must lie in one straight line, as the fundamental triangle is a straight line.

386. Three circles have their centres in the three vertices, B, C and D of a parallelogram. Place a parallelogram, which shall have given angles, with one vertex in the fourth vertex, A, of the first parallelogram and with the three other vertices in the circumferences of the three circles.

Multiplying the circle C by $\frac{1}{2}$ in regard to A we obtain a new circle; this one and the circles B and D have for their fundamental triangle a straight line, the two parts of which are equal. The diagonal, B_1D_1, of the sought parallelogram must consequently intersect these three circles in similarly situated points and is seen from *A* under a given angle. Revolve BB_1 to DD_1 and *A* will fall in a known point A_1, $\angle AD_1A_1$ being known.

387. To find the locus of the points, from which tangents drawn to two given circles, have a given ratio.

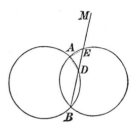

Let the circles intersect in *A* and *B*, *M* being one of the sought points; line *MB* intersects the two circles in *D* and *E*, and the ratio between $MD \times MB$ and $ME \times MB$ is constant, according to the given conditions; consequently the ratio of *MD* and *ME* is a constant; as, in addition, the angles of $\triangle ADE$ are constant, the whole figure *ADEM* will have a constant form and while revolving around *A*, *D* and *E* describing circles, *M* must describe a circle too. *A* being the common pivot point of this and the given circles, the former must pass through *A*. *DEM* represents the fundamental triangle, and as the triangle, formed by the lines, which join the three centres, must be similar to the fundamental triangle, it is evident, that the three centres must be situated in one straight line, the distances of the sought centre from the given having the same ratio as *MD*∶*ME*, which is the square of the given ratio.

388. Draw two lines, which shall form a given angle and touch two circles in such a manner, that the line, joining the points of contact, shall pass through a given point.

By **14** the problem is reduced to 364.

389. Draw two lines, which shall form a given angle and touch two circles in such a manner, that the line, joining the points of contact, shall have a given direction.

This problem is a special case of the preceding, the given point being infinitely distant.

390. In a triangle to inscribe another, which, being similar to a given, shall have a side, which passes through a given point.

We determine three similarly situated points in the given lines, taking as the fundamental triangle the one, which shall be inscribed. The problem is now reduced to 364.

391. In a triangle to inscribe another, which shall be similar to a given; the centre of gravity of the sought triangle shall be situated in one of the medians of the given triangle.

Inscribe any two triangles, similar to the given; the line, which joins the centres of gravity of these two triangles, will intersect the given median in the sought centre of gravity. The vertices are now easily determined; for a system of three vertices in one side of the given triangle will determine parts, which have the same ratio as the parts, determined by the three centres of gravity.

392. In a triangle to inscribe another, of which two sides shall have given directions and the third side a given length.

Let abc be the inscribed triangle, of which bc is given. A circle, circumscribing abc, will intersect the side, to which a belongs, in two points, viz., a and another point d. All the sides of the triangle dbc are known.

393. We shall draw three circles, having given the point, from which the three circles appear to be of equal size, a point in the circumference of each circle, the ratios of the radii and the angles, under which the centerlines are seen from the given point.

We know the common pivot point of the three circles, the angles of revolution and the ratios of revolution; consequently, we can revolve two of the given points to the circle through the third point, and then construct the circle through the three points.

394. Given two circles, which intersect in A and B, and two points, P and R. In each of the circles draw a chord, which shall pass through P and R respectively; the lines, which join the ends of the chords, shall pass through A.

If we consider the two chords similar figures, B will be the pivot point of these and of the circles. The angle of revolution and the ratio of revolution being known, we may revolve one of the given points into the chord, containing the other point; two points in this chord are then known.

395. The point X is the pivot point of AB and CY, of which A, B and C are given points; which curve will be described by X, while Y describes a given curve?

Translate the triangle BAX to the parallel position $B_1 CX_1$. The similar triangles show that $B_1 Y$ and CX_1 have a constant product and revolve in opposite directions with the same angular velocity. X and Y will therefore describe inverse curves.

396. A surveyor can see three points, A, B and C in the field; the corresponding points, a, b and c are platted on the plane table. He shall determine the point, O, on the plane table, which corresponds to his station in the field. (The three point problem).

The sought point is the pivot point of the triangles ABC and abc. Draw through a, b and c the sightlines to A, B and C, which lines form the so called triangle of error; call this $a\beta\gamma$, the lines through a and b intersecting in γ etc. The angles, a, β and γ may be considered constant for small changes in the position of the plane table on account of the great distance to A, B and C; consequently the sought point is that, in which the circles $a\gamma b$ and $a\beta c$ intersect.

To draw these circles correctly is not practical in the field, and their centres will not always be on the table. If we take the inverse figures of the circles, a being the centre of inversion and $a\beta \times a\gamma$ the power of inversion, the point corresponding to the required will be the point of intersection of two straight lines, passing respectively through β and γ and forming with $\beta\gamma$ respectively angles equal to $ab\gamma$ and $ac\beta$. The construction is therefore:

Draw the two lines through β and γ making with $\beta\gamma$ the above mentioned two known angles and intersecting in a point O_1. Turn the plane table till O_1a points to A; then the triangles ABC and abc are similarly situated, and the triangle of error is reduced to a point, O, which is the demanded.

Making $\angle \beta\gamma O_1 = \beta ca$ and $\angle \gamma\beta O_1 = \gamma ba$, the equal angles being described in the same direction of revolution, the construction will hold for any situation of the known points.

APPENDIX.

ABOUT THE INTERSECTION OF ARCS OF CIRCLES.

In the preceding we have seen, how important it is to carefully examine a figure, in order to find the simple relations, which exist between the elements of the figure, especially those of the angles. This may generally be accomplished by the theorems treating of the relations between angles and arcs of circles, and similar elementary theorems; but are the figures complicated, it will often be difficult to discover the simple relations on account of the great number of angles. It is therefore appropriate to procure means, by which such an examination may be made easy. One of these will be, to consider the very angles, formed by arcs of circles. It is not my intention in this place to fully treat this question, but only to cite some theorems, the application of which will be found convenient in a great number of cases.

I. *In a polygon, formed by arcs of circles, the sum of the sides plus the sum of the angles, adjacent to those of the polygon, is equal to 4R.*

Let a straight line roll around the polygon, commencing at one vertex and touching one side till it shall have reached the next angular point; then revolving around this till it becomes a tangent to the next side, and so forth, finally returning to the position, from which it started; the line will then successively have described angles, which are equal to the sides of the polygon and to the angles adjacent to the angles of the polygon, but as the line has made one complete revolution, the sum of those angles must be $4R$.

We have here made the supposition, that the line returns to the position, from which it started, after *one* revolution; in the case of polygons, which are not convex, the line may have made several revolutions (or none); the sum of the angles may therefore be any multiple of $4R$.

Shall the theorem hold generally, we must take the angles and the arcs as positiv or negativ according to the direction of the revolution.

2. *In a triangle the sum of the angles minus the sum of the sides is equal to $2R$. Do the sides pass through the same point* (which is not an angular point of the triangle), *the sum of the angles is equal to $2R$, the sum of the sides $= 0$.*

The last theorem is easily proved, if we for the angles of the triangle substitute the angles at the point of intersection of the sides, these angles being equal to the former.

3. *In a twosided figure the two angles have the same size and are equal to half the sum of the sides.*

4. *An angle at the circumference is equal to half the sum of the legs and the arc, which it subtends.*

Prolong the legs, thus forming a twosided figure, in which half the sum of the sides is equal to the angle; but the sum of the two prolongations is equal to the arc, which the angle at the circumference subtends (**2**). This arc, being considered a side in one or the other of the two triangles, in which the figure is divided, must have opposite signs in the two cases.

5. *If of two pair of circles, the points of intersection of each pair are situated each on one circle of the other pair, the two pair of circles make equal angles.* (**2**).

6. *In an inscribed quadrilateral the sum of one pair of opposite angles is equal to the sum of the other pair. Do the four sides pass through the same point, the equal sums are $2R$, and the sum of the sides $= 0$.* (**4**).

7. *If in a quadrilateral the sum of one pair of oppo-site angles equals the sum of the other pair, the quadrilateral is inscribable.*

According to I the sum of one pair of opposite angles minus half the sum of the sides is equal to $2R$. This sum is the same as the sum of the opposite angles of the straight-lined quadrilateral, the angular points of which coincide with those of the given.

8. *If two circles touch two other circles in the same manner,* (externally or internally) *the four points of contact lie all in the circumference of a circle.* (**7**).

9. *Every circle, which passes through the point, in which two fixed circles intersect, will intersect a system of circles, touching the two fixed circles* (in the same manner) *under equal angles.*

We have formerly (198) proved this theorem by inversion, but shall now prove it directly, including the case where the two fixed circles do not intersect, understanding by a circle through their points of intersection a circle, which has a common radical axis with the two fixed circles.

We may for one circle take the common tangent; be A and B the points of contact of the common tangent and the fixed circles S_1 and S_2, while C and D are the points of con-tact of another circle S. The circle through the points of intersection of the fixed circles, intersects the common tangent in E, the circle S in F. The lines AC and BD meet in that point O of S, the tangent to which is parallel to the common tangent. The points A, B, C and D being situated in one circle, O must have the same power in regard to S_1 and S_2, and has consequently the same power in regard to the circles ACF, EF and BDF; O must therefore be a point of the ra-dical axis for any two of these three circles. F being a common point of the three circles, OF will be their common radical axis, and the circles will have another common point in the line OF. The circles having two common points, their centres must be situated in one straight line. As the circles ACF and BDF pass through the points of contact, each of them will intersect the common tangent and the tangent to F under equal angles, and their centres must be points of the line, which bisects the angle between the two tangents. The centre of circle EF being a point of the same line, EF must intersect the common tangent and the tangent to F, or the circle S, under equal angles.

SYSTEMS OF CIRCLES.

Among the conditions, which determine a circle, we will especially notice, 1) the circle shall pass through a given point, 2) the circle shall touch a given straight line and 3) the circle shall touch a given circle. By selecting the three conditions, which determine a circle from these, we obtain a group of problems, which, with exception of four, have been solved in the preceding. Before proceding to the solution of these and a few other problems, we will state two theorems, which will be applied in the following.

10. *If A and B are the points, in which a circle touches two other circles, then the line AB passes through one of the centres of similitude of the two circles.*

Call the second point b, in which line AB intersects the circle through B. It is easily seen, that the radius to b is parallel to the radius to A in the other circle. A and b are consequently similarly situated points in the two circles, considered as similarly situated, and the line Ab must therefore pass through the centre of similitude.

If the circle touches the two circles in the same manner, i. e. touches both externally or internally, the line passes through the external centre of similitude; if it touches one externally and the other internally, the line passes through the internal centre of similitude.

O being the centre of similitude, the two circles are inverse curves in regard to O as the centre of inversion; the product $OA \times OB$ is therefore a constant.

11. *The three external centres of similitude for each pair of three circles lie in a straight line.*

Be the circles A, B and C, γ the centre of similitude of A and B, β of A and C, α of B and C. Draw two tangents to the circle B, which shall be parallel to the common tangents to the circles A and C;

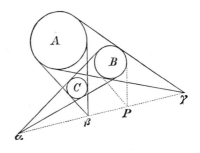

the former intersect in P. P and β are similarly situated points in regard to the circles A and B and the line $P\beta$ must therefore pass through the centre of similitude, γ, of A and B. P and β are likewise similarly situated in regard to B and C consequently the line $P\beta$ passes through α; hence α, β and γ must be in one straight line.

App. 1. In analogy with the above, a straight line through two of the internal centres of similitude will pass through the external centre of similitude of the third pair of circles.

App. 2. The theorem holds for any three similar curves being similarly situated in pairs; add to the curves three similarly situated circles; the theorem holds for the centres of similitude of these circles, which are the same as the centres of similitude of the curves.

EXAMPLES.

397. To describe a circle, which shall touch two given circles; the line through the points of contact shall pass through a given point.

398. Describe a circle, which shall touch two given circles in the same manner and shall intercept a chord of a given length of a line through the external centre of similitude of the given circles.

399. Given two circles, A and B, and the points D, E and F. Describe a circle, C, passing through D, so that the radical axis of A and C shall pass through E, and the radical axis of B and C shall pass through F.

400. In a quadrilateral, $ABCD$, the side AB is fixed, and the ratios between the parts of the diagonals are constant. Find the locus of CD.

Call the point, in which the diagonals intersect, O, and
$$AO : OC = m : n,$$
$$BO : OD = p : q;$$

Let the point O describe one or another curve, K; multiplying this curve in regard to A by $\dfrac{m+n}{m}$ and in regard to B by $\dfrac{p+q}{p}$, we obtain the curves, simultaneously described by C and D; these curves are similar curves in the ratio $\dfrac{p\,(m+n)}{m\,(p+q)}$, and their centre of similitude is a point M situated in the line AB (**II**, *App.* *2*). As C and D are similarly situated, CD passes through M, the ratio $MC : MD$ being the above stated. Similarly we find the ratio $MB : MA$ to be constant, consequently M to be a fixed point and the locus of CD.

401. To describe a circle, which shall pass through a given point and touch two given circles.

We know the power of the centre of similitude in regard to the required circle; thereby we determine another point in that circle, and the problem is reduced to 238.

402. To describe a circle, which shall pass through a given point and touch a given line and a given circle.

The problem is a special case of 401, the given line being considered a circle with infinitely large radius.

403. To draw a circle, which shall touch three given circles.

By applying the method of parallel translation, mentioned on pag. 52, we reduce the problem to 401.

The problem may also be solved by a proceeding, similar to the one in 201. The triangle, we seek to construct, will in this case be the one, the vertices of which are the sought points of contact; the sides will pass through three of the centres of similitude; are these taken as centres of inversion, and the powers of inversion so chosen, that the circles, in pairs, will be exchanged by the inversion, any one of the circles will after three inversions return to its first place. There will thus be no essential difference between this problem and the one formerly solved.

The simplest and most elegant solution is obtained by applying the theorem, that the radical axis of two circles intersects a circle, touching both, and one of the common tangents under equal angles. According to this theorem, the tangents to the required circle drawn through the points, in which the radical axis of the two circles intersect this circle, will be parallel to those common tangents, which belong to the same system of touching circles, as the one under consideration. (The external common tangents belong to the system of circles, which touch in the same manner, the internal to the system of circles, which touch in different manners). Let A, B and C be the given circles. If we consider the required circle and circle A as similarly situated, the point of contact being the centre of similitude, then the radical axis of A and B will be similarly situated to the line, which in circle A joins the points of contact of the common tangents to A and B; under the same supposition the radical axis of A and C will be similarly situated to the line, which in circle A joins the points of contact of the common tangents to A and C. These two lines intersect in the point, which is similarly situated to the radical centre of the given circles; the line joining these two points will therefore pass through the point of contact, which we seek.

The other problems, in which the circle is determined by three of the above named conditions, may all be treated as special cases of this.

404. In a triangle ABC to inscribe three circles S_a, S_b and S_c, each of them touching the other two circles and two sides of the triangle.

This famous problem has been solved for the first time by the italian mathematician *Malfatti* († 1807), who calculated the radii of the circles and found their values, which could easily be constructed. In 1826 *Steiner* stated, that the common tangent to two of the circles at their point of contact would also be a tangent to two of the circles, inscribed in the triangles, in which the given triangle is divided by the lines, bisecting the angles; this theorem gives at once an easy construction. Steiner, however, did not prove the theorem, but stated, that it could be proved by a series of theorems, in regard to centres of similitude, radical axes, power-circles etc., which he deducted. It was as late as 1874, that the first proof of Steiners construction, by aid of his theorems was given by *Schröter*, yet by assistance of some complicated inversions. We will now, at this place, deduct Steiners construction from the most elementary theorems.

Let us name the points of contact with the sides, so that by following the perimeter we meet successively points A, c_1, c_2, B, a_1, a_2, C, b_1, b_2; call γ the point of contact of S_a and S_b, β that of S_a and S_c and α that of S_b and S_c. A circle, touching S_a and S_c in β and passing through the point c_2, will intersect AC in a point D under the same angle, which it forms with AB at c_2 (**9**). The tangents to this circle at c_2 and D meet in the line, which bisects angle A, and form with the two sides an inscribable quadrilateral, consequently the arc $c_2 D$ is equal to $\angle A$. The circle $c_2 a\beta$ passes through the point c_1; this circle and $\beta D b_2$ intersecting in E, we have $\angle c_1 E b_2 = \angle c_1 c_2 \beta + \angle b_2 D\beta = 180° - \frac{1}{2}A$; hence it follows, that the circle $c_1 E b_2$ has its centre in A. The circle $c_1 c_2 a\beta$ cuts off equal chords of AB, AE and the tangent to $D\beta c_2$ at c_2; for $Ac_1 = AE$ and the circle intersects AB and $D\beta c_2$ under equal angles. Similarly we see, that circle $E\beta D b_2$ cuts off equal chords of AE and the tangent to D. Call F the point, in which the tangents to D and c_2 intersect, while these lines intersect AE respectively in G and H; of $c_2F = DF$, $c_2G = EG$, $DH = EH$ follows, that one side in the triangle GFH is equal to the sum of the other two. The points G and H will therefore be the same as F, and line AEF will bisect the angle A. The circle $c_1c_2\alpha\beta$ intersects consequently AB, AE and the tangents to α and β under equal angles, and we may thus describe a circle, concentric with $c_1c_2\alpha\beta$, which shall touch the four lines. In the same way we prove, that this circle touches the line, which bisects the angle B, and thus Steiners theorem is proved.

If we would consider the circles, touching the prolongations of the sides, the problem would have other solutions, easily obtained by simple alterations in the above deduction.

If we in the problem for the sides of the triangle substitute three circles, we may invert the figure using for centre of inversion one of the points, in which the circles intersect. It is evident, that the theorem proved above may be extended to include this case, if we for the line bisecting the angles substitute the circles, which bisect the angles between two of the given circles, and for the tangent to β substitute the corresponding circle of the inverse figure etc.

ABOUT THE POSSIBILITY OF SOLVING A GIVEN PROBLEM BY STRAIGHT EDGE AND PAIR OF COMPASSES.

If we have not succeded in finding the solution of a given problem, the reason may be either, that we have not been able to find the right method, or that the problem belongs to those, which can not be solved by straight edge and compasses. In the following we will give the means to decide this question in most cases.

If a problem can be solved, the solution, be it ever so complicated, must be combined of the two operations: to draw a straight line through two given points and to describe a circle, the centre and the radius of which are given. Every point is determined as the point of intersection of two straight lines, or of a straight line and a circle, or of two circles. If we suppose, that by the methods and formulas of the analytical geometry, we calculate the coordinates of the points successively as they are constructed, all the equations to be solved will be of the first or the second degree. It will therefore be possible to express all the elements, determined by the construction, by the given elements so that the determined quantities are expressed rationally or irrationally by square roots; as, on the other hand, any such expression may be constructed, *the necessary and sufficient condition for the possibility of the demanded construction by straight edge and compasses is*, *that the required quantities may be expressed in terms of the given*, *rationally or irrationally only by square roots.*

An examination of the equations, which can be solved by square roots, we find in the authors work „Om Ligninger, der loses ved Kvadratrod" and in his „Theorie der algebraischen Gleichungen" (Kopenhagen 1878). In those works the following theorems are proved:

1. *There are no other curves than the conic sections, of which we can determine the intersections with a straight line by straight edge and compasses.*

2. *There are no other curves than the conic sections to which tangents may be drawn from any point by straight edge and compasses.*

3. *If we are able by straight edge and compasses to determine the points, in which any line of a pencil of lines intersects a curve,* (which does not pass through the vertex of the pencil), *the order of this curve must be a power of* **2** *and there will be at least two lines in the pencil, of which the points of intersection with the curve coincide in pairs.*

From these theorems we may by transformations deduct new ones, as well as we may extend the examinations to other systems of lines, than the pencil of lines, to systems of circles etc. We will here only mention the following:

4. *There are no other curves than the circle and the straight line, of which the points of intersection with any circle can be determined by straight edge and compasses.*

This theorem is easily deducted from I, the circle and the straight line being the only curves, which by any inversion form conic sections.

These theorems suffice in a great number of cases.

Let us suppose for instance, that in a problem it is given, that a point X shall fall in a line, the situation of which may be chosen at will. Remove this condition, and X will have a locus, which according to I must be a conic section, if the problem shall be solved by straight edge and compasses. We can apply the second theorem in a similar way, when the figure contains a point, the situation of which may be chosen at will.

Examining more specially the first case, we see that a sort of general graphic method for the solution of the problems results from the preceding. Removing the line and constructing any two figures, which satisfy the rest of the conditions, we have two positions of X; call these X_1 and X_2. Line $X_1 X_2$ will intersect the removed line in a point, which will be the demanded, if the locus of X is a straight line. If this point is not the demanded, we try once more, determining a third point X_3. Should the circle $X_1 X_2 X_3$ not intersect the removed line in the sought points, then we make two more trials, determining X_4 and X_5. The points, in which the removed line and the conic section, determined by the five points, intersect can be determined by straight edge and compasses. Are the last points not the demanded, the problem can not be solved by straight edge and compasses. In the second case we proceed in a similar manner.

Having solved a problem by straight edge and compasses, we generally conclude, according to the above theorems, that the loci of certain points are conic sections; and it will ordinarily be easy to decide, whether these conic sections are circles or straight lines or other conics.

APPLICATIONS.

405. Through a given point to draw a line, of which the legs of a given angle cut off a certain length.

Removing one leg of the angle, the locus of the free point will be a conchoïd. As the position of the removed leg is entirely independent of the conchoid, the problem can not be solved by straight edge and compasses. In special cases (f. inst. the given point being situated in the line, which bisects the angle) the line may have such a special position in regard to the conchoid, that the problem can be solved.

406. From two fixed points lines are drawn to any point of a given circle; join the points, in which the drawn lines intersect the circle the second time, with a straight line; prove that the locus of this line is a conic section.

We have seen that problem 201 can be solved by straight edge and compasses, which proves the theorem.

407. Place a given triangle with its vertices on three given circles.

This problem can not be solved; for if we remove one circle, the free vertex will have a locus, which can neither be a circle nor a straight line, for in the special case, where two of the circles are straight lines and the triangle is also a straight line, the locus will be an ellipse.

408. Construct a triangle of a, c and $B - C$.

Draw BC and from B two lines, of which one forms an angle with BC equal to half the given angle, the other line being perpendicular to this, then the problem is reduced to the following: From C to draw a line, of which the legs of the right angle shall cut off the length $2c$. This problem being a special case of 405 we must examine it more specially. Removing point C, the line $2c$ will, in moving with its extremities on the legs of the right angle, describe a hypocycloid. As a and the given angle may vary thus, that C gets any position, while the hypocycloid does not change, the problem can not be solved by straight edge and compasses.

409. To trisect a given angle.

The problem is easily altered to the following: Through a given point, A, of the circumference of a circle to draw a line AX, which shall intersect any given diameter in Y, so that XY shall be equal to the radius of the circle. By removing the diameter, we obtain as the locus of Y a curve of the fourth order, having double points in the infinitily distant imaginary points of any circle and in A, passing also through the centre. As the diameters form a pencil of lines, the vertex of which is an ordinary point of the curve, it is a necessary condition for the solution of the problem, that the order of the curve shall surpass a power of two with one. The problem can therefore not be solved by straight edge and compasses.

While we have thus proved, that this old famous problem can not be solved, this is not proved of the equally famous problem, to square a circle. The point is here to prove, that π can not be expressed by square root, which, as yet, nobody has been able to prove.

410. A point, P, and two circles are given; draw a line through P and a tangent to each of the circles; in the triangle, thus formed, P and the two points of contact shall be the middle points of the sides.

Let X and Y be the two points of contact; the triangle XYP shall be so placed, that the altitudes from X and Y pass through the centres. Revolve the circle through

X around P to cover the circle through Y, and X will fall in a point X_1, PY and PX_1 forming equal angles with the line from P to the centre. The radius to X_1 forms a known angle with PY, as it was perpendicular to PY before the revolution and has been revolved a known angle. In trying to construct the triangle PX_1O, O being the centre, the problem is reduced to 408 and can therefore not be solved by straight edge and compasses.

THE ELEMENTS OF
NON-EUCLIDEAN PLANE GEOMETRY
AND TRIGONOMETRY

BY

H. S. CARSLAW

Sc.D. (Camb.), D.Sc. (Glasg.)

PROFESSOR OF MATHEMATICS IN THE UNIVERSITY OF SYDNEY
FORMERLY FELLOW OF EMMANUEL COLLEGE, CAMBRIDGE

WITH DIAGRAMS

PREFACE

In this little book I have attempted to treat the Elements of Non-Euclidean Plane Geometry and Trigonometry in such a way as to prove useful to teachers of Elementary Geometry in schools and colleges. Recent changes in the teaching of Geometry in England and America have made it more than ever necessary that the teachers should have some knowledge of the hypotheses on which Euclidean Geometry is built, and especially of that hypothesis on which Euclid's Theory of Parallels rests. The historical treatment of the Theory of Parallels leads naturally to a discussion of the Non-Euclidean Geometries; and it is only when the logical possibility of these Non-Euclidean Geometries is properly understood that a teacher is entitled to form an independent opinion upon the teaching of Elementary Geometry.

The first two chapters of this book are devoted to a short discussion of the most important of the attempts to prove Euclid's Parallel Postulate, and to a description of the work of the founders of Non-Euclidean Geometry, Bolyai, Lobatschewsky and Riemann.

In Chapters III. V. the Non-Euclidean Geometry of Bolyai and Lobatschewsky, now known as the Hyperbolic Geometry, is developed in a systematic manner. The feature of this treatment is that in Chapter III. no use is made of the Principle of Continuity, and that both the Geometry and the Trigonometry of the Hyperbolic Plane are built up without the use of Solid Geometry.

In Chapters VI.-VII. a similar treatment, though in less detail, is given for the Elliptic Geometry.

Chapter VIII. deals with Poincaré's representation of the Non-Euclidean Geometries by the geometry of the families of circles orthogonal or diametral to a fixed circle. From these representations an elementary proof of the impossibility of proving Euclid's Parallel Postulate can be obtained, and they throw fresh light upon the Non-Euclidean Geometries themselves.

This little book could never have been written had it not been for the work of Bonola. It was from him that I first learnt that an elementary treatment of the subject was possible. Both to his historical work, an English translation of which I had the privilege of undertaking, and to his article in Enriques' *Questioni riguardanti la geometria elementare*, especially in its extended form in the German edition of that work, this book owes a very great deal.

The other writers on the same subject to whom I am most indebted are Liebmann and Stäckel. The treatment of Plane Hyperbolic Trigonometry is due to Liebmann; and to the second edition of his well-known *Nichteuklidische Geometrie*, as well as to his original papers, most of which he has sent to me as they appeared, I am much indebted. A similar acknowledgment is due to Stäckel. When he learnt that I was engaged on this work, I received from him, in the most generous way, a set of all his papers on the subject, many of which were inaccessible to me in Australia; and the gift of a copy of his book on *Wolfgang and Johann Bolyai*, immediately on its publication, allowed me to make some use of his final account of the discovery of the Hyperbolic Geometry in reading my proofs.

Other acknowledgments will be found in their proper place in the text. However, I would mention here the frequent use I have made of Halsted's work and of the *Bibliography* of Sommerville; also the assistance which I have received

from Dr. F. S. Macaulay, who read all the proofs and made
many valuable suggestions and amendments. The work
of another of the Editors of this Series, Mr. C. S. Jackson,
has made my labour lighter, and one of my colleagues in
Sydney, Mr. R. J. Lyons, has also read a great part of the
final proofs.

H. S CARSLAW.

SYDNEY, *September*, 1914.

NOTE.

The final proofs of this book had been corrected, and the
foregoing preface written and set up in type before the
outbreak of the war.

In the course of years the time may come when such co-
operation as I have here acknowledged will again be possible.

H. S. C.

SYDNEY, *January*, 1916.

CONTENTS

CHAPTER I.

THE PARALLEL POSTULATE, AND THE WORK OF SACCHERI, LEGENDRE AND GAUSS.

CHAPTER II.

THE WORK OF BOLYAI, LOBATSCHEWSKY, AND RIEMANN, THE FOUNDERS OF THE NON-EUCLIDEAN GEOMETRIES.

CONTENTS

CHAPTER III.

THE HYPERBOLIC PLANE GEOMETRY.

CHAPTER IV.

THE HYPERBOLIC PLANE TRIGONOMETRY.

CONTENTS

CHAPTER V.

MEASUREMENTS OF LENGTH AND AREA, WITH THE AID OF THE INFINITESIMAL CALCULUS.

CHAPTER VI.

THE ELLIPTIC PLANE GEOMETRY.

CHAPTER VII.

THE ELLIPTIC PLANE TRIGONOMETRY.

CHAPTER VIII.

THE CONSISTENCY OF THE NON-EUCLIDEAN GEO-METRIES AND THE IMPOSSIBILITY OF PROVING THE PARALLEL POSTULATE.

NON-EUCLIDEAN GEOMETRY.

CHAPTER I.

THE PARALLEL POSTULATE, AND THE WORK OF SACCHERI, LEGENDRE AND GAUSS.

§ 1. By the term Non-Euclidean Geometry we understand a system of Geometry built up without the aid of the Euclidean Parallel Hypothesis, while it contains an assumption as to parallels incompatible with that of Euclid.

The discovery that such Non-Euclidean Geometries are logically possible was a result of the attempts to deduce Euclid's Parallel Hypothesis from the other assumptions which form the foundation of his *Elements of Geometry*. It will be remembered that he defines Parallel Lines as follows :

Parallel straight lines are straight lines which, being in the same plane and being produced indefinitely in both directions, do not meet one another in either direction.[*]

Then in I. 27 he proves that

If a straight line falling on two straight lines make the alternate angles equal to one another, the straight lines will be parallel to one another.

And in I. 28 that

If a straight line falling on two straight lines make the exterior angle equal to the interior and opposite angle on the same side,

---

[*] Here and in other places where the text of Euclid's *Elements* is quoted, the rendering in Heath's Edition (Cambridge, 1908) is adopted. This most important treatise will be cited below as Heath's *Euclid*.

or the interior angles on the same side equal to two right angles, the straight lines will be parallel to one another.

In order to prove the converse of these two propositions, namely (I. 29), that

A straight line falling on parallel straight lines makes the alternate angles equal to one another, the exterior angle equal to the interior and opposite angle, and the interior angles on the same side equal to two right angles,

he found it necessary to introduce the hypothesis as to parallel lines, which he enunciates as follows :

If a straight line falling on two straight lines make the interior angles on the same side less than two right angles, the two straight lines, if produced indefinitely, meet on that side on which are the angles less than the two right angles.

This hypothesis we shall refer to as Euclid's Parallel Postulate. It is true that in some of the MSS. it finds a place among the Axioms. In others it is one of the Postulates, and it seems to belong more properly to that group. No use is made of it in the earlier propositions of the First Book. Accordingly these would find a place in the Non-Euclidean Geometries, which differ only from the Euclidean in substituting for his Parallel Postulate another incompatible with it. Other theorems of the Euclidean Geometry will belong to the Non-Euclidean, if they have been proved, or can be proved, without the aid of the Parallel Postulate, and if these geometries adopt the other assumptions, explicit and implicit, made by Euclid.

§ 2. It is not within the scope of this book to discuss the modern treatment of the assumptions on which the Euclidean and Non-Euclidean Geometries are based. We shall deal simply with the assumption regarding parallels. But it is right to mention that the idea of motion or displacement, which forms part of the method of superposition, itself involves an axiom. The fourth proposition of Euclid's First Book now finds a place among the Axioms of Congruence, and upon this group of axioms the idea of motion is founded. Apparently Euclid recognised that the use of the method of superposition was a blot upon the *Elements*. He adopted it only in I. 4, and refrained from employing it in other places, where it would have shortened the demonstration.

Again, Postulate I., which asserts the possibility of drawing a straight line from any one point to any other, must be held to declare that the straight line so drawn is unique, and that two straight lines cannot enclose a space. And Postulate II., which asserts the possibility of producing a finite straight line continuously in a straight line, must also be held to assert that the produced part in either direction is unique ; in other words, that two straight lines cannot have a common segment.

But the following more fundamental and distinct assumptions are made by Euclid, without including them among the axioms or postulates :

(i) *That a straight line is infinite.*

This property of the straight line is required in the proof of I. 16. The theorem that the exterior angle is greater than either of the interior and opposite angles does not hold in the Non-Euclidean Geometry in which the straight line is regarded as endless, returning upon itself, but not infinite.

(ii) *Let* A, B, C *be three points, not lying in a straight line, and let* a *be a straight line lying in the plane* ABC, *and not passing through any of the points* A, B, *or* C. *Then, if* a *passes through a point of the segment* AB, *it must also pass through a point of the segment* BC, *or of the segment* AC (*Pasch's Axiom*).

From this axiom it can be deduced that a ray passing through an angular point, say A, of the triangle ABC, and lying in the region bounded by AB and AC, must cut the segment BC.

(iii) Further, in the very first proposition of the First Book of the *Elements* the vertex of the required equilateral triangle is determined by the intersection of two circles. It is assumed that these circles intersect. A similar assumption is made in I. 22 in the construction of a triangle when the sides are given. The first proposition is used in the fundamental constructions of I. 2 and I. 9-11.

Again, in I. 12, in order to be sure that the circle with a given centre will intersect the given straight line, Euclid makes the circle pass through a point on the side opposite to that in which the centre lies. And in some of the propositions of Book III. assumptions are made with regard to the inter- section of the circles employed in the demonstration. Indeed right through the *Elements* constructions are effected by means of straight lines and circles drawn in accordance with Postulates I.-III. Such straight lines and circles determine by their intersection other points in addition to those given ; and these points are used to determine new lines, and so on. The existence of these points of intersection must be postulated or proved, in the same way as the existence of the other straight lines and circles in the construction has been postulated or proved.

The *Principle of Continuity*, as it is called, is introduced to fill this gap. It can be stated in different ways, but probably the simplest is that which Dedekind originally adopted in discussing the idea of the irrational number. His treatment of the irrational number depends upon the following geometrical axiom :

If all the points of a straight line can be separated into two classes, such that every point of the first class is to the left of every point of the other class, then there exists one, and only one, point which brings about this division of all the points into two classes, this section of the line into two parts.*

This statement does not admit of proof. The assumption of this property is nothing less than an axiom by which we assign its continuity to the straight line.

The *Postulate of Dedekind*, stated for the linear segment, can be readily applied to any angle, (the elements in this case being the rays from the vertex), and to a circular arc. By this means demonstrations can be obtained of the theorems as to the intersection of a straight line and a circle, and of a circle with another circle, assumed by Euclid in the propositions above mentioned.† The idea of continuity was adopted by Euclid without remark. What was involved in the assumption and the nature of the irrational number were unknown to the mathematicians of his time.

This Postulate of Dedekind also carries with it the important

---

* Dedekind, *Stetigkeit und irrationale Zahlen*, p. 11 (2nd ed., Braunschweig, 1892) ; English translation by Beman (Chicago, 1901).

† This question is treated fully in the article by Vitali in Enriques' volume, *Questioni riguardanti la geometria elementare* (Bologna, 1900) ; German translation under the title, *Fragen der Elementargeometrie*, vol. i. p. 129 (Leipzig, 1911). See also Heath's *Euclid*, vol. i. p. 234.

Postulate of Archimedes, which will be frequently referred to in the following pages :

If two segments are given, there is always some multiple of the one which is greater than the other.*

§ 3. An interesting discovery, arising out of the recent study of the Foundations of Geometry, is that a great part of Elementary Geometry can be built up without the Principle of Continuity. In place of the construction of Euclid I. 2, the proof of which depends upon this Principle, the following Postulate † is made :

If A, B *are two points on a straight line* a, *and if* A′ *is a point upon the same or another straight line* a′, *then we can always find on the straight line* a′, *on a given ray from* A′, *one and only one point* B′, *such that the segment* AB *is congruent to the segment* A′B′.

In other words, we assume that we can always set off a given length on a given line, from a given point upon it, towards a given side. By the term *ray* is meant the half-line starting from a given point.

With this assumption, for Euclid's constructions for the bisector of a given angle (I. 9), for the middle point of a given straight line (I. 10), for the perpendicular to a given straight line from a point upon it (I. 11), and outside it (I. 12), and, finally, for an angle equal to a given angle (I. 23)—all of which, in the *Elements,* depend upon the Principle of Continuity— we may substitute the following constructions, which are independent, both of that Principle and of the Parallel Postulate.‡

---

* For the proof of the *Postulate of Archimedes* on the assumption of Dedekind's Postulate, see Vitali's article named above, § 3. Another treatment of this question will be found in Hilbert's *Grundlagen der Geometrie,* 3rd ed. § 8. An English translation of the first edition was made by Townsend (Chicago, 1902). The Postulate of Archimedes stated above for linear segments is adopted also for angles, areas, and volumes.

† Cf. Hilbert, *loc. cit.* 3rd ed. § 5, Axioms of Congruence.

‡ The constructions in Problems 1, 2, 3 and 5 are given by Halsted in his book, *Rational Geometry* (2nd ed. 1907). Those for Problems 4 and 6 in the text are independent of the Parallel Postulate, and replace those given by Halsted, in which the Euclidean Hypothesis is assumed.

PROBLEM 1. **To bisect a given angle.**

Construction. On one of the lines bounding the given angle **A** take any two points **B**, **C**.

On the other bounding line take **AB′ = AB** and **AC′ = AC**.

Join **BC′** and **B′C**.

Let them intersect at **D**.

Then **AD** is the desired bisector.

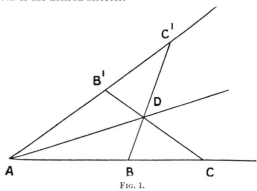

FIG. 1.

Proof. The triangles **BAC′** and **B′AC** are congruent.

Therefore ∠ **ACB′** = ∠ **AC′B** and ∠ **DBC** = ∠ **DB′C′**.

It follows that the triangles **BDC** and **B′DC′** are congruent, since

$$BC = B'C'.$$

Therefore $$DB' = DB.$$

Finally the triangles **BAD** and **B′AD** are congruent, and **AD** bisects the given angle.

PROBLEM 2. **To draw a perpendicular to a given straight line.**

Construction. Let **AB** be the given straight line.

Take any other straight line **AC** through **A**.

Upon **AB** take **AD = AC**.

Join **CD**.

Bisect ∠ **CAD** (by Problem 1), and let the bisector cut **CD** at **G**.

On **AB** take **AF = AG**, and on the ray **AG** take **AH = AD**.

Join **FH**.

Then **FH** is perpendicular to **AB**.

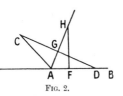

FIG. 2.

Proof. From the triangles **ACG** and **ADG**, we have ∠ **AGD** equal to a right angle.

Also the triangles **AGD** and **AFH** are congruent.

Therefore ∠ **AFH** = ∠ **AGD** = 1 right angle.

PROBLEM 3.   At a given point on a given straight line to erect the perpendicular.

Construction.   Let A be the given point and BC the given straight line.
Draw the perpendicular ZOY (by Problem 2), meeting BC in O.
Take OY = OZ, and join AY and AZ.
Produce YA through A to X.
Bisect ∠ XAZ by AD (by Problem 1).
Then AD is the perpendicular to BC through A.

Proof.   By the construction, the triangles OAZ and OAY are congruent.

Therefore   ∠ ZAO = ∠ YAO

$$= ∠ XAC.$$

But   ∠ DAZ = ∠ XAD.

Therefore AD is perpendicular to BC.

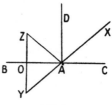

FIG. 3.

PROBLEM 4.   From a given point outside a given straight line to draw the perpendicular to the line.

Construction.   Let A, B be two points on the given line, and C the point outside it.
Join AC and BC.
On the segment AB take a point D, and (by Problem 3) draw the perpendicular at D to AB.
By Pasch's Axiom, this line must cut either AC or BC.
Let it cut AC, and let the point of intersection be E.
Produce ED through D to F, so that DE = DF.
Join AF and produce AF to G, such that AG = AC.
Join CG, and let it be cut by AB, or AB produced, at H.
Then CH is the required perpendicular.

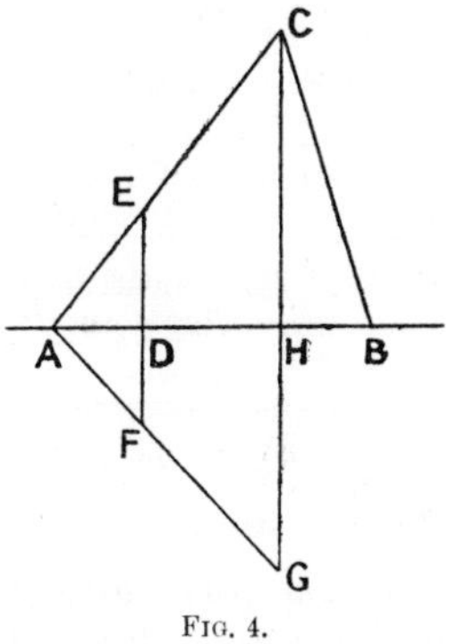

Proof.   From the construction, the triangles ADE and ADF are congruent, so that AB bisects ∠ CAG.

FIG. 4.

It follows that the triangles ACH and AGH are congruent, and that ∠ AHC is a right angle.

PROBLEM 5.   At a given point on a given straight line to make an angle equal to a given angle.

Construction.   Let A be the point on the given line *a*.   (Cf. Fig. 5.)
Let D be the given (acute) angle.
From a point E on one of the lines bounding the angle, draw (by Problem 4) the perpendicular EF to the other bounding line.

On A*a* take AC = DF.

At C erect the perpendicular C*c* to A*a* (by Problem 3).

Make BC = EF, and join AB.

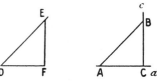

FIG. 5.

Proof. By the construction, the triangles DEF and ABC are congruent.

Therefore   ∠BAC = ∠EDF.

PROBLEM 6. **To bisect a given finite straight line.**

Construction. Let AB be the given segment.

At B draw the perpendicular B*b* to AB (by Problem 3).

Upon B*b* take any point C and join AC.

At B make ∠ABE = ∠BAC (by Problem 5).

Let the line BE cut AC at D.

Bisect ∠ADB by the line cutting AB at F (by Problem 1).

Then F is the middle point of AB.

Proof. From the construction it follows that the triangles ADF and DBF are congruent.

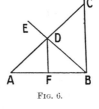

FIG. 6.

Thus   AF = FB.

Note. This construction has to be slightly modified for the Elliptic Geometry. The point C must lie between B and the pole of AB. [Cf. § 78.]

§ 4. Two Theorems independent of the Parallel Postulate.

1. *The perpendicular to the base of any triangle through its middle point is also perpendicular to the line joining the middle points of the two sides.*

Let ABC be any triangle, and let F and E be the middle points of the sides AB and AC.

Join F and E; and draw AA′, BB′, and CC′ perpendicular to EF from A, B, and C.

Let H be the middle point of BC, and K the middle point of B′C′.

Join HK.

We shall prove that HK is perpendicular to BC and EF.

From the triangles AFA′ and BFB′, which are congruent, we have AA′ = BB′.

Similarly   AA′ = CC′.

Therefore   BB′ = CC′.

Join BK and KC.

In the triangles BB′K and CC′K we have

$$BB' = CC', \quad B'K = C'K,$$

and the angles at B′ and C′ are equal.

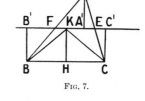

Fig. 7.

Therefore the triangles are congruent, and BK = CK.

Again, in the triangles BHK and CHK, we have the three sides equal, each to each.

Therefore the triangles are congruent, and

$$\angle BHK = \angle CHK = \text{a right angle.}$$

Also ∠ BKH = ∠ CKH.

But, from the triangles BB′K and CC′K, we have

$$\angle BKB' = \angle CKC'.$$

Therefore ∠ HKB′ = ∠ HKC′ = a right angle.

Thus HK is perpendicular to both BC and EF.

2. *The locus of the middle points of the segments joining a set of points* ABC... *on one straight line and a set* A′B′C′... *on another straight line is a straight line, provided that* AB = A′B′, BC = B′C′, *etc.*

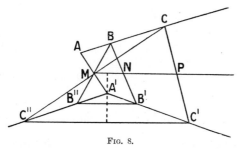

Fig. 8.

Let M, N, and P be the middle points of AA′, BB′, and CC′.

Join BM and produce it to B″, so that BM = MB″.

Join B″A′ and B″B′.

The sides of the triangle BB′B″ are bisected at M and N. Therefore the line bisecting B′B″ at right angles is also perpendicular to MN.

But this line bisects ∠ B′A′B″, since A′B′ = A′B″.

Now produce A′B″ to C″, so that B″C″ = BC = B′C′.

Join C′ C″, MC″ and MC.

The triangles MAC and MA′C″ are congruent, and it follows that MC and MC″ are in one straight line.

Since A′C′ = A′C″, the line bisecting C′C″ at right angles coincides with the line bisecting B′B″ at right angles.

Therefore MN and MP are perpendicular to the same straight line.

Therefore MNP are collinear.

Proceeding to the points A, B, D, A′, B′, D′ we have a corresponding result, and in this way our theorem is proved.

§ 5. From the *Commentary* of Proclus * it is known that not long after Euclid's own time his Parallel Postulate was the subject of controversy. The questions in dispute remained unsolved till the nineteenth century, though many mathematicians of eminence devoted much time and thought to their investigation. Three separate problems found a place in this discussion :

(i) Can the Parallel Postulate be deduced from the other assumptions on which Euclid's Geometry is based ?

(ii) If not, is it an assumption demanded by the facts of experience, so that the system of propositions deduced from the fundamental assumptions will describe the space in which we live ?

(iii) And finally, are both it and assumptions incompatible with it consistent with the other assumptions, so that the adoption of the Euclidean Hypothesis can be regarded as an arbitrary specialisation of a more general system, accepted not because it is more true than the others, but because the Geometry founded upon it is simpler and more convenient ?

There can be little doubt that Euclid himself was convinced that the first of these questions must be answered in the negative. The place he assigned to the Parallel Postulate and

---

* Cf. Friedlein, *Procli Diadochi in primum Euclidis elementorum librum commentarii* (Leipzig, 1873). Also Heath's *Euclid*, vol. i. Introduction, chapter iv.

his refusal to use it earlier than I. 29 are evidence that with him it had only the value of an hypothesis. It seems at least very probable that he realised the advantage of proving without that postulate such theorems as could be established independently ; just as he refrained from using the method of superposition, when other methods were available and sufficient for the demonstration.

But the followers of Euclid were not so clear sighted. Fruitless attempts to prove the Parallel Postulate lasted well into the nineteenth century. Indeed it will be surprising if the use of the vicious *direction*-theory of parallels, advocated at present in some influential quarters in England, does not raise another crop of so-called demonstrations—the work of those who are ignorant of the real foundations on which the Theory of Parallels rests.

The assumption involved in the second question had also an effect on the duration of the controversy. Had it not been for the mistake which identified Geometry—the logical doctrine—with Geometry—the experimental science—the Parallel Postulate would not so long have been regarded as a blemish upon the body of Geometry. However, it is now admitted that Geometry is a subject in which the assertions are that such and such consequences follow from such and such premises. Whether entities such as the premises describe actually exist is another matter. Whenever we think of Geometry as a representation of the properties of the external world in which we live, we are thinking of a branch of Applied Mathematics. That the Euclidean Geometry does describe those properties we know perfectly well. But we also know that it is not the only system of Geometry which will describe them. To this point we shall return in the last pages of this book.

In the answer to the third question the solution of the problem was found. This discovery will always be associated with the names of Lobatschewsky and Bolyai. They were the first to state publicly, and to establish rigorously, that a consistent system of Geometry can be built upon the assumptions, explicit and implicit, of Euclid, when his Parallel Postulate is omitted, and another, incompatible with it, put in its place. The geometrical system constructed upon these foundations is as consistent as that of Euclid. Not only so, by a proper choice of a parameter entering into it, this system can be made to describe and agree with the external relations of things.

This discovery, which was made about 1823-1830, does not detract from the value of Euclid's work. The Euclidean Geometry is not to be replaced by the Non-Euclidean Geometries. The latter have thrown light upon the true nature of Geometry as a science. They have also shown that Euclid's Theory of Parallels, far from being a blot upon his work, is one of his greatest triumphs. In the words of Heath : " When we consider the countless successive attempts made through more than twenty centuries to prove the Postulate, many of them by geometers of ability, we cannot but admire the genius of the man who concluded that such a hypothesis, which he found necessary to the validity of his whole system of geometry, was really indemonstrable." *

§ 6. The Work of Saccheri (1667-1733).

The history of these attempts to prove the Parallel Postulate does not lie within the scope of this work.† But we must refer to one or two of the most important contributions to that discussion from their bearing on the rise and development of the Non-Euclidean Geometries.

Saccheri, a Jesuit and Professor of Mathematics at the University of Pavia, was the first to contemplate the possibility of hypotheses other than that of Euclid, and to work out the consequences of these hypotheses. Indeed it required only one forward step, at the critical stage of his memoir, and the discovery of Lobatschewsky and Bolyai would have been anticipated by one hundred years. Nor was that step taken by his immediate successors. His work seems to have been quickly forgotten. It had fallen completely into oblivion when the attention of the distinguished Italian mathematician Beltrami was called to it towards the end of the nineteenth century. His Note entitled " *un precursore italiano di Legendre e di Lobatschewsky* " ‡ convinced the scientific world of the importance of Saccheri's work, and of the fact that theorems, which had been ascribed to Legendre, Lobatschewsky, and Bolyai, had been discovered by him many years earlier.

---

* Heath's *Euclid*, vol. i. p. 202.

† Cf. Bonola, *La geometria non-euclidea* (Bologna, 1906) ; English translation (Chicago, 1912). In quoting this work, we shall refer to the English translation.

‡ *Rend. Acc. Lincei* (4), t. v. pp. 441-448 (1889).

Saccheri's little book—*Euclides ab omni nœvo vindicatus*—
is now easily accessible.* It was published in 1733, the last
year of his life. Much of it has been incorporated in the
elementary treatment of the Non-Euclidean Geometries. A
great deal more would be found therein were it not for the fact
that he makes very frequent use of the Principle of Continuity.

It must not be forgotten that Saccheri was convinced of the
truth of the Euclidean Hypothesis. He discussed the contradictory assumptions with a definite purpose—not, like
Bolyai and Lobatschewsky, to establish their logical possibility—but in order that he might detect
the contradiction which he was persuaded
must follow from them. In other words,
he was employing the *reductio ad absurdum*
argument.

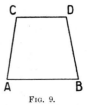

Fig. 9.

The fundamental figure of Saccheri is
the two right-angled isosceles quadrilateral
ABDC, in which the angles at A and B are
right angles, and the sides AC and BD equal.
It is easy to show by congruence theorems that the angles
at C and D are equal. [Cf. § 28.]

On the Euclidean Hypothesis they are both right angles.
Thus, if it is assumed that they are both obtuse, or both acute,
the Parallel Postulate is implicitly denied.

Saccheri discussed these three hypotheses under the names :

The Hypothesis of the Right Angle ... ∠ C = ∠ D = a right angle.

*The Hypothesis of the Obtuse Angle ... ∠ C = ∠ D = an obtuse
angle.*

*The Hypothesis of the Acute Angle ... ∠ C = ∠ D = an acute
angle.*

He showed that

*According as the Hypothesis of the Right Angle, the Obtuse
Angle, or the Acute Angle is found to be true, the sum of the
angles of any triangle will be respectively equal to, greater than,
or less than two right angles.*

Also that

*If the sum of the angles of a single triangle is equal to, greater
than, or less than two right angles, then this sum will be equal*

---

* Cf. Engel u. Stäckel, *Die Theorie der Parallellinien von Euclid bis
auf Gauss*, pp. 31-136 (Leipzig, 1895).

to, greater than, or less than two right angles in every other triangle.

Again, he showed that

The Parallel Postulate follows from the Hypothesis of the Right Angle, and from the Hypothesis of the Obtuse Angle.

He was thus able to rule out the Hypothesis of the Obtuse Angle ; since, if the Parallel Postulate is adopted, the sum of the angles of a triangle is two right angles, and the Hypothesis of the Obtuse Angle is contradicted. It should be remarked that he assumes in this argument that the straight line is infinite. When that assumption is dropped, the Hypothesis of the Obtuse Angle remains possible.

As we have already mentioned, Saccheri's aim was to show that both the Hypothesis of the Acute Angle and that of the Obtuse Angle must be false. He hoped to establish this by deducing from these hypotheses some result, which itself would contradict that from which it was derived, or be inconsistent with a previous proposition. So, having demolished the Hypothesis of the Obtuse Angle, he turned to that of the Acute Angle. In the system built upon this Hypothesis, after a series of propositions, which are really propositions in the Geometry of Lobatschewsky and Bolyai, he believed that he had found one which was inconsistent with those preceding it. He concluded from this that the Hypothesis of the Acute Angle was also impossible ; so that the Hypothesis of the Right Angle alone remained, and the Parallel Postulate must be true.

In his belief that he had discovered a contradiction in the sequence of theorems derived from the Hypothesis of the Acute Angle, Saccheri was wrong. He was led astray by the prejudice of his time in favour of the Euclidean Geometry as the only possible geometrical system. How near he came to the discovery of the Geometry of Lobatschewsky and Bolyai will be clear from the following description of the argument contained in his Theorems 30 to 32 :

He is dealing with the pencil of rays proceeding from a point A on the same side of the perpendicular from A to a given line *b*, and in the same plane as that perpendicular and the line.

He considers the rays starting from the perpendicular AB and ending with the ray AX at right angles to AB.

In addition to the last ray AX, he shows that, on the hypothesis of the Acute Angle, there are an infinite number of rays which have a common perpendicular with the line b. These rays obviously cannot intersect the line b.

There is no last ray of this set, although the length of the common perpendicular decreases without limit; but there is a lower limit to the set.

Also, proceeding from the line AB, we have a set of rays which intersect the line b. There is no last ray of this set; but there is an upper limit to the set.

The upper limit of the one set and the lower limit of the other, he showed to be one and the same ray.

Thus, there is one ray, the line a_1, which divides the pencil of rays into two parts, such that all the rays on the one side of the line a_1, beginning with AB, intersect the line b; and all the rays on the other side of the line a_1, beginning with the line AX, perpendicular to the line AB, do not intersect b. The line a_1 is the boundary between the two sets of rays, and is asymptotic to b.

The result which Saccheri obtained is made rigorous by the introduction of the Postulate of Dedekind. According to that postulate a division of the two classes such as is described above carries with it the existence of a ray separating the one set of lines from the other.

This ray, which neither intersects b nor has with it a common perpendicular, is the right-handed (or left-handed) parallel of Bolyai and Lobatschewsky to the given line.

§ 7. The Work of Legendre (1752-1833).

The contribution of Legendre must also be noticed. Like Saccheri, he attempted to establish the truth of Euclid's Postulate by examining in turn the Hypothesis of the Obtuse Angle, the Hypothesis of the Right Angle, and the Hypothesis of the Acute Angle. In his work these hypotheses entered as assumptions regarding the sum of the angles of a triangle.

If the sum of the angles of a triangle is equal to two right angles, the Parallel Postulate follows; at any rate, if we assume, as Euclid did, the Postulate of Archimedes.[*]

Legendre thus turned his attention to the other two cases. He gave more than one rigorous proof that the sum of the angles of a triangle could not be greater than two right angles.

---

[*] Cf. Heath's *Euclid*, vol. i. pp. 218-9.

In these proofs the infinity of the line is assumed. One of them is as follows :

Let the sum of the angles of the triangle ABC be $\pi + \alpha$, and let A be the smallest angle.

Bisect BC at D and produce AD to E, making DE = AD. Join BE.

Then from the triangles ADC and BDE, we have

$$\angle CAD = \angle BED,$$
$$\angle ACD = \angle DBE.$$

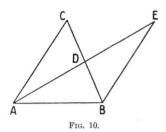

Fig. 10.

Thus the sum of the angles of the triangle AEB is also equal to $\pi + \alpha$, and one of the angles BAD or AEB is less than or equal to $\frac{1}{2} \angle CAB$.

Apply the same process to the triangle ABE, and we obtain a new triangle in which one of the angles is less than or equal to $\frac{1}{2^2} \angle CAB$, while the sum is again $\pi + \alpha$.

Proceeding in this way after n operations we obtain a triangle, in which the sum of the angles is $\pi + \alpha$, and one of the angles is less than or equal to $\frac{1}{2^n} \angle CAB$.

But we can choose n so large that $2^n \alpha > \angle CAB$, by the Postulate of Archimedes.

It follows that the sum of two of the angles of this triangle is greater than two right angles, which is impossible (when the length of the straight line is infinite).

Thus, we have Legendre's First Theorem that

The sum of the angles of a triangle cannot be greater than two right angles.

Legendre also showed that

If the sum of the angles of a single triangle is equal to two right angles, then the sum of the angles of every triangle is equal to two right angles.

From these theorems it follows that

If the sum of the angles of a single triangle is less than two right angles, then the sum of the angles of every triangle is less than two right angles.

All these results had been obtained many years earlier by Saccheri.

Legendre made various attempts to prove that the sum cannot be less than two right angles, even in a single triangle ; but these efforts all failed, as we now know they were bound to do. He published several so-called proofs in the successive editions of his text-book of geometry, the *Éléments de Géométrie*. All contained some assumption equivalent to the hypothesis which they were meant to establish.

For example, in one he assumes that there cannot be an absolute unit of length ; * an alternative hypothesis already noted by Lambert (1728-1777).†

In a second he assumes that from any point whatever, taken within an angle, we can always draw a straight line which will cut the two lines bounding the angle.

In a third he shows that the Parallel Postulate would be true, if a circle can always be drawn through any three points not in a straight line.

In another [cf. p. 279, 14th Ed.] he argues somewhat as follows :

A straight line divides a plane in which it lies into two congruent parts. Thus two rays from a point enclosing an angle less than two right angles contain an area less than half the plane. If an infinite straight line lies wholly in the region bounded by these two rays, it would follow that the area of half the plane can be enclosed within an area itself less than half the plane.

Bertrand's well-known " proof " (1778) of the Parallel Postulate ‡ and another similar to it to be found in *Crelle's Journal* (1834) fail for the same reason as does Legendre's. They depend upon a comparison of infinite areas. But a process of reasoning which is sound for finite magnitudes need not be valid in the case of infinite magnitudes. If it is to be extended to such a field, the legitimacy of the extension must be proved. Lobatschewsky himself dealt with these proofs, and pointed out the weakness in the argument. First of all, the idea of congruence, as applied to finite areas, is used in dealing with infinite regions, without any exact statement of its meaning in this connection. Further—and here it seems best to quote his

---

* See below, p. 90.   Also Bonola, *loc. cit.* § 20.

† Cf. Engel u. Stäckel, *loc. cit.* p. 200.

‡ Cf. Frankland, *Theories of Parallelism*, p. 26 (Cambridge, 1910).

own words : " when we are dealing with areas extending to infinity, we must in this case, as in all other parts of mathematics, understand by the ratio of two of these infinitely great numbers, the limit to which this tends when the numerator and denominator of the fraction continually increase." *

It is not a little surprising that at the present day mathematicians of distinction have been found quoting Bertrand's argument with approval.†

§ 8. Both Legendre and Saccheri, in their discussion of these hypotheses, make use of the axiom that the length of the straight line is infinite, and they also assume the Postulate of Archimedes. Hilbert ‡ showed that the Euclidean Geometry could be built up without the Postulate of Archimedes. Dehn § investigated what effect the rejection of the Postulate of Archimedes would have on the results obtained by Saccheri and Legendre. He found that the sum of the angles of a triangle can be greater than two right angles in this case. In other words, the Hypothesis of the Obtuse Angle is possible. Again, he showed that without the Postulate of Archimedes we can deduce from the angle-sum in a single triangle being two right angles, that the angle-sum in every triangle is two right angles. But his most important discovery was that, when the Postulate of Archimedes is rejected, the Parallel Postulate does not follow from the sum of the angles of a triangle being equal to two right angles. He proved that there is a Non-Archimedean Geometry in which the angle-sum in every triangle is two right angles, and the Parallel Postulate does not hold.

His discovery has been referred to in this place because it shows that the Euclidean Hypothesis is superior to the others, which have been suggested as equivalent to it. Upon the Euclidean Hypothesis, without the aid of the Postulate of Archimedes, the Euclidean Geometry can be based. If we

---

* Cf. Lobatschewsky, *New Principles of Geometry with a Complete Theory of Parallels*, Engel's translation, p. 71, in Engel u. Stäckel's *Urkunden zur Geschichte der nichteuklidischen Geometrie*, I. (Leipzig, 1898).

† Cf. Frankland, *The Mathematical Gazette*, vol. vii. p. 136 (1913) and p. 332 (1914) ; *Nature*, Sept. 7, 1911, and Oct. 5, 1911.

‡ Cf. *loc. cit.* chapter iii.

§ Cf. *Math. Ann.* vol. liii. p. 404 (1900).

substitute for it the assumption that the sum of the angles of a
triangle is two right angles—or that the locus of the points
equidistant from a straight line is another straight line—
different geometries can be created.   One of these is the
Euclidean Geometry, in which only one parallel can be drawn
to a straight line from a point outside it.   Another is what
Dehn calls the Semi-Euclidean Geometry, in which an infinite
number of parallels can be drawn.*

§ 9. The Work of Gauss (1777-1855).

Though Bolyai and Lobatschewsky were the first to
publicly announce the discovery of the possibility of a Non-
Euclidean Geometry and to explain its content, the great
German mathematician Gauss had also independently, and
some years earlier, come to the same conclusion.   His results
had not been published, when he received from Wolfgang
Bolyai, early in 1832, a copy of the famous *Appendix*, the
work of his son John.

This little book reached Gauss on February 14, 1832.   On
the same day he wrote to Gerling, with whom he had been
frequently in correspondence on mathematical subjects : †

" . . . Further, let me add that I have received this day a
little book from Hungary on the Non-Euclidean Geometry.   In
it I find all *my own ideas and* RESULTS, developed with
remarkable elegance, although in a form so concise as to offer
considerable difficulty to anyone not familiar with the subject.
The author is a very young Austrian officer, the son of a friend
of my youth, with whom, in 1798, I have often discussed these
matters.   However at that time my ideas were still only
slightly developed and far from the completeness which they
have now received, through the independent investigation of
this young man.   I regard this young geometer v. Bolyai as a
genius of the highest order. . . ."

The letter in which Gauss replied to Wolfgang Bolyai three
weeks later is better known, but deserves quotation from the
light it throws upon his own work : ‡

" . . . If I commenced by saying *that I am unable to praise
this work* (by John), you would certainly be surprised for a
moment.   But I cannot say otherwise.   To praise it would be to

---

* Cf. Halsted, *Science*, N.S. vol. xiv. pp. 705-717 (1901).

† Cf. Gauss, *Werke*, vol. viii. p. 220.

‡ Gauss, *Werke*, vol. viii. p. 220.

praise myself. Indeed the whole contents of the work, the path taken by your son, the results to which he is led, coincide almost entirely with my meditations, which have occupied my mind partly for the last thirty or thirty-five years. So I remained quite stupefied. So far as my own work is concerned, of which up till now I have put little on paper, my intention was not to let it be published during my lifetime. Indeed the majority of people have not clear ideas upon the questions of which we are speaking, and I have found very few people who could regard with any special interest what I communicated to them on this subject. To be able to take such an interest one must have felt very keenly what precisely is lacking, and about that most men have very confused ideas. On the other hand, it was my idea to write all this down later, so that at least it should not perish with me. It is therefore a pleasant surprise for me that I am spared this trouble, and I am very glad that it is just the son of my old friend who takes the precedence of me in such a remarkable manner. . . ."

Wolfgang sent a copy of this letter to his son with the remark :

" Gauss's answer with regard to your work is very satisfactory, and redounds to the honour of our country and nation. A good friend says, That's very satisfactory ! " *

John Bolyai was the reverse of pleased. That he would be disappointed at the news that Gauss had already reached the same conclusions as himself was natural. But his chagrin led him to doubt whether Gauss had really made these discoveries independently of his work. He conceived the absurd idea that his father must have sent his papers to Gauss some time earlier (they had been in his hands for several years), and that Gauss had made use of them, jealous of being beaten by this young Hungarian. In this he relied upon a remark made by Gauss in 1804, in a letter to his father, when both of them were trying to demonstrate the Parallel Postulate. Wolfgang had sent him what he thought was a rigorous proof, and Gauss replied that his demonstration was invalid, and that he would try as clearly as possible to bring to light the stumbling-

---

* Cf. Stäckel, " Die Entdeckung der nichteuklidischen Geometrie durch Johann Bolyai," *Math. u. Naturwissenschaftliche Berichte aus Ungarn*, Bd. xvii. p. 17 (1901). Also by the same author in Engel u. Stäckel's *Urkunden zur Geschichte der nichteuklidischen Geometrie, II.*, *Wolfgang u. Johann Bolyai*, vol. i. p. 72 (Leipzig, 1913).

block which he found therein. That this was not unlike the
obstacle which so far had baffled his own efforts. " However,
I am always hopeful," he added, "that some day, and that
in my own lifetime, a way over this obstacle will be revealed." *

Though John Bolyai afterwards saw how groundless his
suspicions were, he always held that Gauss had treated him
badly in this matter ; and it does seem unfortunate that Gauss
did not more effectively use his great influence to rescue from
ill-merited neglect the notable work of the two comparatively
unknown young mathematicians, Bolyai and Lobatschewsky.
Not till years after they had passed away did the scientific
world realise the immense value of their discoveries.

§ 10. Bolyai's discovery was made in 1823, and first published in 1832. Far away in Kasan, Lobatschewsky—one of
the Professors of Mathematics in the local University—not
later than 1829, and probably as early as 1826, had also discovered this new Geometry, of which the Euclidean was a
special case. Thus it is interesting to trace, so far as we can,
Gauss's attitude to the Theory of Parallels at that time. The
chief available authorities are some letters of his which still
survive, and some notes found among his papers.†

In the early years of the nineteenth century he shared the
common belief that a proof of the Euclidean Hypothesis might
possibly be found. But in 1817 we find him writing to Olbers
as follows :

" Wachter has published a little paper on the ' First Principles of Geometry,' of which you will probably get a copy
through Lindenau. Although he has got nearer the root of
the matter than his predecessors, his proof is no more rigorous
than any of the others. I am becoming more and more
convinced that the necessity of our geometry cannot be
proved . . ." ‡

In 1819 he learnt from Gerling in Marburg that one of his
colleagues, Schweikart—a Professor of Law, but formerly a
keen student of Mathematics—had informed him that he was
practically certain that Euclid's Postulate could not be proved
without some hypothesis or other ; and that it seemed to him

---

* Gauss, *Werke*, vol. viii. p. 160.

† See Gauss, *Werke*, vol. viii.

‡ Gauss, *Werke*, vol. viii. p. 177.

not improbable that our geometry was only a special case of a more general one. At the same time Gerling sent him, at Schweikart's request, a Memorandum, which the latter had given him, desiring to know Gauss's opinion upon it.

This Memorandum is as follows : *

" Marburg, December, 1818.

" There are two kinds of geometry—a geometry in the strict sense—the Euclidean ; and an astral geometry.

" Triangles in the latter have the property that the sum of their three angles is not equal to two right angles.

" This being assumed, we can prove rigorously :

(a) That the sum of the three angles of a triangle is less than two right angles ;

(b) That the sum becomes always less, the greater the area of the triangle ;

(c) That the altitude of an isosceles right-angled triangle continually grows, as the sides increase, but it can never become greater than a certain length, which I call the *Constant*.

" Squares have, therefore, the following form (Fig. 11) :

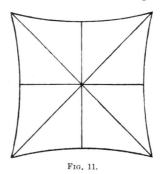

FIG. 11.

" If this Constant were *for us* the radius of the earth (so that every line drawn in the universe from one fixed star to another, distant 90° from the first, would be a tangent to the surface of the earth), it would be infinitely great in comparison with the spaces which occur in daily life.

* Gauss, *Werke*, vol. viii. p. 180.

" The Euclidean geometry holds only on the assumption that the Constant is infinite. Only in this case is it true that the three angles of every triangle are equal to two right angles ; and this can easily be proved, as soon as we admit that the Constant is infinite."

This document is of peculiar importance, as it is in all probability the earliest statement of the Non-Euclidean Geometry. From a passage in a letter of Gerling's,* we learn that Schweikart made his discovery when in Charkow. As he left that place for Marburg in 1816, he seems by that date to have advanced further than the stage which Gauss had reached in 1817, according to the letter quoted above.

To Gerling, Gauss replied as follows : †

" . . . Schweikart's Memorandum has given me the greatest pleasure, and I beg you to convey to him my hearty congratulations upon it. It could almost have been written by myself. (Es ist mir fast alles aus der Seele geschrieben). . . . I would only further add that I have extended the Astral Geometry so far, that I can fully solve all its problems as soon as the Constant = C is given, e.g. not only is the Defect‡ of the angles of a plane triangle greater, the greater the area, but it is exactly proportional to it ; so that the area has a limit which it can never reach ; and this limit is the area of the triangle formed by three lines asymptotic in pairs. . . ."

From Bolyai's papers it appears that at this date he was attempting to prove the truth of the Parallel Postulate. Also in 1815-17 Lobatschewsky was working on the same traditional lines.

§ 11. The above Memorandum is the only work of Schweikart's on the Astral Geometry that is known. Like Gauss, he seems not to have published any of his researches. However, at his instigation, and encouraged by Gauss, his nephew Taurinus devoted himself to the subject. In 1825 he published a *Theorie der Parallellinien*, containing a treatment of Parallels on Non-Euclidean Lines, the rejection of the Hypothesis of the Obtuse Angle, and some investigations resembling those of Saccheri and Lambert on the Hypothesis of the Acute Angle. For various reasons he decided that the Hypothesis of

---

* Cf. Gauss, *Werke*, vol. viii. p. 238.

† Gauss, *Werke*, vol. viii. p. 181.   ‡ See p. 54.

the Acute Angle must also be rejected, though he recognised the logical possibility of the propositions which followed from it.

Again, it is from a letter which Gauss wrote to Taurinus in 1824, before the publication of his book, that we obtain the fullest information of his views : *

" Your kind letter of the 30th October with the accompanying little theorem I have read not without pleasure, all the more as up till now I have been accustomed to find not even a trace of real geometrical insight in the majority of the people who make new investigations upon the so-called Theory of Parallels. In criticism of your work I have nothing (or not much) more to say than that it is incomplete. It is true that your treatment of the proof that the sum of the angles of a plane triangle cannot be greater than 180° is still slightly lacking in geometrical precision. But there is no difficulty in completing this ; and there is no doubt that that impossibility can be established in the strictest possible fashion. The position is quite different with regard to the second part, that the sum of the angles cannot be smaller than 180°. This is the real hitch, the obstacle, where all goes to pieces. I imagine that you have not occupied yourself with this question for long. It has been before me for over thirty years, and I don't believe that anyone can have occupied himself more with this second part than I, even though I have never published anything upon it. The assumption that the sum of the three angles is smaller than 180° leads to a peculiar Geometry, quite distinct from our Euclidean, which is quite consistent. For myself I have developed it quite satisfactorily, so that I can solve every problem in it, with the exception of the determination of a Constant, which there is no means of settling *a priori*. The greater we take this Constant, the nearer does the geometry approach the Euclidean, and when it is given an infinite value the two coincide. The theorems of that Geometry appear almost paradoxical, and to the ignorant, absurd. When considered more carefully and calmly, one finds that they contain nothing in itself impossible. For example, the three angles of a triangle can become as small as we please, if only we may take the sides large enough ; however, the area of a triangle cannot exceed a definite limit, no matter how great the sides are taken, nor can it reach that limit. All my attempts to find a

* Cf. Gauss, *Werke*, vol. viii. p. 186.   This letter is reproduced in facsimile in Engel u. Stäckel's *Theorie der Parallellinien* (Leipzig, 1895).

contradiction, an inconsistency, in this Non-Euclidean Geometry, have been fruitless. The single thing in it, which is opposed
to our reason, is that if it were true, there must exist in space
a linear magnitude, *determined in itself* (although unknown to
us). But methinks, in spite of the meaningless Word-Wisdom
of the Metaphysicians, we know too little or nothing at all
about the real meaning of space, to stamp anything appearing
unnatural to us as *Absolutely Impossible.* If the Non-Euclidean
Geometry were the true one, and that Constant were in some
ratio to such magnitudes as we meet in our measurements on
the earth or in the heavens, then it might be determined *a
posteriori.* Thus I have sometimes in jest expressed the
wish, that the Euclidean Geometry were not the true one,
because then we would have *a priori* an absolute measure.

"I have no fear that a man who has shown himself to me
as possessed of a thinking mathematical head will misunder-
stand what I have said above. But in every case take it as
a private communication, of which in no wise is any public
use to be made, or any use which might lead to publicity.
Perhaps, if I ever have more leisure than in my present cir-
cumstances, I may myself in the future make my investigations
known."

§ 12. Finally, in 1831, after Bolyai's *Appendix* was in print,
but before a copy had reached him, we find Gauss writing to
Schumacher, who thought he had proved that the sum of the
angles of a triangle must be two right angles, by a method
practically the same as the rotation method of Thibaut, which
so unfortunately has lately received official sanction in England
and crept into our text-books of Elementary Geometry. He
pointed out to him the fallacy upon which that so-called proof
rests. Then he added : *

"In the last few weeks I have commenced to put down a
few of my own meditations which are already to some extent
forty † years old. These I had never put in writing, so that I
have been compelled three or four times to think out the
whole question afresh. Nevertheless I did not want it to
perish with me."

---

* Cf. Gauss, *Werke,* vol. viii. p. 213.

† Forty years before the date of this letter Gauss would be just a
little over 14 years old !

The Notes on Parallels,* found among his papers, probably belong to this period. Some use of them will be made below in the formal development of the Geometry of Bolyai and Lobatschewsky.

However his plans were changed when, in February, 1832, Bolyai's work reached his hands. He saw that it was now unnecessary for him to proceed with this work. The enthusiasm with which he read the *Appendix* we have already seen.

I have entered at some length into this story, partly because of its intrinsic interest; partly because of the unfortunate claim made by some mathematicians that to Gauss should be ascribed the discovery of the Non-Euclidean Geometry; partly, also, because it has been suggested that the work of Bolyai and Lobatschewsky had been inspired by the investigations of Gauss.

The claim and the suggestion we now know to be unfounded. The wonderful discovery, which revolutionised the science of Geometry, must always be associated with the names of Bolyai and Lobatschewsky, who, independently and without any knowledge of the work of Gauss, fully developed the new Geometry. While the glory of the discovery is theirs, we must not forget the advance which Gauss, and also Schweikart, had made along the same lines.

---

* Cf. Gauss, *Werke*, vol. viii. p. 202; also Bonola, *loc. cit.* p. 67.

CHAPTER II.

THE WORK OF BOLYAI, LOBATSCHEWSKY, AND RIEMANN, THE FOUNDERS OF THE NON-EUCLIDEAN GEOMETRIES.

§ 13. John Bolyai (1802-1860).

As we have already seen, John Bolyai, a Hungarian officer in the Austrian army, had in 1823 built up a consistent system of geometry in which the Parallel Postulate of Euclid was replaced by another, contradictory to the former. His discovery was published in 1832 as an Appendix to his father's work : *Tentamen juventutem studiosam in elementa matheseos purae, elementaris ac sublimioris, methodo intuitiva, evidentiaque huic propria, introducendi.* This work is usually referred to as the *Tentamen.* The title of the Appendix contributed by the son, and placed at the end of vol. i. of the *Tentamen,* is : *Appendix. Scientiam spatii absolute veram exhibens : a veritate aut falsitate Axiomatis XI Euclidei (a priori haud unquam decidenda) independentem : adjecta ad casum falsitatis, quadratura circuli geometrica. Auctore Johanne Bolyai de eadem, Geometrarum in Exercitu Caesareo Regio Austriaco Castrensium Capitaneo.*

If we omit the title page, a page explaining the notation, and two pages of errata, the Appendix contains only twenty-four pages.

Bolyai's discovery was made as early as 1823, when he was but 21 years old. At the time, we find him writing to his father as follows : *

" I have resolved to publish a work on the theory of parallels, as soon as I shall have put the material in order, and my cir-

---

* Stäckel u. Engel, " Gauss die beiden Bolyai und die nichteuklidische Geometrie, *Math. Ann.* vol. xlix. p. 155 (1897). Also Stäckel, *loc. cit.* vol. i. p. 85.

cumstances allow it. At present I have *not yet* completed this work, but the road, which I have followed, has made it almost certain that the goal will be attained, if that is at all possible : the goal is not yet reached, but I have made such wonderful discoveries that I have been almost overwhelmed by them, and it would be the cause of continual regret if they were lost. When you will see them, my dear father, you too will recognise it. In the meantime I can only say this : *I have created a new universe from nothing.* All that I have sent you till now is but a house of cards compared to a tower. I am as fully persuaded that it will bring me honour, as if I had already completed the discovery."

Wolfgang suggested that his son should publish his work, and offered to insert it as an Appendix in the *Tentamen.* He advised him, if he had really succeeded, not to lose time in letting the fact be known, for two reasons : *

" First, because ideas pass easily from one to another, who can anticipate its publication ; and, secondly, there is some truth in this, that many things have an epoch, in which they are found at the same time in several places, just as the violets appear on every side in spring. Also every scientific struggle is just a serious war, in which I cannot say when peace will arrive. Thus we ought to conquer when we are able, since the advantage is always to the first comer."

But the publication of the *Tentamen* was delayed for some years. In the meantime the MSS. was placed in his father's hands, and he called some parts of it in question. His doubts were partly removed, and the work was inserted in the first volume, an advance copy of which reached Gauss at Göttingen in February, 1832. The younger Bolyai attached immense importance to the approval of Gauss, at that time the greatest authority in the world of mathematics. The high praise which Gauss gave to his work we have already mentioned.

§ 14. We now give a short description of the Appendix.

(i) It opens with a definition of parallels. *If the ray* AM *is not cut by the ray* BN, *situated in the same plane, but is cut by every ray* BP *comprised in the angle* ABN, *this will be denoted by* BN ||| AM.

---

* Stäckel, " Die Entdeckung der nichteuklidischen Geometrie durch Johann Bolyai," *Math. u. Naturw. Berichte aus Ungarn*, vol. xvii. p. 14 (1901). Also *loc. cit.* vol. i. p. 86.

In a footnote he adds " pronounced BN *asymptotic* to AM."

Bolyai always used the word *parallel* and the symbol ‖ in the sense of equidistant, while he reserved the word *asymptotic* and this symbol ⫴ for the new parallels, in the sense in which we shall see Lobatschewsky used the term.

The properties of the new parallels are then established.

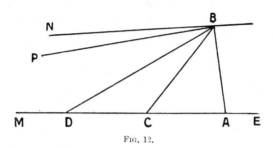

Fig. 12.

(ii) The properties of the circle and sphere of infinite radius are obtained. It is shown that the geometry on the sphere of infinite radius is identical with ordinary plane geometry.

(iii) Spherical Geometry is proved to be independent of the Parallel Postulate.

(iv) The formulae of the Non-Euclidean Plane Trigonometry are obtained with the help of the sphere of infinite radius.

(v) Various geometrical problems are solved for the Non-Euclidean Geometry ; *e.g.* the construction of a " square " whose area shall be the same as that of a given circle.*

Bolyai laid particular stress upon the demonstration of the theorems which can be established without any hypothesis as to parallels. He speaks of such results as *absolutely true,* and they form part of Absolute Geometry or the Absolute Science of Space. As the title of the Appendix shows, one of his chief objects was to build up this science.

In the Appendix he says little about the question of the impossibility of proving the truth of the Euclidean Parallel

---

* Of course the Non-Euclidean "square" is not a quadrilateral with equal sides and all its angles right angles. A rectangle is impossible in the Non-Euclidean plane. The square of Bolyai is simply a regular quadrilateral. The angles are equal, but their size depends on the sides.

Postulate. He refers to the point more than once ; but he postpones fuller treatment till a later occasion ; an occasion which, so far as the public are concerned, never came. The last sentences of the Appendix (Halsted's translation) are as follows :

" It remains finally, (that the thing may be completed in every respect), to demonstrate the impossibility (apart from any supposition), of deciding *a priori*, whether Σ, or some S (and which one) exists.* This, however, is reserved for a more suitable occasion."

§ 15. Bolyai retired from the army in 1833 and lived till 1860. So far as we know he published nothing further, either in extension of the Appendix or on any other mathematical subject. From several sources, chiefly notes found among his papers, we learn that he occupied himself with some of the problems of the Non-Euclidean Geometry. He carried his work further in the direction of Solid Geometry. He investigated more fully the relation between the Non-Euclidean Geometry and Spherical Trigonometry ; and he pondered the question of the possibility or impossibility of proving Euclid's Hypothesis.

An unpublished version of part of the Appendix exists in German,† in which he gives clearer expression to his views upon the last of these topics than is to be found in the corresponding section of the original. In this version, which dates from 1832, the first part of § 33 reads as follows :

" Now I should briefly state the essential result of this theory, and what it is in a position to effect :

" I. Whether Σ or S actually exists, remains here (and, as the author can prove, for ever) undecided.

" II. Now there is a Plane Trigonometry absolutely true (*i.e.* free from every hypothesis), in which, however, (according to I.), the constant i and its very existence remain wholly undetermined. With the exception of this unknown everything is determined. But Spherical Trigonometry was

---

* Bolyai calls Σ the system of Geometry resting upon Euclid's Hypothesis ; and S the system founded upon his own definition of parallels.

† Cf. Stäckel, "Untersuchungen aus der absoluten Geometrie aus Johann Bolyai's Nachlass," *Math. u. Naturw. Berichte aus Ungarn*, vol. xviii. p. 280, 1902. Also *loc. cit.* vol. ii. p. 181.

developed absolutely and completely in § 26 ; so that the
ordinary familiar Spherical Trigonometry is not in the least
dependent upon Axiom XI. and is unconditionally true.

" III. By means of these two trigonometries and several
subsidiary theorems (to be found in the text of § 32) one is able
to solve all the problems of Solid Geometry and Mechanics,
which the so-called Analysis in its present development has in
its power (a statement which requires no further qualification),
and this can be done downright without the help of Axiom XI.
(on which until now everything rested as chief-foundation-
stone), and the whole theory of space can be treated in the
above-mentioned sense, from now on, with the analytical
methods (rightly praised within suitable limits) of the new
(science).

" Taking now into consideration the demonstration of the
impossibility of deciding between Σ and S (a proof which the
author likewise possesses), the nature of Axiom XI. is at
length fully determined ; the intricate problem of parallels
completely solved ; and the total eclipse completely dispelled,
which has so unfortunately reigned till the present (for minds
thirsting for the truth), an eclipse which has robbed so many of
their delight in science, and of their strength and time.

" Also, in the author, there lives the perfectly purified conviction (such as he expects too from every thoughtful reader)
that by the elucidation of this subject one of the most important
and brilliant contributions has been made to the real victory
of knowledge, to the education of the intelligence, and consequently to the uplifting of the fortunes of men."

His proof of the impossibility of proving the Euclidean
Hypothesis seems to have rested upon the conviction that
the Non-Euclidean Trigonometry would not lead to any contradiction. The following sentences are to be found among
his papers :

" We obtain by the analysis of a system of points on a
plane obviously quite the same formulae as on the sphere ;
and since continued analysis on the sphere cannot lead to any
contradiction (for Spherical Trigonometry is absolute), it is
therefore clear that in the same way no contradiction could
ever enter into any treatment of the system of points in a
plane." *

---

* Cf. Stäckel, *loc. cit.* vol. i. p. 121.

And lower down in the same passage :

" But there still remains the question, whether in some way or other the considerations of space would not avail for the establishment of Σ."

Indeed, owing to a mistake in his analysis, he thought for a time that he had actually obtained a proof of the Euclidean Hypothesis on these lines. But he discovered his error later.

From the fact that at one time he was willing to admit that, with the aid of Solid Geometry, evidence against the logical consistency of the Non-Euclidean Geometry might be obtained, we must not imagine that he had failed to grasp the significance of his earlier work. On the contrary, his argument shows that he had seen more deeply into the heart of the matter than Lobatschewsky himself. The latter, as we shall see below, relied simply upon the formulae for the plane. Even when it has been established that the Non-Euclidean Plane Geometry is a perfectly logical and consistent system, the question still remains, whether, somewhere or other, contradictory results might not appear in the theorems of Solid Geometry.

This question, raised for the first time by Bolyai, was settled many years later by Klein,* following upon some investigations of Cayley. We shall give, in the last chapter of this book, an elementary and rigorous demonstration of the logical possibility of the Non-Euclidean Geometry of Bolyai-Lobatschewsky, and shall show how the same argument can be applied to the Non-Euclidean Geometry associated with the name of Riemann.

§ 16. The Work of Lobatschewsky (1793-1856).

Nicolaus Lobatschewsky—Professor of Mathematics in the University of Kasan—was a pupil of Bartels, the friend and fellow-countryman of Gauss. As early as 1815 he was working at the Theory of Parallels, and in notes of his lectures (1815-1817), carefully preserved by one of his students, and now in the Biblioteca Lobatschewskiana of the Kasan Physical-Mathematical Society, no less than three " proofs " of the Parallel Postulate are to be found. From a work on Elementary Geometry, completed in 1823, but never published, the MSS. of which was discovered in 1898 in the archives of the University of Kasan, we know that by that date he had made some

---

* Cf. " Über die sogenannte Nicht-Euklidische Geometrie," *Math. Ann.* vol. iv. (1871).

advance ; for he says regarding the Parallel Postulate, " a rigorous proof of this truth has not hitherto been discovered ; those which have been given can only be called explanations, and do not deserve to be considered as mathematical proofs in the full sense." *

Between 1823 and 1826 Lobatschewsky had entered upon the path which finally led him to his great discovery. It is known that in 1826 he read a paper to the Physical-Mathematical Society of Kasan, entitled, *Exposition succincte des principes de la géométrie, avec une démonstration rigoureuse du théorème des parallèles*. The MSS. of this work does not survive, and the last clause in the title is ominous, for it suggests that he had not yet reached his goal. But in 1829-30 he published a memoir in Russian, *On the Principles of Geometry*,† and in a footnote to the first page he explains that the work is an extract from the *Exposition succincte*.

This memoir and many other works of Lobatschewsky have come down to us, for, unlike Bolyai, he was a prolific writer. He published book after book, hoping to gain for the Non-Euclidean Geometry the recognition it deserved—a recognition which in his lifetime it wholly failed to receive. But his first published work contains all that is essential to the treatment of the subject ; and fully establishes the truth and value of his discovery. Thus, if the year 1826 cannot, with absolute certainty, be taken as the date at which Lobatschewsky had solved the problem, there is not the least doubt that his discovery of the Non-Euclidean Geometry was an accomplished fact in the year 1829.

§ 17. This memoir consists of nearly seventy pages. The earlier sections, §§ 1 to 7, deal with the ordinary geometrical notions of surface, line, point, distance, etc. In § 8 he introduces his theory of parallels.

This section reads as follows : ‡

---

* I am indebted to Dr. D. M. Y. Sommerville for a rendering of the Appendix I. by Vasiliev to the Russian translation of Bonola's *La geometria non-euclidea*. From this Appendix the sentence in the text is taken.

† When Lobatschewsky's works appeared in Russian, we give the titles in English. This work is available in German in Engel's translation. See Engel u. Stäckel's *Urkunden zur Geschichte der nicht-euklidischen Geometrie*, I. (Leipzig, 1898).

‡ Cf. Engel, *loc. cit.* p. 10.

" We have seen that the sum of the angles of a rectilinear triangle cannot be greater than π. There still remains the assumption that it may be equal to π or less than π. Each of these two can be adopted without any contradiction appearing in the deductions made from it ; and thus arise two geometries : the one, the *customary*, it is that until now owing to its simplicity, agrees fully with all practical measurements ; the other, the *imaginary*, more general and therefore more difficult in its calculations, involves the possibility of a relation between lines and angles.

" If we assume that the sum of the angles in a single rectilinear triangle is equal to π, then it will have the same value in all. On the other hand, if we admit that it is less than π in a single triangle, it is easy to show that as the sides increase, the sum of the angles diminishes.

" In all cases, therefore, two lines can never intersect, when they make with a third, angles whose sum is equal to π. It is also possible that they do not intersect in the case when this sum is less than π, if, in addition, we assume that the sum of the angles of a triangle is smaller than π.

" In relation to a line, all the lines of a plane can therefore be divided into *intersecting* and *not-intersecting* lines. The latter will be called *parallel*, if in the pencil of lines proceeding from a point they form the limit between the two classes ; or, in other words, the boundary between the one and the other.

" We imagine the perpendicular a dropped from a point to a given line, and a parallel drawn from the same point to the same line. We denote the angle between a and the parallel by $\mathsf{F}(a)$. It is easy to show that the angle $\mathsf{F}(a)$ is equal to $\dfrac{\pi}{2}$ for every line, when the sum of the angles of a triangle is equal to π ; but, on the other hypothesis, the angle $\mathsf{F}(a)$ alters with a, so that as a increases, it diminishes to zero, and it remains always less than $\dfrac{\pi}{2}$.

" To extend the meaning of $\mathsf{F}(a)$ to all lines a, on the latter hypothesis, we shall take

$$\mathsf{F}(0) = \frac{\pi}{2}, \quad \mathsf{F}(-a) = \pi - \mathsf{F}(a).$$

In this way we can associate with every acute angle A a positive line a, and with every obtuse angle A, a negative line a, such that

$$A = F(a).$$

Further parallels, in both cases, possess the following properties :

" If two lines are parallel, and two planes passing through them intersect, their intersection is a line parallel to both.

" Two lines parallel to a third are parallel to each other.

" When three planes intersect each other in parallel lines, the sum of the inner plane angles is equal to π."

In § 9 the circle and sphere of infinite radius are introduced ; the *Limiting-Curve* and *Limiting-Surface** of the Non-Euclidean Geometry.

In §§ 11 to 15 he deals with the measurement of triangles and the solution of the problems of parallels.

At the end of § 13 are to be found the fundamental equations (17) connecting the angles and sides of a plane triangle.

§ 16, and those which follow it, are devoted to the determination, in the Non-Euclidean Geometry, of the lengths of curves, the areas of surfaces, and the volumes of solids.

After the most important cases have been examined, he adds a number of pages dealing with definite integrals, which have only an analytical interest.

From the conclusion I make the following extract, as it is related to the question already touched upon in the sections dealing with Bolyai's work—the logical consistency of the new geometry :

" After we obtained the equations (17), which express the relations between the sides and angles of a triangle, we have finally given general expressions for the elements of lines, surfaces, and volumes. After this, all that remains in Geometry becomes Analysis, where the calculations must necessarily agree with one another, and where there is at no place the chance of anything new being revealed which is not contained in these first equations. From them all the relations of the geometrical magnitudes to each other must be obtained. If anyone then asserts that somewhere in the argument a contradiction compels us to give up the fundamental assumption, which we have adopted in this new geometry, this contradiction can only be hidden in equations (17) themselves. But we

---

* See note on p. 80.

remark that these equations are transformed into the equations
(16) of Spherical Trigonometry by substituting ia, ib, and ic for
the sides a, b, and c. And in ordinary geometry and Spherical
Trigonometry there enter only the relations between lines. It
follows that the ordinary geometry, (Spherical) Trigonometry
and this new geometry must always be in agreement with
one another." *

§ 18. The writings of Lobatschewsky were brought under
the notice of Gauss as early as 1841, and we gather from his
letters how much impressed he was with them. Indeed it
almost appears as if he had thrown himself into the study of
Russian that he might be able to read the numerous papers
which he hears this " clear-sighted mathematician " had
published in that tongue. Through Gauss the elder Bolyai
learnt in 1848 of the Russian's work, and in particular of the
Geometrische Untersuchungen zur Theorie der Parallellinien of
1840. The astonishing news and the volume, which Lobatschewsky had written as a summary of his work, were passed
on from the father to his son. How he received the intelligence
we learn from the following passage in some unpublished Notes
upon *Nicolaus Lobatschewsky's Geometrische Untersuchungen* : †

" Even if in this remarkable work many other methods are
adopted, yet the spirit and the result so closely resemble the
Appendix to the *Tentamen matheseos*, which appeared in Maros-
Vásárhely in 1832, that one cannot regard it without astonishment. If Gauss was, as he says, immensely surprised, first by
the *Appendix* and soon after by the remarkable agreement of
the Hungarian and Russian mathematician, not less so am I.

" The nature of absolute truth can indeed only be the same
in Maros-Vásárhely as in Kamschatka and on the Moon, or, in
a word, anywhere in the world ; and what one reasonable
being discovers, that can also quite possibly be discovered by
another."

---

* The same point is referred to in Lobatschewsky's other works :
cf. (i) *Imaginary Geometry* (Liebmann's translation, p. 8) ; (ii) *Geometrische Untersuchungen zur Theorie der Parallellinien* (Halsted's
translation, p. 163) ; (iii) *Pangéométrie*, § 8 (quoted by Bonola, *loc. cit.*
p. 93).

† Cf. Kürschák u. Stäckel, "Johann Bolyai's Bemerkungen über
Nicolaus Lobatschewsky's Geometrische Untersuchungen zur Theorie
der Parallellinien," *Math. u. Naturw. Berichte aus Ungarn*, vol. xviii.
p. 256 (1902). Also, Stäckel, *loc. cit.* vol. i. p. 140.

Then he goes on to remark that in the world of science discoveries are not unlikely to be made about the same time ; but
he cannot help wondering whether someone had not brought
his own work to Lobatschewsky's notice ; after which the
latter might have attempted to reach the same goal by another
path. And he also makes the absurd suggestion that Lobatschewsky's work might really be due to Gauss himself ; that
Gauss, unable to endure that anyone should have anticipated
him in this matter, and yet powerless to prevent it, might have
himself written this work under Lobatschewsky's name. Bolyai
was undoubtedly a great genius, but he seems to have been the
possessor of an extraordinarily suspicious nature !

The opinion of Gauss on the same work is given in a letter
to Schumacher of 1846 : *

" . . . I have lately had occasion again to go through the
little book . . . by Lobatschewsky. It contains the outlines
of that geometry which must exist, and could quite consistently
exist, if the Euclidean Geometry is not true. A certain Schweikart called such a geometry the Astral ; Lobatschewsky calls it
the Imaginary. You are aware that for fifty-four years (since
1792) † I have had the same conviction (with some extension
later, of which I shall not say more here). I have found nothing
really new to myself in Lobatschewsky's work ; but the
development is made on other lines than I had followed, and by
Lobatschewsky, indeed, in a most masterful fashion and with
real geometrical spirit. I feel compelled to bring the book under
your notice. It will give you exquisite pleasure. . . ."

Lobatschewsky died in 1856 and Bolyai four years later :
one of them, probably, a disappointed man ; the other,
certainly, an embittered one. Public recognition they had
not gained, and in all likelihood the number of mathematicians
acquainted with their work was extremely small. Had Gauss
only made public reference to their discoveries, instead of
confining himself to praise of their work, cordial and enthu-
siastic though it was, in conversation and correspondence, the
world would earlier have granted them the laurels they
deserved.

A few years after they had passed away the correspondence
of Gauss and Schumacher was published, and the numerous

---

* Gauss, *Werke*, vol. viii. p. 238.

† Rather an early date, surely, for Gauss was born in 1777.

references to the works of Lobatschewsky and Bolyai showed the mathematicians of that day in what esteem Gauss had held these two still unknown and obscure names. Soon afterwards, thanks chiefly to Lobatschewsky's works, and to the labours of some well-known French, German, and Italian geometers, the Non-Euclidean Geometry, which Bolyai and Lobatschewsky had discovered and developed, began to receive full recognition. To every student of the Foundations of Geometry their names and their work are now equally familiar.

§ 19. The Work of Riemann (1826-1866).

The later development of Non-Euclidean Geometry is due chiefly to Riemann, another Professor of Mathematics at Göttingen. His views are to be found in his celebrated memoir : *Über die Hypothesen welche der Geometrie zu Grunde liegen*. This paper was read by Riemann to the Philosophical Faculty at Göttingen in 1854 as his *Habilitationsschrift*, before an audience not composed solely of mathematicians. For this reason it does not contain much analysis, and the conceptions introduced are mostly of an intuitive character. The paper itself was not published till 1866, after the death of the author ; and the developments of the Non-Euclidean Geometry due to it are mostly the work of later hands.

Riemann regarded the postulate that the straight line is infinite—adopted by all the other mathematicians who had devoted themselves to the study of the Foundations of Geometry—as a postulate which was as fit a subject for discussion as the Parallel Postulate. What he held as beyond dispute was the *unboundedness* of space. The difference between the *infinite* and *unbounded* he puts in the following words :

" In the extension of space construction to the infinitely great, we must distinguish between *unboundedness* and *infinite extent* ; the former belongs to the extent relations ; the latter to the measure relations. That space is an unbounded threefold manifoldness is an assumption which is developed by every conception of the outer world ; according to which every instant the region of real perception is completed, and the possible positions of a sought object are constructed, and which by these applications is for ever confirming itself. The unboundedness of space possesses in this way a greater empirical certainty than any external experience, but its infinite extent by no means follows from this ; on the other hand, if we

assume independence of bodies from position, and therefore
ascribe to space constant curvature, it must necessarily be
finite, provided this curvature has ever so small a positive
value." *

§ 20. Riemann, therefore, substituted for the hypothesis
that the straight line is *infinite*, the more general one that it is
unbounded. With this assumption the Hypothesis of the
Obtuse Angle need not be rejected. Indeed the argument which
led Saccheri, Legendre, and the others to reject that hypothesis
depended upon the theorem of the external angle (I. 16). In
the proof of this theorem it is assumed that the straight line is
infinite.

The Hypothesis of the Obtuse Angle being available, another
Non-Euclidean Geometry appeared. The importance of this
new Geometry was first brought to light, when the ideas of
the Non-Euclidean Geometry were considered in their bearing
upon Projective Geometry.

A convenient nomenclature was introduced by Klein.† He
called the three geometries *Hyperbolic, Elliptic,* or *Parabolic,*
according as the two infinitely distant points on a straight
line are *real, imaginary,* or *coincident.* The first case we meet
in the Geometry of Lobatschewsky and Bolyai ; the second
in the Geometry of Riemann ; the third in the Geometry of
Euclid. These names are now generally adopted, and the
different Non-Euclidean Geometries will be referred to below
by these terms.

It is evident that at this stage the development of the Non-
Euclidean Geometries passes beyond the confines of Elementary
Geometry. For that reason the Elliptic Geometry will not
receive the same treatment in this book as the simpler Hyperbolic Geometry. Also it should perhaps be pointed out here—
the question will meet us again later—that the Elliptic Geometry really contains two separate cases, and that probably only
one of these was in the mind of Riemann. The twofold nature
of this Geometry was discovered by Klein.

* This quotation is taken from Clifford's translation of Riemann's
memoir (*Nature*, vol. viii. 1873). The surface of a sphere is *unbounded*:
it is not infinite. A two-dimensional being moving on the surface of a
sphere could walk always on and on without being brought to a stop.

† Cf. Klein, "Über die sogenannte Nicht-Euklidische Geometrie,"
Math. Ann. vol. iv. p. 577 (1871), and a paper in *Math. Ann.* vol. vi.
Also Bonola, *loc. cit.* English translation, App. iv.

CHAPTER III.

THE HYPERBOLIC PLANE GEOMETRY.

§ 21. In this chapter we proceed to the development of the Plane Geometry of Bolyai and Lobatschewsky—the Hyperbolic Geometry. We have already seen that we are led to it by the consideration of the possible values for the sum of the angles of a triangle, at any rate when the Postulate of Archimedes is adopted. This sum cannot be greater than two right angles, assuming the infinity of the straight line. If it is equal to two right angles, the Euclidean Geometry follows. If it is less than two right angles, then two parallels can be drawn through any point to a straight line.

It is instructive to see how Lobatschewsky treats this question in the *Geometrische Untersuchungen,** one of his later works, written when his ideas on the best presentation of this fundamental point were finally determined.

" All straight lines in a plane which pass through the same point," he says in § 16, " with reference to a given straight line, can be divided into two classes, those *which cut the line,* and those *which do not cut it.* That line which forms the *boundary* between these two classes is said to be *parallel* to the given line.

" From the point A (Fig. 13) draw the perpendicular AD to the line BC, and at A erect the perpendicular AE to the line AD. In the right angle EAD either all the straight lines going out from A will meet the line DC, as, for example, AF ; or some of them, as the perpendicular AE, will not meet it.

" In the uncertainty whether the perpendicular AE is the only line which does not meet DC, let us assume that it is

---

* *Geometrische Untersuchungen zur Theorie der Parallellinien* (Berlin, 1840). English translation by Halsted (Austin, Texas, 1891).

possible that there are other lines, such as AG, which do not cut DC however far they are produced.

" In passing from the lines AF, which cut DC, to the lines AG, which do not cut DC, we must come upon a line AH, parallel to DC, that is to say, a line on one side of which the lines AG do not meet the line DC, while, on the other side, all the lines AF meet DC.

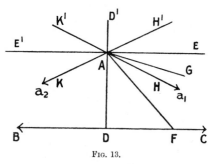

FIG. 13.

" The angle HAD, between the parallel AH and the perpendicular AD, is called *the angle of parallelism*, and we shall denote it by $\Pi(p)$, p standing for the distance AD."

Lobatschewsky then shows that if the *angle of parallelism* were a right angle for the point A and this straight line BC, the sum of the angles in every triangle would have to be two right angles. Euclidean Geometry would follow, and the *angle of parallelism* would be a right angle for any point and any straight line.

On the other hand, if the *angle of parallelism* for the point A and this straight line BC were an acute angle, he shows that the sum of the angles in every triangle would have to be less than two right angles, and the *angle of parallelism* for any point and any straight line would be less than a right angle.

The assumption $\Pi(p) = \dfrac{\pi}{2}$ serves as the foundation for the ordinary geometry, and the assumption $\Pi(p) < \dfrac{\pi}{2}$ leads to the new geometry, to which he gave the name *Imaginary Geometry*. In it two parallels can be drawn from any point to any straight line.

In this argument Lobatschewsky relies upon the idea of

continuity without stating the assumptions underlying that term. The same remark applies to the argument of Bolyai. Indeed their argument does not prove the existence of the two parallels. The existence of the two parallels in this geometry is an axiom, just as the existence of only one parallel is an axiom in the Euclidean Geometry.

§ 22. Hilbert's Axiom of Parallels.

Hilbert makes the matter clearer by definitely inserting in his treatment of the Hyperbolic Plane Geometry * the following Axiom of Parallels :

If b is any straight line and A any point outside it, there are always two rays through A, a_1, and a_2, which do not form one and the same straight line, and do not intersect the line b, while every other ray in the region bounded by a_1 and a_2, which passes through A, does intersect the line b.

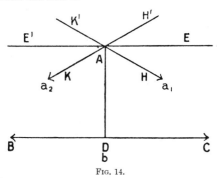

Fɪɢ. 14.

Let BC be the line *b* and AH, AK the rays a_1 and a_2.

From Pasch's Axiom † it follows that no line in the regions H'AH, K'AK cuts BC (Fig. 14).

Hence the rays a_1 (AH) and a_2 (AK) form the boundary between the rays through A which cut BC and the rays through A which do not cut BC.

Through A draw the perpendicular AD to the line *b* (BC), and also the perpendicular E'AE to the line AD.

Now E'AE cannot intersect BC, for if it cut BC on one side of D, it must cut it at a corresponding point on the other.

---

* Hilbert, *loc. cit.* p. 160.   † Cf. p. 3.

Also it cannot be parallel to BC, because according to the Axiom the two parallels are not to form one and the same straight line.

Therefore the angles between a_1, a_2, and AD must be acute.

We shall now show that they are equal.

If the angles are unequal, one of them must be the greater. Let a_1 make the greater angle with AD, and at A make

$$\angle DAP = \angle DAK.$$

Then AP must cut BC when produced.

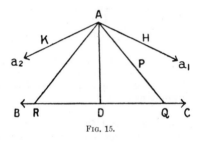

Fig. 15.

Let it cut it at Q.

On the other side of D, from the line b cut off DR = DQ and join AR.

Then the triangles DAQ and DAR are congruent, and AR makes the same angle with AD as a_2, so that AR and a_2 must coincide.

But a_2 does not cut BC; therefore the angles which a_1, a_2 make with AD are not unequal.

Thus we have shown that the perpendicular AD bisects the angle between the parallels a_1 and a_2.

The angle which AD makes with either of these rays is called the *angle of parallelism* for the distance AD, and is denoted, after Lobatschewsky, by $\Pi(p)$, where AD $=p$.

The rays a_1 and a_2 are called the *right-handed* and *left-handed* parallels from A to the line BC.

§ 23. In the above definition of parallels, the starting point A of the ray is material. We shall now show that

A straight line maintains its property of parallelism at all its points.

In other words, *if the ray* AH *is the right-handed (or left-handed) parallel through* A *to the line* BC, *then it is the right-handed (or left-handed) parallel through any point upon the ray* AH, *or* HA *produced, to the given line.*

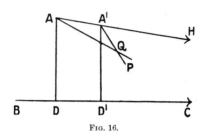

FIG. 16.

Case I. Let A′ be any point upon the ray AH other than A. Through A′ draw A′D′ perpendicular to BC.

In the region bounded by A′D′ and A′H draw any ray A′P, and take Q any point upon A′P.

Join AQ.

Then AQ produced must cut DC.

It follows from Pasch's Axiom that A′Q must cut D′C.

But A′H does not cut D′C, and A′P is any ray in the region D′A′H.

Therefore A′H is a parallel through A′ to the line BC.

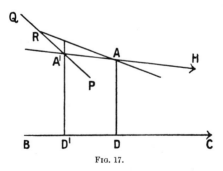

FIG. 17.

Case II. Let A′ be any point upon the ray AH produced backwards through A.

Draw A′D′ perpendicular to BC.

In the region bounded by A′D′ and A′H draw through A′ any ray A′P, and produce PA′ through A′ to Q.

Upon A′Q take any point R and join AR.

Then RA produced must intersect DC.

It follows that A′P must intersect D′C.

Therefore, as above, the ray A′H is a parallel through any point A′, on HA produced, to the line BC.

In both cases the parallels are *in the same sense* or *direction* as the original ray (*i.e.* both right-handed or both left-handed). We are thus entitled to speak of a line AB as a right-handed (or left-handed) parallel to another line CD, without reference to any particular point upon the line AB.

§ 24. Another property of parallels with which we are familiar in Euclidean Geometry also holds for the Hyperbolic Geometry.

If the line AB is parallel to the line CD, then the line CD is parallel to the line AB.

From A draw AC perpendicular to CD, and from C draw CE perpendicular to AB.

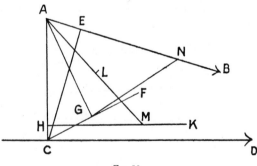

Fig. 18.

In the region DCE draw any ray CF, and from A draw AG perpendicular to CF.

It is easy to show that the point G must lie in the region ECD.

Further, since ∠ ACG is an acute angle and ∠ AGC is a right angle, AC > AG.

From AC cut off AH = AG, and draw HK perpendicular to AH on the same side as CD.

Make   ∠ HAL = ∠ GAB.

Then the ray AL must cut CD, and it follows that HK must cut AL.

Let HK cut AL at M.

From AB cut off AN = AM, and join GN.

Then the triangles HAM and GAN are congruent.

Thus   ∠ AGN = a right angle.

Therefore GN and GF coincide, and CF produced intersects AB.

But CF was any ray in the region between CE and CD, and CD itself does not cut AB.

Therefore CD is parallel to AB, in the same sense as AB is parallel to CD.*

§ 25. A third important property of parallels must also be proved :

If the line (1) is parallel to the line (2) and to the line (3), the three lines being in the same plane, then the line (2) is also parallel to (3).

Case I. Let the line (1) lie between (2) and (3). (Cf. Fig. 19.)

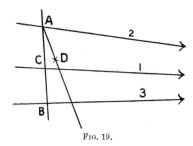

Fɪɢ. 19.

Let A and B be two points upon (2) and (3), and let AB cut (1) in C.

Through A let any arbitrary line AD be drawn between AB and (2).

---

*The proof in the text is adapted from that of Lobatschewsky in *New Principles of Geometry with a Complete Theory of Parallels*, § 96 (Engel's translation, p. 169).

Then it must cut (1), and on being produced must also cut (3).

Since this holds for every line such as AD, (2) is parallel to (3).

Case II. Let the line (1) be outside both (2) and (3), and let (2) lie between (1) and (3). (Fig. 20.)

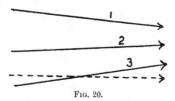

Fᴵᴳ. 20.

If (2) is not parallel to (3), through any point chosen at random upon (3), a line different from (3) can be drawn which is parallel to (2).

This, by Case I., is also parallel to (1), which is absurd.*

§ 26. We shall now consider the properties of the figure [cf. Fig. 21] formed by two parallel rays through two given points and the segment of which these two points are the ends.

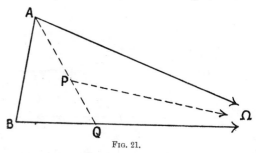

Fᴵᴳ. 21.

It is convenient to speak of two parallel lines as meeting at infinity. In the Hyperbolic Geometry each straight line will have two points at infinity, one for each direction of parallelism. With this notation the parallels through A, B may be said to meet at Ω, the common point at infinity on these lines.

---

* The proof in the text is due to Gauss, and is taken from Bonola, *loc. cit.* p. 72.

Also, a straight line will be said to pass through this point Ω, when it is parallel to these two lines in the same sense.

1. *If a straight line passes through one of the angular points* A, B, *or* Ω, *and through a point inside this figure, it must cut the opposite side.* (Fig. 21.)

Let P be the point within the figure. Then AP must cut BΩ, by the Axiom of Parallels. Let it cut BΩ at Q. The line PΩ must cut one of the sides AB or BQ of the triangle ABQ, by Pasch's Axiom. It cannot cut BQ, since it is parallel to BΩ. Therefore it must cut AB.

2. *A straight line in the plane* ABΩ, *not passing through an angular point, which cuts one of the sides, also cuts one, and only one, of the remaining sides of this figure.*

Let the straight line pass through a point C on AB. Let CΩ be drawn through C parallel to AΩ and BΩ. If the given line lies in the region bounded by AC and CΩ, it must cut AΩ ; and if it lies in the region bounded by BC and CΩ it must cut BΩ.

Again, if the line passes through a point D on AΩ, and B, D are joined, it is easy to show that it must cut either AB or BΩ.

We shall now prove some further properties of this figure.

3. *The exterior angle at* A *or* B *is greater than the interior and opposite angle.*

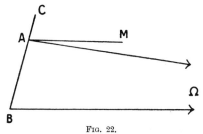

Fig. 22.

Consider the angle at A, and produce the line BA to C. Make $\angle$ CAM $= \angle$ ABΩ. AM cannot intersect BΩ, since the exterior angle of a triangle is greater than the interior and opposite angle. Also it cannot coincide with AΩ, because then the perpendicular to AΩ from the middle point of AB would also be perpendicular to BΩ. The angle of parallelism for this common perpendicular would be a right angle, and this is contrary to Hilbert's Axiom of Parallels.

Therefore $\angle\, CA\Omega > \angle\, CAM$, which is equal to $\angle\, AB\Omega$.

Thus the exterior angle at A is greater than the interior angle at B.

A similar proof applies to the angle at B.

We take now two figures of this nature ; each consisting of a segment and two parallels through the ends of the segment.

4. *If the segment* AB =*the segment* A′B′, *and the angle at* A =*the angle at* A′, *then the angles at* B *and* B′ *are equal.*

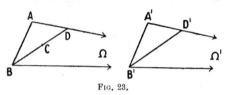

Fig. 23.

If $\angle\, AB\Omega$ is not equal to $\angle\, A′B′\Omega′$, one of them must be the greater.

Let $\angle\, AB\Omega > \angle\, A′B′\Omega′$.

Make $\angle\, ABC = \angle\, A′B′\Omega′$.

Then BC must cut $A\Omega$.

Let it cut it at D ; and on $A′\Omega′$ take A′D′ =AD, and join B′, D′.

Then the triangles ABD and A′B′D′ are congruent, so that $\angle\, A′B′D′ = \angle\, ABD = \angle\, A′B′\Omega′$, which is absurd.

It follows that $\angle\, AB\Omega$ is not greater than $\angle\, A′B′\Omega′$, and that the angles are equal.

5. *If the segment* AB =*the segment* A′B′, *and the angles at* A *and* B *are equal, as also the angles at* A′ *and* B′, *then the four angles at* A, B, A′ *and* B′ *are equal to each other.*

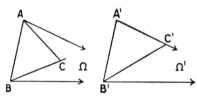

Fig. 24.

If the angle at A is not equal to the angle at A′, one of them must be the greater. Let it be the angle at A.

At A and B draw the rays which make with AB an angle equal to the angle at A'.

These rays must intersect ; let them meet at C.

From A'Ω' cut off A'C' = AC, and join B'C'.

The triangles ABC and A'B'C' are congruent, so that

$$\angle \text{A}'\text{B}'\text{C}' = \angle \text{ABC} = \angle \text{A}'\text{B}'\Omega',$$

which is absurd.

Thus the angles at A and A' must be equal ; and it follows that the angles at A, B, A' and B' are equal to each other.

6. *If the angles at* A *and* A' *are equal, and the angles at* B *and* B' *are also equal, then the segment* AB =*the segment* A'B'.

If AB is not equal to A'B', one of them must be the greater. Let it be AB.

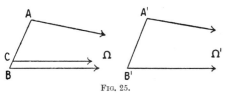

Fɪɢ. 25.

From AB cut off AC = A'B', and draw CΩ parallel to AΩ.

Then, by (4), $\angle \text{AC}\Omega = \angle \text{A}'\text{B}'\Omega' = \angle \text{AB}\Omega.$

But by (3), $\angle \text{AC}\Omega > \angle \text{AB}\Omega.$

Therefore AB cannot be greater than A'B', and the two segments are equal.

§27. The Angle of Parallelism.

From § 26 (4), we can at once deduce that *the angles of parallelism corresponding to equal distances are equal.*

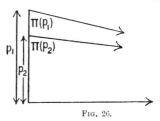

Fɪɢ. 26.

Combining this result with § 26 (3), we can assert that

If $p_1 > p_2$, then $\Pi(p_2) > \Pi(p_1)$.

We shall see later (§ 41) that to any given segment we can find the angle of parallelism, and that to any given acute angle (§ 45) we can find the corresponding distance.

Thus, we can say that

$$\text{If } \quad p_1 = p_2, \quad \text{then} \quad \Pi(p_1) = \Pi(p_2).$$
$$\text{If } \quad p_1 > p_2, \quad \text{then} \quad \Pi(p_1) < \Pi(p_2).$$
$$\text{If } \quad p_1 < p_2, \quad \text{then} \quad \Pi(p_1) > \Pi(p_2).$$

Also
$$\Pi(0) = \frac{\pi}{2},$$
$$\Pi(\infty) = 0.$$

It is convenient to use the notation

$$\alpha = \Pi(a), \quad \beta = \Pi(b), \text{ etc.}$$

Again, if the segment a is given, we can find the angle α [cf. § 41], and thus $\frac{\pi}{2} - \alpha$. And to $\frac{\pi}{2} - \alpha$ there corresponds a distance of parallelism [cf. § 45]. It is convenient to denote this *complementary* segment by a'.

Thus we have
$$\Pi(a') = \frac{\pi}{2} - \Pi(a).$$

Further, in the words of Lobatschewsky,* " we are wholly at liberty to choose what angle we will denote by the symbol $\Pi(p)$, when the line p is expressed by a negative number, so we shall assume $\quad \Pi(p) + \Pi(-p) = \pi$."

§ 28. Saccheri's Quadrilateral.

The quadrilateral in which the angles at A and B are right angles, and the sides AC, BD equal, we shall call Saccheri's Quadrilateral. We have seen that Saccheri made frequent use of it in his discussion of the Theory of Parallels.

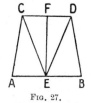

Fig. 27.

In Saccheri's Quadrilateral, when the right angles are adjacent to the base, the vertical angles are equal acute angles, and the line which bisects the base at right angles also bisects the opposite side at right angles.

Let AC and BD be the equal sides, and the angles at A and B right angles.

---

* *Geometrische Untersuchungen zur Theorie der Parallellinien*, § 23.

Let E, F be the middle points of AB and CD respectively.
Join EF, CE, and DE.

Then the triangles ACE and EDB are congruent, and the congruence of CFE and EFD follows.

Thus the angles at C and D are equal, and EF is perpendicular both to AB and CD.

Further, the angles at C and D are acute.

To prove this, at C and D draw CΩ and DΩ parallel to AB.

Then, by §26 (4), ∠ACΩ =∠ BDΩ.
Produce CD to E.

By §26 (3), ∠EDΩ > ∠DCΩ.
Therefore, since ∠ACD =∠ BDC, it follows that

∠EDB > ∠CDB.

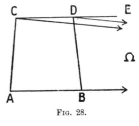

Fig. 28.

Thus ∠ACD and ∠BDC are both acute angles.

§ 29. *If in the quadrilateral* ABDC, *the angles at* A *and* B *are right angles, and the side* AC *is greater than* BD, *the angle at* C *is less than the angle at* D.

Since we are given AC > BD, we can cut off from AC the segment AE = BD. When this has been done, join DE.

It follows from § 28 that ∠AED =∠ BDE.
But ∠AED > ∠ACD and ∠BDC > ∠BDE.
Therefore ∠BDC > ∠ACD.

The converse of these theorems is easily proved indirectly, namely, that, if the angles at A *and* B *are right angles, according as* ∠ACD ⪋∠ BDC, *so is* AC⪌BD.

§ 30. *If* ABDC *is a quadrilateral in which the angles at* A, B, *and* C *are right angles, then the angle at* D *must be acute.*

Produce BA through A to B′, making AB′ = AB. (Fig. 30.)
Draw B′D′ perpendicular to B′A and equal to BD.
Join CD′, D′A, and DA.

From the congruent triangles D′B′A and DBA, we have

D′A =DA and ∠D′AB′ =∠ DAB.

Thus $\angle$ D'AC $=\angle$ DAC, and the triangles D'AC and DAC are congruent.

Therefore $\angle$ D'CA is a right angle, and DC, CD' form one straight line.

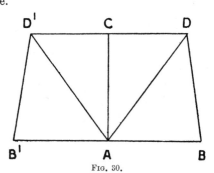

Fig. 30.

Applying the result of § 28 to the quadrilateral D'B'BD, it follows that the angles at D' and D are equal and acute.

§ 31. The sum of the angles of every triangle is less than two right angles.

Case I. Let the triangle ABC be any right-angled triangle with C $=90°$.

At A make $\angle$ BAD $=\angle$ ABC.

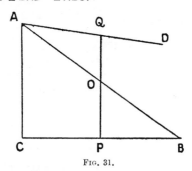

Fig. 31.

From O, the middle point of AB, draw the perpendiculars OP and OQ to CB and AD respectively.

Then the triangles POB and AOQ are congruent, and it follows that OP and OQ are in one and the same straight line.

Thus the quadrilateral ACPQ has the angles at C, P, and Q right angles.

Therefore, by § 30, the angle at A, namely ∠ CAD, must be acute.

It follows that the sum of the angles of any right-angled triangle must be less than two right angles.

Case II. Consider now any triangle, not right-angled. Every triangle can be divided into two right-angled triangles by drawing the perpendicular from at least one angular point to the opposite side (Fig. 32).

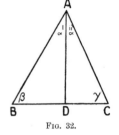

Let AD be the perpendicular referred to in the triangle ABC, and let the angles α', α'', β, γ be as in the figure.

Then $A + B + C = (\alpha' + \beta) + (\alpha'' + \gamma).$

But $\alpha' + \beta < 1$ right angle

and $\alpha'' + \gamma < 1$ right angle.

Therefore $A + B + C < 2$ right angles.

Fig. 32.

It should be noticed that no use has been made of the Postulate of Archimedes in proving this result.

The difference between two right angles and the sum of the angles of a triangle will be called the Defect of the Triangle.

COROLLARY. *There cannot be two triangles with their angles equal each to each, which are not congruent.*

It is easy to show that if two such triangles did exist, we could obtain a quadrilateral with the sum of its angles equal to four right angles. We have simply to cut off from one of the triangles a part congruent with the other. But the sum of the angles of a quadrilateral cannot be four right angles, if the sum of the angles of every triangle is less than two right angles.

§ 32. Not-intersecting Lines.

It follows from the Theorem of the External Angle (I. 16) that if two straight lines have a common perpendicular, they cannot intersect each other. And they cannot be parallel, since this would contradict Hilbert's Axiom of Parallels [cf. § 26 (3)].

The converse is also true, namely, that

If two straight lines neither intersect nor are parallel, they must have a common perpendicular.

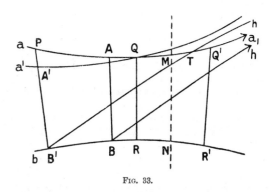

Fig. 33.

Let a and b be the two given lines, which neither intersect nor are parallel.

From any two points A and P on the line a, draw AB and PB′ perpendicular to the line b.

If AB = PB′, the existence of a common perpendicular follows from § 28. Therefore we need only discuss the case when AB is not equal to PB′.

Let PB′ be the greater.

Cut off A′B′ from PB′ so that A′B′ is equal to AB.

At A′ on the line A′B′, and on the same side of the line as AB, draw the ray a' making with A′B′ the same angle as a, or PA produced, makes with AB.

We shall now prove that a' must cut the line a.

Denote the ray PA by a_1, and draw from B the ray h parallel to a_1.

Since a, b are *not-intersecting lines*, the ray h must lie in the region between BA and B′B produced.

Through B′ draw the ray h', on the same side of B′A′ as h is of BA, and making the same angle with the ray B′B as h does with B′B produced.

From § 26 (3), it follows that the parallel from B′ to h and a_1 lies in the region between h' and B′B.

* This proof is due to Hilbert ; cf. *loc. cit.* p. 162.

Therefore h' must cut a_1.

Let it cut this line at T.

Since a' is parallel to B'T, it follows that the ray a' must cut PT (Pasch's Axiom).

Let these rays a_1, a' intersect at Q.

From Q draw QR perpendicular to the line b, and from the line b cut off BR' equal to B'R and on the opposite side of B from B'.

In the same way, from the line a cut off AQ' equal to A'Q, and on the opposite side of A from P.

In this way we obtain a quadrilateral ABR'Q' congruent with A'B'RQ.

Thus QRR'Q' is a Saccheri's Quadrilateral, and the line joining the middle points of QQ', RR' is perpendicular to a and b.

§ **33.** *Two parallel lines approach each other continually, and their distance apart eventually becomes less than any assigned quantity.*

Let a and b be two parallel lines.

Upon a take any two points P and Q, PQ being the direction of parallelism for the lines.

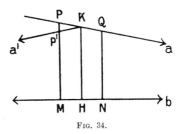

Fig. 34.

From P and Q draw the perpendiculars PM and QN to b.

Bisect MN at H, and draw the perpendicular at H to the line b.

This must intersect the segment PQ ; let it do so at K.

At K draw the ray a' parallel to b in the other direction.

This ray must intersect PM, since it enters the triangle PKM at the vertex K.

Let it cut PM at P'.

Since the triangles KHM and KHN are congruent, and ∠ HKP′ =∠ HKQ, it easily follows that P′M is equal to QN.

But P′ lies on the segment PM.

Therefore PM is greater than QN, and we have shown that as we pass along the line a, in the direction of parallelism, the distance from b continually diminishes.

We have now to prove the second part of the theorem.

Let a and b be two parallel lines as before, and P any point on the line a.

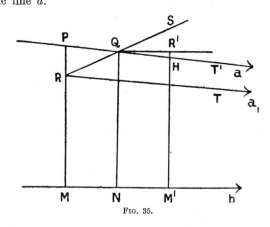

Fig. 35.

Draw PM perpendicular to b, and let ϵ be any assigned length as small as we please.

If PM is not smaller than ϵ, cut off MR $= \epsilon$.

Through R draw the ray a_1 (RT) parallel to a and b in the same sense.

Also draw through R the ray RS perpendicular to MR.

RS must cut the ray a, since ∠ PRT is an obtuse angle.

Let it cut a at Q and draw QN perpendicular to b.

Now the lines RQS and the line b have a common perpendicular.

Therefore they are not-intersecting lines.

It follows that ∠ NQR is greater than the angle of parallelism for the distance QN.

At Q make ∠ NQR′ =∠ NQR.

Then ∠ NQR′ >∠ NQT′, T′ being any point upon PQ produced.

From the line b cut off NM$' =$ NM, on the other side of N from M, and from QR$'$ cut off QR$' =$ QR.

Join R$'$M$'$.

Then R$'$M$'$ is perpendicular to b, and is cut by the ray PQ between R$'$ and M$'$.

Let the point of section be H.

Then M$'$H $<$ M$'$R$'$, and M$'$R$' =$ MR.

Therefore we have found a point on the line a whose distance from b is less than the given length ϵ.

§ **34.** *The shortest distance between any two not-intersecting lines is their common perpendicular, and as we proceed along either of the lines from the point at which it is cut by the common perpendicular the distance from one to the other continually increases.*

Let the common perpendicular to two not-intersecting lines a and b meet them at A and B.

Let P and Q be two other points on one of the lines on the same side of A, and such that AP $<$ AQ.

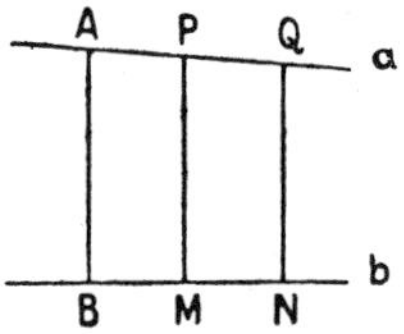

Draw PM and QN perpendicular to the other line.

Then in the quadrilateral ABMP, the angle A is a right angle and the angle APM is acute (cf. § 30).

Fig. 36.

Therefore PM $>$ AB (cf. § 29).

Also in the quadrilateral PQMN, the angle MPQ is obtuse and PQN is acute.

Therefore QN $>$ PM.

Thus, as we pass along the ray APQ... the distance from the line b continually increases from its value at A.

It can be shown that two parallel lines continually diverge towards the side opposite to the direction of parallelism, and that two intersecting lines continually diverge from the point of intersection. Also, the distance apart, both in the case of intersecting lines, of parallel lines, in the direction opposite to that of parallelism, and of not-intersecting lines will become eventually greater than any assigned length.

The theorems of §§ 33-4 were all proved by Lobatschewsky; cf. *New Principles of Geometry with a Complete Theory of Parallels* (Engel's translation), § 108 *et seq.*

§ 35. The correspondence between a Right-Angled Triangle and a Quadrilateral with Three Right Angles and One Acute Angle.

The sides of a right-angled triangle ABC, in which C is the right angle, are denoted as usual by a, b, and c; the angles A and B by λ and μ; and the distances corresponding to the angles of parallelism λ and μ are denoted by l and m. Between these quantities a, b, c, l, m, λ, and μ certain relations hold.

Similarly the elements of a quadrilateral, in which three angles are right angles, the remaining angle being necessarily acute, are connected by certain relations.

We proceed to find the equations connecting these quantities, and to establish a very important correspondence between the two figures.

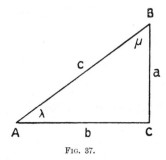

Fig. 37.

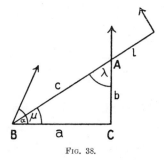

Fig. 38.

I. *The Right-Angled Triangle.*

Let ABC be any right-angled triangle. Produce the hypothenuse through A a distance l, and at the other end of the segment l draw the parallel to the line CA. Also draw through B the parallel to both these lines.

It follows from Fig. 38 that

$$\mu + \Pi(c + l) = \Pi(a) = \alpha, \quad \dots\dots\dots\dots(1)$$

and in the same way we have

$$\lambda + \Pi(c + m) = \Pi(b) = \beta. \quad \dots\dots\dots\dots(1')$$

Now draw through A the parallel to the line BC (Fig. 39).

Also draw the line perpendicular to c, which is parallel to BC in the same sense. This line will cut the hypothenuse, or the hypothenuse produced, according as m is less than or greater than c.

If $m < c$, we have

$$\lambda + \beta = \Pi(c - m). \quad\ldots\ldots\ldots\ldots\ldots\ldots(2)$$

If $m > c$, then we would have

$$\pi - \lambda - \beta = \Pi(m - c).$$

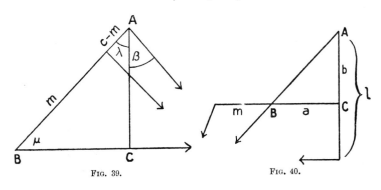

FIG. 39.   FIG. 40.

With the usual notation (cf. § 27) this reduces to

$$\lambda + \beta = \Pi(c - m).$$

In the same way we have

$$\mu + \alpha = \Pi(c - l). \quad\ldots\ldots\ldots\ldots\ldots\ldots(2')$$

Finally, produce CB through B, and draw the perpendicular to CB produced which is also parallel to AB (Fig. 40). Also produce AC through C, and draw the perpendicular to AC which is parallel to AB.

From Fig. 40, if we suppose a line drawn through C parallel to AB, it is clear that

$$\Pi(l - b) + \Pi(m + a) = \frac{\pi}{2}, \quad\ldots\ldots\ldots\ldots(3)$$

and similarly

$$\Pi(m - a) + \Pi(l + b) = \frac{\pi}{2}. \quad\ldots\ldots\ldots\ldots(3')$$

II. *The Quadrilateral with Three Right Angles and an Acute Angle.*

Let PQRS be a quadrilateral in which the angles P, Q, R are right angles.   We denote the sides, for reasons that will presently appear, by l_1, a_1, m_1', and c_1; the acute angle by β_1; and l_1, c_1 contain this angle β_1.

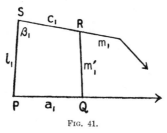

Fɪɢ. 41.

Produce c_1 through R a distance m_1, and draw the perpendicular at the end of that segment.   Since $\Pi(m_1) + \Pi(m_1') = \dfrac{\pi}{2}$, if the parallel through R to PQ is supposed drawn, it follows that this perpendicular is parallel to PQ (Fig. 41).

It follows that
$$\lambda_1 + \Pi(c_1 + m_1) = \beta_1, \quad \dotsc\dotsc\dotsc\dotsc\dotsc\text{(I.)}$$
and correspondingly
$$\gamma_1 + \Pi(l_1 + a_1') = \beta_1. \quad \dotsc\dotsc\dotsc\dotsc\dotsc\text{(I'.)}$$

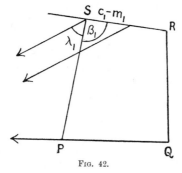

Fɪɢ. 42.

From RS cut off the segment m_1; then it is obvious from Fig. 42 that
$$\lambda_1 + \beta_1 = \Pi(c_1 - m_1), \quad \dotsc\dotsc\dotsc\dotsc\dotsc\text{(II.)}$$
and correspondingly
$$\gamma_1 + \beta_1 = \Pi(l_1 - a_1'). \quad \dotsc\dotsc\dotsc\dotsc\dotsc\text{(II'.)}$$

Finally, from QP cut off the segment m_1, and from PS produced the segment b_1, and raise the perpendiculars at the ends of these lines (Fig. 43).

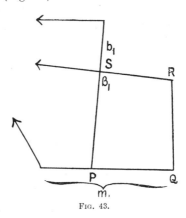

FIG. 43.

It follows that

$$\Pi(l_1 + b_1) + \Pi(m_1 - a_1) = \frac{\pi}{2}, \quad \dots\dots\dots\dots(\text{III.})$$

and correspondingly

$$\Pi(c_1 + b_1) + \Pi(a_1' - m_1') = \frac{\pi}{2}. \quad \dots\dots\dots(\text{III}'.)$$

III. We are now able to establish the correspondence between the two figures.

A right-angled triangle is fully determined when we know c and μ; a quadrilateral of this nature, when we know c_1 and m_1'.

Let $\qquad c_1 = c$ and $\Pi(m_1') = \dfrac{\pi}{2} - \mu,$

so that $\qquad\qquad m_1 = m.$

Then it follows from (1′) and (2) that

$$\lambda + \beta = \Pi(c - m),$$
$$-\lambda + \beta = \Pi(c + m),$$

and therefore $\qquad 2\lambda = \Pi(c - m) - \Pi(c + m),$

$$2\beta = \Pi(c - m) + \Pi(c + m).$$

But from (I.) and (II.) we have

$$\lambda_1 + \beta_1 = \Pi(c_1 - m_1) = \Pi(c - m),$$
$$- \lambda_1 + \beta_1 = \Pi(c_1 + m_1) = \Pi(c + m).$$

Therefore $\lambda_1 = \lambda$ and $\beta_1 = \beta$.

From (3') and (III.), we now obtain

$$\Pi(m - a) = \frac{\pi}{2} - \Pi(l + b),$$

$$\Pi(m_1 - a_1) = \Pi(m - a_1) = \frac{\pi}{2} - \Pi(l_1 + b_1) = \frac{\pi}{2} - \Pi(l + b).$$

Thus $m - a_1 = m - a,$

and $a_1 = a.$

Therefore we have obtained the important result :

If a, b, c, (λ, μ) *are the five elements of a right-angled triangle, then there exists a quadrilateral with three right angles and one acute angle, in which the sides are* c, m', a, *and* l, *taken in order, and the acute angle* β *lies between* c *and* l.*

The converse of this theorem also holds.

§ 36. The Closed Series of Associated Right-Angled Triangles.

We have seen that to the right-angled triangle $a, b, c, (\lambda, \mu)$ there corresponds a quadrilateral with three right angles and

---

* This result was given by Lobatschewsky in his earliest work, *On the Principles of Geometry* (cf. §§ 11, 16, Engel's translation, pp. 15 and 25), but his demonstration requires the theorems of the Non-Euclidean Solid Geometry. The proof in the text is due to Liebmann (*Math. Ann.* vol. lxi. p. 185 (1905), and *Nichteuklidische Geometrie*, 2nd ed. § 10), who first established the correspondence between the right-angled triangle and the quadrilateral with three right angles and an acute angle by the aid of Plane Geometry alone.

This is an important development, as the Parallel Constructions depend upon this correspondence, and the Non-Euclidean Plane Geometry and Trigonometry is now self-contained.

Further, as we shall see below (§ 45), the existence of a segment corresponding to any given angle of parallelism can be established without the use of the Principle of Continuity, on which Lobatschewsky's demonstration depends. Therefore, though the existence of p, when $\Pi(p)$ is given, is assumed in the above demonstration, the correspondence between the triangle and quadrilateral is independent of that principle.

an acute angle β, the two sides enclosing the acute angle being c and l, and the other two a and m'.

If we interchange c and l, and m' and a, we obtain the same quadrilateral. It follows that, given the right-angled triangle a, b, c, (λ, μ), there exists another right-angled triangle whose elements are a_1, b_1, c_1, (λ_1, μ_1), where

$$a_1 = m', \ b_1 = b, \ c_1 = l, \ \lambda_1 = \gamma, \ \mu_1 = \frac{\pi}{2} - \alpha.$$

Thus, starting with the right-angled triangle

$$a, \ b, \ c, \ (\lambda, \ \mu), \ \dots\dots\dots\dots\dots\dots(1)$$

we obtain a second right-angled triangle whose elements are

$$m', \ b, \ l, \ \left(\gamma, \ \frac{\pi}{2} - \alpha\right). \ \dots\dots\dots\dots\dots(2)$$

If we now take the sides and opposite angles of this triangle in the reverse order, $i.e.$ write it as the triangle

$$b, \ m', \ l, \ \left(\frac{\pi}{2} - \alpha, \ \gamma\right),$$

we obtain another right-angled triangle with the elements

$$c', \ m', \ a', \ \left(\lambda, \ \frac{\pi}{2} - \beta\right). \ \dots\dots\dots\dots(3)$$

Writing this as

$$m', \ c', \ a', \ \left(\frac{\pi}{2} - \beta, \ \lambda\right),$$

we obtain another with the elements

$$l', \ c', \ b', \ \left(\frac{\pi}{2} - \alpha, \ \mu\right). \ \dots\dots\dots\dots(4)$$

From this we obtain in its turn

$$l', \ a, \ m, \ \left(\gamma, \ \frac{\pi}{2} - \beta\right). \ \dots\dots\dots\dots(5)$$

Again, from this we have

$$b, \ a, \ c, \ (\mu, \ \lambda), \ \dots\dots\dots\dots\dots\dots(6)$$

the last being the original triangle.

The relation between the elements of these triangles can be put in the form of the following rule :

Let a, b, c, ($\lambda = \Pi(l)$, $\mu = \Pi(m)$) *be the sides, hypothenuse, and the angles opposite the sides of a right-angled triangle. Write the letters* a$'$, l, c, m, b$'$ *in cyclic order on the sides of a pentagon. The six triangles which form the closed series of associated triangles are obtained, if we write the letters* a$_r'$, l$_r$, c$_r$, m$_r$, b$_r'$ *in the same or reverse order on the sides, starting with any one side, and take the elements with the suffices equal to those on the same sides without the suffices.*

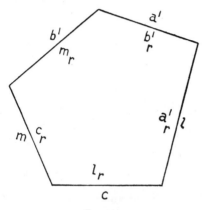

Fɪɢ. 44.

E.g. from Fig. 44,

$$a_r' = l, \quad i.e. \quad a_r = l' ;$$
$$b_r' = a', \quad i.e. \quad b_r = a ;$$
$$m_r = b', \quad i.e. \quad \mu_r = \frac{\pi}{2} - \beta ;$$
$$c_r = m ;$$
$$l_r = c, \quad i.e. \quad \lambda_r = \gamma ;$$

giving the triangle (5) above.

These results have an important bearing on certain problems of construction. For example, the problem of constructing a right-angled triangle when the hypothenuse c and a side a are given, with the usual construction involves the assumption as to the intersection of a circle and a straight line ; an assumption which depends upon the Principle of Continuity. But we know that with the triangle a, b, c, (λ, μ) there is associated a triangle l', a, m, $\left(\gamma, \dfrac{\pi}{2} - \beta\right)$. In this triangle we are given a side a and the adjacent angles γ, $\dfrac{\pi}{2}$; and it can be constructed without that assumption. The associated triangle gives us the second side b of the required triangle. This argument depends upon the theorem proved in §§41-3, that we can always find $\Pi(p)$ when p is given, and that proved in §45, that given $\Pi(p)$, we can always find p.

§ 37. Proper and Improper Points.

In the Euclidean Plane two lines either intersect or are parallel. If we speak of two parallels as intersecting at " a point at infinity " and assign to every straight line " a point at infinity," so that the plane is completed by the introduction of these *fictitious* or *improper* points, we can assert that any two given straight lines in the plane intersect each other.

On this understanding we have two kinds of pencils of straight lines in the Euclidean Plane : the ordinary pencil whose vertex is a *proper* point, and the set of parallels to any given straight line, a pencil of lines whose vertex is an *improper* point.

Also, in this Non-Euclidean Geometry, there are advantages to be gained by introducing *fictitious* points in the plane. If two coplanar straight lines are given they belong to one of three classes. They may intersect in the ordinary sense ; they may be parallel ; or they may be *not-intersecting lines* with a common perpendicular. Corresponding to the second and third classes we introduce two kinds of *fictitious* or *improper* points. Two parallel lines are said to intersect at *a point at infinity*. And every straight line will have two points at infinity, one corresponding to each direction of parallelism. All the lines parallel to a given line in the same sense will thus have a common point—*a point at infinity* on the line.

Two *not-intersecting* lines have a common perpendicular. The lines are said to intersect in *an ideal point* corresponding to this perpendicular. And all the lines perpendicular to one and the same straight line are said to intersect in *the ideal point* corresponding to this line.

We shall denote an ordinary point—a *proper* point—by the usual capital letter, *e.g.* A. An *improper* point—*a point at infinity*—by the Greek capital letter, *e.g.* Ω ; and a point belonging to the other class of improper points—*an ideal point* —by a Greek capital letter with a suffix, to denote the line to which the *ideal point* corresponds, *e.g.* Γ_c.

Thus any two lines in the hyperbolic plane determine a pencil.

(i) If the lines intersect in an ordinary point A, the pencil is the set of lines through the point A in the plane.

(ii) If the lines are parallel and intersect in the improper point Ω, the pencil is the set of lines in the plane parallel to the given lines in the same sense.

(iii) If the two lines are perpendicular to the line c, and thus intersect in the ideal point which we shall denote by Γ_c, the pencil is the set of lines all perpendicular to the line c.

§ 38. We now enumerate all the cases in which two points in the Hyperbolic Plane fix a straight line and the corresponding constructions :

(1) Two ordinary points A and B. The construction of the line joining any two such points is included in the assumptions of our geometry.

(2) An ordinary point [A] and a point at infinity [Ω]. The line $A\Omega$ is constructed by drawing the parallel through A to the line which contains Ω, in the direction corresponding to Ω. This construction is given below in §§ 41-3.

(3) An ordinary point [A] and an ideal point [Γ_c]. This line is constructed by drawing the perpendicular from A to the representative line c of the ideal point.

(4) Two points at infinity [Ω, Ω']. The line $\Omega\Omega'$ is the common parallel to the two given lines on which Ω, Ω' lie. These lines are not parallel to each other or Ω and Ω' would be the same point. The construction of this line is given below in § 44.

(5) An ideal point [Γ_c] and a point at infinity [Ω] not lying on the representative line c of the ideal point. The line $\Gamma_c\Omega$ is the line which is parallel to the direction given by Ω and perpendicular to the representative line c of the ideal point. The construction of this line is given below in § 45.

(6) Two ideal points $[\Gamma_c,\ \Gamma'_{c'}]$, when the lines c and c' do not intersect and are not parallel. The line $\Gamma_c\Gamma'_{c'}$ is the common perpendicular to the two not-intersecting lines c and c'. The construction of this line was given in § 32.

The pairs of points which do not determine a line are as follows :

(i) An ideal point and a point at infinity lying on the representative line of the ideal point.

(ii) Two ideal points, whose representative lines are parallel or meet in an ordinary point.*

§ **39.** With this notation the theorems as to the concurrence of the lines bisecting the sides of a triangle at right angles, the lines bisecting the angles of a triangle, the perpendiculars from the angular points to the opposite sides, which hold in the Euclidean Geometry, will be found also to be true in this Non-Euclidean Geometry. Lines will be said to intersect in the sense of §§ 37, 38. Also, in speaking of triangles, it is not always necessary that they should have ordinary points for their angular points. The figure of § 26 is a triangle with one angular point at an improper point—a point at infinity. It will be seen that a number of the theorems of that section are analogous to familiar theorems for ordinary triangles.

With regard to the concurrence of lines in the triangle we shall only take one case—the perpendiculars through the middle points of the sides.

The perpendiculars to the sides of a triangle at their middle points are concurrent.

Let ABC be the triangle and D, E, F the middle points of the sides opposite A, B and C.

Case (i) If the perpendiculars at the middle points of two of the sides intersect in an ordinary point, the third perpendicular must also pass through this point. The proof depends on the congruence theorems as in the Euclidean case.

---

* In the foundation of Projective Geometry independent of the Parallel Postulate, this difficulty is overcome by the introduction of new entities, called *improper* lines, and *ideal* lines, to distinguish them from the ordinary or *proper* lines. Cf. Bonola, *loc. cit.* English translation, App. IV.

Case (ii) Let the perpendiculars at D and E be not-intersecting lines, and let D′E′ be the line perpendicular to both.

From A, B, and C draw AA′, BB′, and CC′ perpendicular to
D′E′.

Then it is not difficult to show from congruent triangles that

$$AA′ = CC′ \text{ and } BB′ = CC′.$$

Thus AA′ = BB′.

Let F′ be the middle point of A′B′.

From § 28 it follows that FF′ is perpendicular to AB and A′B′.

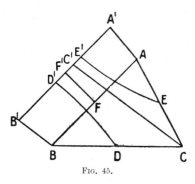

Fɪɢ. 45.

Therefore, in this case the three perpendicular bisectors of
the sides meet in *an ideal point*.

Case (iii) There remains the case when the lines through
D and E perpendicular to the sides are parallel. It follows
from Cases (i) and (ii) that the perpendicular to the third side
through F cannot intersect the other perpendiculars either in
an ordinary point, or in an ideal point. It must therefore be
parallel to these two lines in the same sense; or it must be
parallel to the first in one sense and to the other in the opposite
sense.

The second alternative we shall show to be impossible; so
the first necessarily will be true.

When the angular points of a triangle are all at infinity
(Ω′, Ω″, Ω‴) a straight line cannot cut all three sides. For
if it cuts two of them at P and Q, say, PQ produced must
be one of the rays through Q which does not intersect the other
side. (Cf. Fig. 46.)

But if BC is the greatest side of the triangle, the angle at A is the greatest angle.

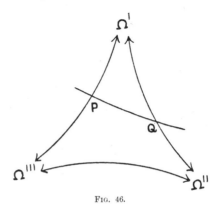

FIG. 46.

If, then, we make ∠ CAP = ∠ ACB, AP produced must cut BC. (Fig. 47.)

Let it cut it at Q.

Then EQ is perpendicular to AC.

A similar argument applies to the perpendicular through F.

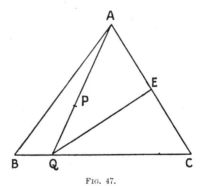

FIG. 47.

Therefore the perpendiculars at E and F both intersect BC.

It follows that the three perpendiculars cannot form a triangle whose angular points are all at infinity.

Therefore they are parallel to one another in the same sense and intersect in an improper point—a point at infinity.

If we take these three cases together, it will be seen that the theorem is established.

§ 40. The Parallel Constructions.

In Hilbert's Parallel Axiom the assumption is made that from any point outside any straight line two parallels can always be drawn to the line. In other words, it is assumed that to any segment p there corresponds an angle of parallelism $\Pi(p)$.

The fundamental problems of construction with regard to parallels are the following :

1. To draw the parallel to a given straight line from a given point towards one end.

2. To draw a straight line which shall be parallel to one given straight line, and perpendicular to another given straight line which intersects the former.

In other words :

1. Given p, to find $\Pi(p)$.

2. Given $\Pi(p)$, to find p.

For both of these problems Bolyai gave solutions ; and one was discussed by Lobatschewsky. In both cases the argument, in one form or other, makes use of the Principle of Continuity.

In the treatment followed in this book the Hyperbolic Geometry is being built up independently of the Principle of Continuity. For that reason neither Bolyai's argument (Appendix, §§ 34, 35), nor Lobatschewsky's discussion * of the second problem, will be inserted.

§ 41. To draw the Parallel to a given Line from a Point outside it. Bolyai's Classical Construction (Appendix, § 34).

To draw the parallel to the straight line AN *from a given point* D, Bolyai proceeds as follows :

Draw the perpendiculars DB and EA to AN (Fig. 48), and the perpendicular DE to the line AE.

---

* Cf. Lobatschewsky, *Geometrische Untersuchungen zur Theorie der Parallelinien*, § 23 (Halsted's translation, p. 135). Also *New Principles of Geometry*, § 102 (Engel's translation).

The angle EDB of the quadrilateral ABDE, in which three angles are right angles, is a right angle, or an acute angle, according as ED is equal to or greater than AB (cf. § 29).

With centre A describe a circle whose radius is equal to ED.

It will intersect DB at a point C, coincident with B, or between B and D.

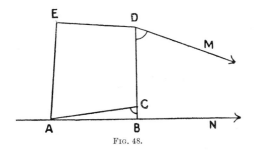

Fig. 48.

The angle which the line AC makes with DB is the angle of parallelism corresponding to the segment BD.

Therefore a parallel to AN can be drawn by making the angle BDM equal to the angle ACB.

Bolyai's proof is omitted for the reasons named above; but it should be remarked that his construction holds both for the Euclidean and Non-Euclidean Geometries; in his language it belongs to the Absolute Science of Space.

§ 42.   The correspondence which we have established in § 35 between the right-angled triangle and the quadrilateral with three right angles and one acute angle, leads at once to Bolyai's construction.

We have seen that, *to the right-angled triangle* a, b, c, (λ, μ), *there corresponds a quadrilateral with three right angles and an acute angle* β, *the sides containing the acute angle being* c *and* l, *and the other two,* a *and* m'.

Therefore we can place the right-angled triangle in the quadrilateral, so that the side a of the triangle coincides with the side a of the quadrilateral, and the side b of the triangle lies along the side l of the quadrilateral. Then the hypothenuse of the triangle will be parallel to the side c of the quadrilateral, since it makes an angle $\dfrac{\pi}{2} - \mu$ with m'.

§ 43. Second Proof of Bolyai's Parallel Construction.

The following proof of the validity of Bolyai's construction is due to Liebmann : * it will be seen that it depends (1) on Theorem (2) of § 4, regarding the locus of the middle points of the segments AA′, BB′, etc., joining a set of points, A, B, C, ..., A′, B′, C′, ..., on two straight lines, such that AB = A′B′, BC = B′C′, etc. ; and (2) on the concurrence of the perpendicular bisectors of the sides of a triangle (cf. § 39).

Let A be the given point, and AF the perpendicular from A to the given line.

It is required to draw from A the parallel to the ray FΩ.

Let us suppose the parallel AΩ drawn.

From AΩ and FΩ cut off equal segments AS and FD, and join SD.

Let M and M′ be the middle points of AF and SD.

From § 4 we know that the line MM′ is parallel to AΩ and FΩ.

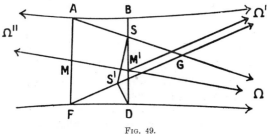

Fɪɢ. 49.

Draw the line Ω″AΩ′ through A perpendicular to AF, and produce M′M through the point M.

Then it is clear that the ray M′M is parallel to the line AΩ″.

Draw from F the parallel FΩ′ to AΩ′, and let it intersect AΩ in G.

From FΩ′ cut off FS′ equal to AS. Join SS′ and S′D.

The line GM bisects SS′ at right angles, and is perpendicular to the line ΩΩ′.

Also the perpendicular bisector of DS′ bisects the angle DFS′, and is perpendicular to ΩΩ′.

* Ber. d. k. sächs. Ges. d. Wiss. Math. Phys. Klasse, vol. lxii. p. 35 (1910) ; also Nichteuklidische Geometrie (2nd ed.), p. 35.

These two bisectors have therefore an ideal point in common, and the perpendicular bisector of SD must pass through the same ideal point (cf. § 39) ; *i.e.* it must also be perpendicular to $\Omega\Omega'$.

Suppose the parallel $M'\Omega'$ drawn through M' to $A\Omega'$.

The bisector of the angle $\Omega'M'\Omega$ is perpendicular to $\Omega\Omega'$, and therefore to SD.

It follows that M'S bisects the angle $\Omega''M'\Omega'$.

But $M'\Omega''$ and $M'\Omega'$ are the parallels from M' to $\Omega''A\Omega'$.

Therefore M'S is perpendicular to $\Omega''A\Omega'$.

And AS was made equal to FD in our construction.

The result to which we are brought can be put in the following words : Let the perpendicular AF be drawn from the point A to the given line a (FΩ), and let the perpendicular $A\Omega'$ be drawn at A to AF. From any point D on the ray FΩ drop the perpendicular DB to $A\Omega'$. This line DB cuts off from the parallel AΩ a length equal to FD.

The parallel construction follows immediately. We need only describe the arc of a circle of radius FD with A as centre. The parallel AΩ is got by joining A to the point at which this arc cuts DB.

The existence of the parallel, given by Hilbert's Axiom, allows us to state that the arc will cut the line once between B and D, without invoking the Principle of Continuity.*

§ 44. Construction of a Common Parallel to two given Intersecting Straight Lines.†

Let OΩ and OΩ' be the two rays a and b meeting at O and containing an angle less than two right angles.

From these rays cut off any two equal segments OA and OB.

From A draw the parallel $A\Omega'$ to the ray OΩ', and from B the parallel BΩ to the ray OΩ.

Bisect the angles $\Omega A\Omega'$ and $\Omega B\Omega'$ by the rays a' and b'.

By § 26 (4), we know that

$$\angle\, OA\Omega' = \angle\, OB\Omega.$$

---

* In Euclid's *Elements* the fundamental problems of construction of Book I. can be solved without the use of Postulate **3** : "To describe a circle with any centre and distance." To draw the parallel from a given point to a given line can be reduced to one of the problems of § **3**. On the other hand, in the Hyperbolic Geometry, the parallel-construction requires this postulate as to the possibility of drawing a circle.

† Cf. Hilbert, *loc. cit.* p. 163.

It follows that $\angle \Omega A \Omega' = \angle \Omega B \Omega'$,

$$\angle \Omega AE = \angle \Omega'BF = \angle \Omega BF.$$

We shall now show that the lines a' and b' neither intersect, nor are parallel.

If possible, let them intersect at M.

The triangle AOB is isosceles, and $\angle OAB = \angle OBA$.

Therefore $\angle BAM = \angle ABM$, and $AM = BM$.

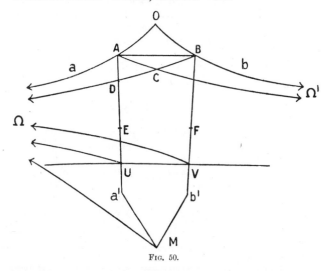

Fig. 50.

Through M draw the parallel $M\Omega$ to $A\Omega$ and $B\Omega$.

Then, since $AM = BM$ and $\angle MA\Omega = \angle MB\Omega$, by § 26 (4), we must have
$$\angle AM\Omega = \angle BM\Omega,$$
which is absurd.

The lines AE and BF therefore do not intersect at an ordinary point, and this proof applies also to the lines produced through A and B.

Next, let us suppose that they are parallel.

Since the ray a' lies in the region $BA\Omega$, it must intersect $B\Omega$. Let it cut that line at D.

Then we have $\angle \Omega AE = \angle DBF$, and $\angle AD\Omega = \angle BDE$.

Also we are supposing DE and BF parallel, and we have $A\Omega$ and $D\Omega$ parallel.

It follows from § 26 (6) that AD = DB.

Therefore we have ∠ DAB = ∠ DBA.

But ∠ BAC = ∠ ABC.

Therefore we have ∠ DAB = ∠ CAB, which is absurd.

Thus, the rays AE and AF cannot be parallel.

Similarly the rays EA, FB produced through A and B cannot be parallel.

We have now shown that the lines a' and b' neither intersect nor are parallel.

They must, therefore, have a common perpendicular (§ 32).

We shall now show that this common perpendicular is parallel to both OΩ and OΩ′.

Let it cut the lines AE and BF at U and V.

Then AU = BV, by § 29.

If VU is not parallel to AΩ, draw through U the ray UΩ parallel to AΩ, and through V the ray VΩ parallel to AΩ.

Then, by § 26 (4), ∠ AUΩ = ∠ BVΩ.

Also the angles AUV and BVU are right angles, so the exterior angle at U would be equal to the interior and opposite angle ΩVU, which is impossible (§ 26 (3)).

Thus we have shown that the ray VU is parallel to OΩ.

The same argument applies to the ray UV and OΩ′.

Therefore we have proved that there is a common parallel to the two given intersecting rays, and we have shown how to construct it.

COROLLARY. *A common parallel can be drawn to any two given coplanar lines.*

If the given lines intersect when produced, the previous proof applies.

If they do not intersect, take any point A on the line (i) and draw a parallel from A to the line (ii).

We can now draw a common parallel to the two rays through A, and by § 25 this line will also be parallel to the two given lines.

§ 45. Construction of the Straight Line which is perpendicular to one of two Straight Lines containing an Acute Angle, and parallel to the other.

Let a(OA) and b(OB) be the two rays containing an acute angle.

At O make $\angle$ AOB$'$ = $\angle$ AOB, and denote the ray OB$'$ by b'.

The common parallel to the rays b and b' will be perpendicular to OA. (Cf. § 22.)

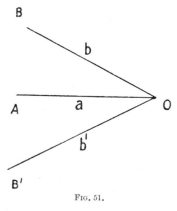

We have thus solved the second fundamental problem of parallels. *To a given angle of parallelism to find the corresponding segment.* In other words, given $\Pi(p)$ to find p.

Incidentally we have also shown that to any acute angle $\Pi(p)$, however small, or however near a right angle, there corresponds a segment p.

COROLLARY. *If two coplanar lines are not-intersecting lines, we can still draw a line parallel to one and perpendicular to the other.*

FIG. 51.

We need only take a point on the line (i), and draw from it a ray parallel to the line (ii). The line perpendicular to (i) and parallel to the ray just drawn will be parallel to the line (ii).

§ 46. Corresponding Points on two Straight Lines.

P *and* Q *are said to be corresponding points on two straight lines when the segment* PQ *makes equal angles with the two lines on the same side.*

If the lines intersect at an ordinary point O, and P is any point upon one of them, we need only take OQ = OP, and the point Q on the second line will correspond to P on the first.

Obviously there is only one point on the second ray corresponding to the point P on the first ; and if R is the point corresponding to Q on a third ray through O, then P and R are corresponding points.

Also the locus of the points on the rays of a pencil, whose vertex is an ordinary point O, which correspond to a given point P on one of the rays, is the circle with centre O and radius OP.

§ 47. We proceed to the case when the lines are parallel and thus intersect at an improper point (a point at infinity).

1. *If* (i) *and* (ii) *are any two parallel straight lines, there exists one and only one point on* (ii) *which corresponds to a given point on* (i).

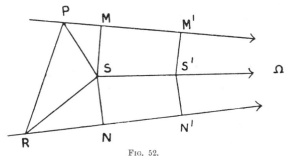

Fig. 52.

Let P be the given point on (i) and take any point R on (ii). Bisect the internal angles at P and R. The bisectors must meet in an ordinary point.

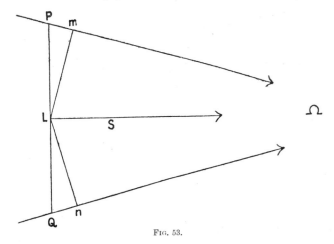

Fig. 53.

Let them meet at S, and from S draw SM and SN perpendicular to (i) and (ii).

Then SM = SN.

Through S draw SΩ parallel to PΩ.

It will also be parallel to RΩ, and it will bisect ∠ MSN, since there is only one angle of parallelism for a given distance.

Let S′ be any point upon the parallel through S to (i) and (ii).

From S′ draw S′M′ and S′N′ perpendicular to these lines.

By congruence theorems, it is easy to show that S′M′ = S′N′, and that S′Ω bisects ∠ M′S′N′.

From P draw PL perpendicular to SΩ, and from L draw L*m* and L*n* perpendicular to (i) and (ii).　(Cf. Fig. 53.)

Cut off *n*Q = *m*P on the opposite side of *n* from Ω, and join LQ.

Then it follows that PLQ is a straight line, and that Q corresponds to P.

It is easy to show that there can only be one point on the second line corresponding to P on the first.

2. *If* P *and* Q *are corresponding points on the lines* (i) *and* (ii), *and* Q *and* R *corresponding points on the lines* (ii) *and* (iii), *the three lines being parallel to each other, then* P, Q, *and* R *cannot be in the same straight line.*

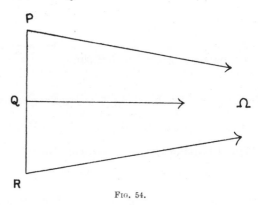

Fɪɢ. 54.

If possible, let PQR be a straight line.

By the definition of corresponding points, we have

$$\angle \Omega PQ = \angle \Omega QP,$$

$$\angle \Omega QR = \angle \Omega RQ.$$

Therefore ∠ΩPR + ∠ΩRP = two right angles, which is impossible, since PR would make equal alternate angles with PΩ and RΩ, and these two parallels would have a common perpendicular.

3. *If* P *corresponds to* Q *on the parallels* (i) *and* (ii), *and* Q *to* R *on the parallels* (ii) *and* (iii), *then* P *corresponds to* R *on the parallels* (i) *and* (iii).

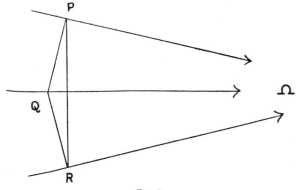

Fig. 55.

This follows from the concurrence of the perpendicular bisectors of the sides of a triangle (§ 39).

The perpendicular bisector of PQ is parallel to the given lines ; the same holds of the perpendicular bisector of QR.

It follows that the line bisecting PR at right angles is parallel to the other two bisectors, and to (i) and (iii).

Therefore P and R correspond.

§ 48. The Limiting-Curve or Horocycle.*

We now come to one of the most important curves in the Hyperbolic Geometry.

The locus of the corresponding points on a pencil of parallel lines is a curve called the Limiting-Curve or Horocycle.

It is clear that this is the circle of infinite radius, and from § 47 (2) it follows that it is not a straight line.

---

* Lobatschewsky uses the terms *grenzkreis, courbe-limite,* and *horicycle* ; Bolyai speaks of the *linea*-L.

Let P *and* P′ *be any two different points upon the same ray of a pencil of parallel lines; the Limiting-Curve through* P *is congruent with the Limiting-Curve through* P′.

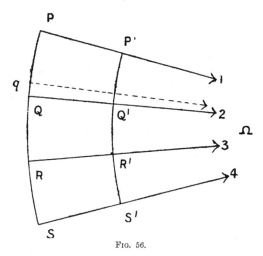

FIG. 56.

We must first explain what we mean by two Limiting-Curves being congruent.

We suppose a set of points obtained on the Limiting-Curve which starts at P′; *e.g.* P′, Q′, R′, S′, etc., on any set of lines 1, 2, 3, 4, ... , of the pencil.

We shall show that a set of points P, *q*, *r*, *s*, etc., exists on the Limiting-Curve through P, such that the segments P*q*, P′Q′ are equal, the segments *qr*, Q′R′ are equal, etc., and these related linear segments make equal angles with the lines of the pencil which they respectively intersect.

To prove this, take the segment P′Q′.

At P make $\angle \Omega P q = \angle \Omega P'Q'$, and take P*q* = P′Q′.

From *q* draw the ray parallel to PΩ.

Then, by § 26 (4), we know that $\angle P q \Omega = \angle P'Q'\Omega$.

But P′ and Q′ are corresponding points.

Therefore P and *q* are corresponding points.

Proceeding now from Q′ and *q* respectively, we find a point *r* on the Limiting-Curve through P, such that the segments *qr* and Q′R′ are equal, while *qr* makes the same angles with the rays passing through its ends, as Q'R' does with the rays through its ends.

We have thus shown that between the two Limiting-Curves there is a one-one correspondence of the nature stated, and in this case we say that the two curves are congruent.

Further, it is clear that it is immaterial at which line of the pencil we begin our Limiting-Curve.

It is convenient to speak of the point at infinity, through which all the parallel lines of the pencil pass, as the *centre* of the Limiting-Curve ; also to call the lines of the pencil the *axes* of the curve. *Concentric* Limiting-Curves will be Limiting-Curves with the same centre.

We can now state the following properties of these curves :

(*a*) The Limiting-Curve in the Hyperbolic Geometry corresponds to the circle with infinite radius in the Euclidean Geometry.

(*b*) Any two Limiting-Curves are congruent with each other.

(*c*) In one and the same Limiting-Curve, or in any two Limiting-Curves, equal chords subtend equal arcs, and equal arcs subtend equal chords.

(*d*) The Limiting-Curve cuts all its axes at right angles, and its curvature is the same at all its points.

§ 49. The Equidistant-Curve.

There remains the pencil of lines through an ideal point : the set of lines all perpendicular to the same line.

1. *If two given lines have a common perpendicular, to any point* P *on the one corresponds one and only one point* Q *on the other.*

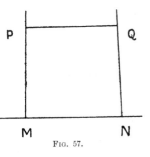

Fig. 57.

Let MN be the common perpendicular to the given lines, and P any point on one of them.

From the other line cut off NQ = MP, Q being on the same side of the common perpendicular as P.

Then PMNQ is one of Saccheri's Quadrilaterals, and the angles at P and Q are equal.

Thus Q corresponds to P, and as before there can only be one point on the second line corresponding to a given point on the first.

2. *If the lines* (i), (ii), *and* (iii) *are all perpendicular to the same straight line, then if the point* Q *on* (ii) *corresponds to the point* P *on* (i), *and the point* R *on* (iii) *to the point* Q *on* (ii), *the points* P *and* R *correspond.*

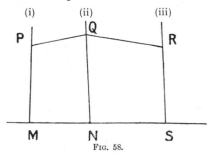

Fig. 58.

Let the common perpendicular meet the lines in M, N, and S.
Then PM = QN and QN = RS.
Therefore PM = RS, and P and R correspond.

3. *The locus of corresponding points upon a pencil of lines whose vertex is an ideal point is called an Equidistant-Curve, from the fact that the points upon the locus are all at the same distance from the line to which all the lines of the pencil are perpendicular. This line is called the base-line of the curve.*

On the Euclidean Plane the Equidistant-Curve is a straight line. On the Hyperbolic Plane *the locus is concave to the common perpendicular.*

This follows at once from the properties of Saccheri's Quadrilateral (cf. § 29). Indeed Saccheri used this curve in his supposed refutation of the Hypothesis of the Acute Angle.

We have thus been led to three curves in this Non-Euclidean Plane Geometry, which may all be regarded as " circles."

(*a*) The locus of corresponding points upon a pencil of lines, whose vertex is an ordinary point, is an ordinary circle, with the vertex as centre and the segment from the vertex to one of the points as radius.

(*b*) The locus of the corresponding points upon a pencil of lines, whose vertex is an improper point—a point at infinity—

is a Limiting-Curve, or Circle of Infinite Radius, with its centre at the vertex of the pencil.

(c) The locus of corresponding points upon a pencil of lines, whose vertex is an improper point—an ideal point—is an Equidistant-Curve, whose base-line is the representative line of the ideal point.

According as the perpendiculars to the sides of a triangle ABC at their middle points meet in an ordinary point, a point at infinity, or an ideal point, the points ABC determine an ordinary circle, a limiting-curve, or an equidistant-curve. (Cf. § 39.)

THE MEASUREMENT OF AREA.

§ 50. Equivalent Polygons.

Two polygons are said to be equivalent when they can be broken up into a finite number of triangles congruent in pairs.

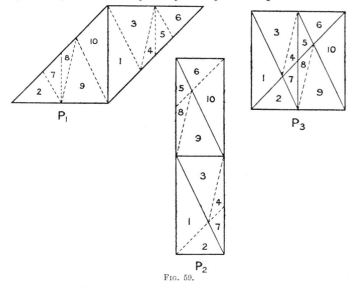

Fig. 59.

With this definition of equivalence, we shall now prove the following theorem :

If two polygons P_1 and P_2 are each equivalent to a third polygon P_3, then P_1 and P_2 are equivalent to each other.

We are given both for P_1 and P_2 a partition into triangles such that to these two partitions correspond two partitions of P_3, the triangles in the partitions of P_3 being congruent in pairs to the triangles in the partitions of P_1 and P_2.

Consider the two partitions of P_3 simultaneously; in general, every triangle of the one partition will be cut into polygons by the sides of the triangles of the second partition.

We now introduce (cf. Fig. 59) a sufficient number of linear segments, so that each of these polygons shall be cut into triangles.

By this means the two partitions of P_3 are further reduced to the same set of triangles, and this can be associated with a set of triangles in P_1 and P_2 respectively.

Therefore the polygons P_1 and P_2 can be broken up into a finite number of triangles congruent in pairs, and they are equivalent to each other.

§51. Equivalent Triangles.

A necessary and sufficient condition that two triangles are equivalent is that they have the same defect.   (Cf. § 31.)

The theorem stated above will now be proved. It has to be taken in several steps.

1. *Two triangles with a side of the one equal to a side of the other, and the same defect, are equivalent.*

Consider the triangle ABC, in which E, F are the middle points of the sides CA and AB.

Let the perpendiculars from A, B, and C on EF meet that line at A', B', and C'.

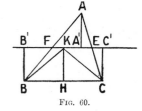

FIG. 60.

Then AA' = BB' = CC', and the quadrilateral BCC'B' is one of Saccheri's Quadrilaterals, the angles at B', C' being right angles, and the sides BB' and CC' being equal.

Further, the acute angles at B and C in that quadrilateral are each equal to half the sum of the angles of the triangle ABC.

Now, the quadrilateral is made up of the triangles BB'F, CC'E, and the figure BCEF.

Also the triangles BB'F and CC'E are congruent, respectively, with AA'F and AA'E.

Therefore the quadrilateral BB'C'C and the triangle ABC are equivalent.

Next, let $A_1B_1C_1$ be another triangle with its side B_1C_1 equal to BC, and the same defect as the triangle ABC.

For this triangle we get in the same way one of Saccheri's Quadrilaterals, the acute angles at B_1 and C_1 being equal to the acute angles at B and C, while the side $B_1C_1 = $ the side BC.

It is easy to see that these quadrilaterals must be congruent, for if they were not, we should obtain a quadrilateral, in which the sum of the angles would be four right angles, by a process which amounts to placing the one quadrilateral upon the other, so that the common sides coincide.

It follows that the triangles ABC and $A_1B_1C_1$ are equivalent. Thus we have shown that triangles with a side of the one equal to a side of the other, and the same defect, are equivalent.

COROLLARY. The locus of the vertices of triangles on the same base, with equal defects, is an Equidistant-Curve.

2. *Any two triangles with the same defect and a side of the one greater than a side of the other are equivalent.*

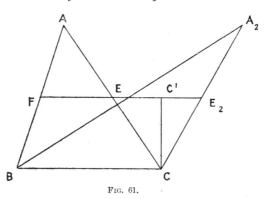

FIG. 61.

Let ABC be the one triangle and $A_1B_1C_1$ the other, and let the side $A_1C_1(b_1)$ be greater than the side AC(b).

Let E, F be the middle points of AC and AB.

From C draw CC' perpendicular to EF ; CC' cannot be greater than $\frac{1}{2}b$.

Construct the right-angled triangle with a side equal to CC' and $\frac{1}{2}b_1$ for the hypothenuse.*

Cut off $C'E_2$ equal to the other side of this triangle.

Join CE_2, and produce it to A_2 making $CE_2 = E_2A_2$.

Join A_2B.

Then the triangle A_2BC has a side equal to b_1, and the same defect as the two given triangles.

Also the triangles ABC and A_2BC are equivalent; and the triangles A_2BC and $A_1B_1C_1$, by (1).

Therefore the triangles ABC and $A_1B_1C_1$ are equivalent (§ 50).

3. *Any two triangles, with the same defect, are equivalent.*

For a side of one must be greater than, equal to, or less than, a side of the other.

When it is a case of equality, the triangles are equivalent by (1).

In the other two cases, the same result follows from (2).

4. The converse of this theorem also holds :

Any two equivalent triangles have the same defect.

From the definition of equivalence, the two triangles can be broken up into a finite number of triangles congruent in pairs. But if a triangle is broken up by transversals † into a set of sub-triangles, it is easy to show that the defect of the triangle is equal to the sum of the defects of the triangles in this partition. Further, following Hilbert,‡ it can be shown that any given partition of a triangle into triangles can be obtained by successive division by transversals. It follows that the sum of the defects of the triangles is equal to the defect of the original triangle.

Now the two equivalent triangles can be broken up into a finite number of triangles congruent in pairs. And the defects of congruent triangles are equal.

---

* The construction of the right-angled triangle from a side and the hypothenuse does not involve the Principle of Continuity. The results of § 36 show that this problem can be reduced to that of constructing a right-angled triangle out of a side and the adjacent angle.

† A triangle is said to be broken up by *transversals*, when the partition into triangles is obtained by lines from the angular points to the opposite sides, either in the original triangle or in the additional triangles which have been obtained from the first by division by transversals.

‡ Cf. Hilbert, *loc. cit.* § 20, or Halsted, *Rational Geometry*, p. 87.

Therefore the defects of any two equivalent triangles are equal.

The theorem enunciated at the head of this section is thus established : a necessary and sufficient condition for equivalence of triangles is equal defect.

5. A triangle is said to be equivalent to the sum of two other triangles, when the three triangles can be broken up into a finite number of triangles, such that the triangles in the partition of the first are congruent in pairs with the sum of the triangles in the partitions of the other two.

Now the defect of each triangle is equal to the sum of the defects of the triangles into which it is divided.

It follows that if a triangle is equivalent to the sum of two other triangles, its defect is equal to the sum of their defects.

§ 52. If we regard *area* as a concept associated with a rectilinear figure, just as *length* is with a straight line, it is obvious that *equivalent* figures have *equal area*.* And if, further, we regard the area of a rectilinear figure as a magnitude to which we can ascribe the relations of sum, equality and inequality, greater and less, we obtain at once from the theorems of § 51 the result that the areas of triangles are proportional to their defects. Indeed if we start with any triangle as the triangle of unit area, a triangle which is *n* times this triangle will have *n* times its defect.

But closer examination of the argument shows that in this treatment of the question of area various assumptions are made ; and the work of some mathematicians of the present day has put the theory of area on a sounder logical basis.† This more exact treatment of the theory of area in the Hyperbolic Plane is simple, and will now be given :

The *measure of area of a triangle* is defined as k^2 multiplied

---

* Hilbert distinguished between *equivalent* polygons, as defined above, and polygons which are *equivalent by completion.* Two polygons are said to be *equivalent by completion,* when it is possible to annex to them *equivalent* polygons, so that the two completed polygons are *equivalent.* If the Postulate of Archimedes is adopted, polygons, which are *equivalent by completion,* are also *equivalent.* Hilbert was able to establish the theory of area on the doctrine of *equivalence by completion* without the aid of the Postulate of Archimedes. *Loc. cit.* Chapter IV.

† Cf. Art. VI. by Amaldi, in Enriques' volume referred to above. Also Finzel, *Die Lehre vom Flächeninhalt in der allgemeinen Geometrie* (Leipzig, 1912).

by its defect, k being a constant depending on the unit triangle, and the unit of angle is chosen so that a right angle has $\frac{\pi}{2}$ for its measure. The number k^2 is introduced to bring the results into agreement with the analytical work in other parts of this book.

It follows from § 51 that

1. If two triangles have the same *measure of area*, they are *equivalent*, and that if two triangles are *equivalent*, they have the same *measure of area*.

2. If a triangle is broken up into a finite number of triangles, the measure of area of the triangle is equal to the sum of the measures of area of the triangles in the partition.

3. If a triangle is equivalent to the sum of two other triangles, the measure of area of this triangle is equal to the sum of the measures of area of the other two triangles.

The measure of area of a polygon is defined to be the sum of the measures of area of the triangles into which it is divided in any given partition.

This sum is independent of the partition which has been chosen. The sum of the defects of the triangles in any partition is equal to $(n-2)$ times two right angles – the sum of the angles of the polygon. This is sometimes called the *Defect of the Polygon*.

With regard to polygons we can now state the following theorems :

1. If two polygons have the same measure of area, they are equivalent. For they are each equivalent to the triangle whose defect is the sum of the defects of the given partitions.

2. If two polygons are equivalent, they have the same measure of area. For they can be broken up into a finite number of triangles congruent in pairs.

3. If a polygon is broken up into a finite number of sub-polygons, the measure of area of the polygon is the same as the sum of the measures of area of the sub-polygons.

4. If a polygon is equivalent to the sum of two other polygons, its measure of area is equal to the sum of the measures of area of these two polygons.

Rectilinear polygons with the same measure of area will be said to have equal area. Thus equivalent polygons have equal area. The area of a polygon will be said to be greater or less than the area of another polygon according as its measure of area is greater or less than the measure of area of the other.

§ 53. In the Euclidean Plane we say that a rectilinear figure contains so many square inches (or sq. ft., etc.), and by considering a curvilinear figure as the limit of a rectilinear figure we obtain a method of measuring curvilinear figures.

In the Hyperbolic Plane there is no such thing as a square inch, or rectangle with equal sides, or any rectangle. To every rectilinear figure there corresponds an equivalent Saccheri's Quadrilateral. To all equivalent rectilinear figures there corresponds one and the same Saccheri's Quadrilateral with a definite acute angle.

This quadrilateral with a given acute angle can be constructed in this geometry immediately. The construction follows from the correspondence established between right-angled triangles and the quadrilateral with three right angles. If the acute angle is β, we obtain the corresponding segment $b\{\beta = \Pi(b)\}$, by the construction of § 45. We draw any right-angled triangle with a side equal to b. The associated quadrilateral has its acute angle equal to β, and the Saccheri's Quadrilateral is obtained by placing alongside it a congruent quadrilateral.

All Saccheri's Quadrilaterals with the same acute angle are equivalent.

Thus it will be seen that there is a fundamental difference between measurement of length and area in the Euclidean and the Hyperbolic Plane.* In the Euclidean, the measures are *relative*. In the Hyperbolic, they are *absolute*. With every linear segment there can be associated a definite angle, namely the angle of parallelism for this segment. With every area, a definite angle can be associated, namely the acute angle of the equivalent Saccheri's Quadrilateral.

---

* Cf. Bonola, *loc. cit.* § 20. Also *supra*, p. 17.

CHAPTER IV.

THE HYPERBOLIC PLANE TRIGONOMETRY.

§ **54.** In this chapter we shall develop the Trigonometry of the Hyperbolic Plane, as in the preceding one we have discussed the Geometry of the Hyperbolic Plane, without introducing the theorems of Solid Geometry into the argument.

The properties of the Limiting-Curve lead to the formulae of Plane Trigonometry, without the use of the Limiting-Surface, as the surface formed by the rotation of a Limiting-Curve about one of its axes is called. The method of Lobatschewsky and Bolyai is founded upon the Geometry upon that Surface.

We begin with some theorems upon Concentric Limiting-Curves.

1. *If* A, B *and* A′, B′ *are the points in which two Concentric Limiting-Curves cut two of their axes, then* AB = A′B′.

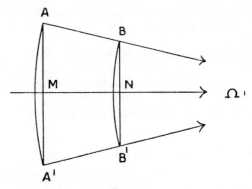

Fɪɢ. 62.

Join AA′ and BB′ (Fig. 62).

Through the middle point M of the chord AA′ draw MΩ parallel to the rays of the pencil.

Then MΩ is perpendicular to the chord BB′, and is symmetrical to the two parallels AB and A′B′ (cf. § 26 (4) and § 47).

Therefore it passes through the middle point N of BB′.

Then it follows from the quadrilateral ABB′A′ that AB = A′B′.

2. *If* A, B *and* A′, B′ *are the points in which two Concentric Limiting-Curves cut two of their axes, and* P, Q *are the middle points of the arcs* AA′ *and* BB′, *then* PQ *is a line of the pencil.*

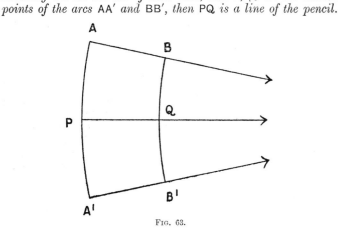

FIG. 63.

Since equal arcs subtend equal chords (cf. § 48), the chords AP and A′P are equal, and the chords BQ and B′Q are equal.

It follows that PQ is the line of symmetry for the two axes AB and A′B′, and is parallel to both (cf. § 47).

COROLLARY. *If the points* P_1, P_2, P_3, P_4, ... , *divide the arc* AA′ *into* n *equal arcs, and the axes through these points are met by the Limiting-Curve* BB′ *in* Q_1, Q_2, Q_3, Q_4, ... , *the points* Q_1, Q_2, Q_3, Q_4, ... *divide the arc* BB′ *into* n *equal arcs.*

3. *If* A, A′, A″, *are three points on a Limiting-Curve, and* B, B′, B″, *are the three points in which a Concentric Limiting-Curve is cut by the axes through* A, A′, *and* A″, *then*

arc AA′ : arc AA″ = arc BB′ : arc BB″.

First, let the arcs AA′ and AA″ be commensurable, and let the one be *m* times the arc AP and the other *n* times the arc AP.

Through P draw the line of the pencil. Let it cut the second Limiting-Curve in Q.

Then we know from (2) that the arc BB′ = m times the arc BQ, and that the arc BB″ = n times the arc BQ.

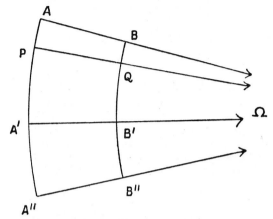

FIG. 64.

Thus the proportion follows.

Secondly, if the arcs are incommensurable, we reach the same conclusion by proceeding to the limit.

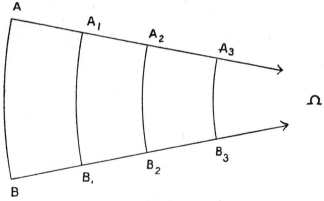

FIG. 65.

§ 55. Let us start with a Limiting-Curve whose centre is Ω, and take any two points A and B upon the curve (Fig. 65).

On the ray $A\Omega$ cut off the equal segments AA_1, A_1A_2, A_2A_3, ...
Let the Concentric Limiting-Curves through A_1, A_2, A_3, ... ,
cut the ray $B\Omega$ in B_1, B_2, B_3, ...
Then we have, by § 54 (1),

$$AA_1 = BB_1 = B_1B_2 = B_2B_3 = \text{etc.}$$

Also, from § 48 and § 54 (3),

arc AB : arc A_1B_1 = arc A_1B_1 : arc A_2B_2 = arc A_2B_2 : arc A_3B_3 = etc.

This ratio is greater than unity, and depends only on the
length of AA_1.
We may choose the unit segment so that the ratio is equal to
e, when $AA_1 = A_1A_2 = A_2A_3 = \ldots =$ the unit segment.
Let the arcs AB, A_1B_1, A_2B_2, etc., be denoted by s, s_1, s_2,
etc., when the segment AA_1 is the unit of length.
Then we have

$$s : s_1 = s_1 : s_2 = s_2 : s_3 = \ldots = e.$$

Thus $s_n = se^{-n}$, when n is a positive integer.

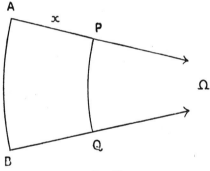

Fig. 66.

It is easy to deduce from this that when the segment AP
(Fig. 66) is x units, x being any rational number, and the arc
PQ is denoted by s_x, then we have

$$s_x = se^{-x}.$$

We obtain the same result for an irrational number x by
proceeding to the limit.

Therefore, with this unit of length we have the following theorem :

If ABDC *(Fig. 67) is a figure bounded by two Concentric Limiting-Curves* AC *and* BD, *and two straight lines* AB *and* CD, *the straight lines being axes of the curves, the lengths* s *and* s_x *of the arcs* AC *and* BD *are connected by the equation*

$$s_x = se^{-x},$$

when the segments AB *and* CD *are* x *units of length, and* AC *is the external curve,* BD *the internal.*

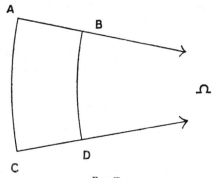

Fig. 67.

If another unit of length had been chosen, so that the ratio of the arc AB (Fig. 65) to the arc A_1B_1 had been $a\,(a > 1)$, when $AA_1 = BB_1 =$ the unit of length, the equation connecting s and s_x would have been

$$s_x = sa^{-x}.$$

Putting $$a = e^{\frac{1}{k}},$$

we have $$s_x = se^{-\frac{x}{k}}.$$

The number k is the parameter of the Hyperbolic Geometry depending upon the unit of length chosen.

§ 56. Since we can find p to satisfy the equation

$$\Pi(p) = \frac{\pi}{4},$$

there is a point Q on the Limiting-Curve through P, such that the tangent at Q is parallel to the axis through P, in the opposite sense to that in which the axis is drawn (Fig. 68).

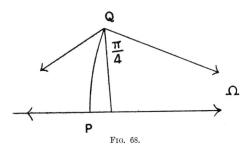

FIG. 68.

We shall for the present denote the length of this arc by S.*
Let B be a point on the Limiting-Curve through A, such that the arc AB is less than S (Fig. 69).

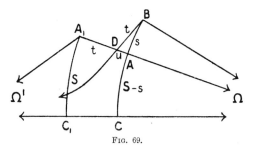

FIG. 69.

It follows that the tangent at B must intersect the axis through A.

Let it cut ΩA in D, and let the segments AD and BD be u and t. It is easy to show that $u < t$.

Produce the arc BA to the point C, such that the arc BC = S.

On ΩD produced take the point A_1, such that $DA_1 = DB = t$.

Then the perpendicular through A_1 to the axis is parallel to BD, and therefore to $C\Omega'$.

Let the Limiting-Curve through A_1 meet $C\Omega'$ in C_1.

Since the tangent at A_1 is parallel to $C\Omega'$, the arc $A_1C_1 = S$.

* Cf. p. 119.

It follows from § 55 that
$$\text{arc } \mathsf{A_1C_1} : \text{arc } \mathsf{AC} = e^{u+t}.$$
Therefore
$$S - s = S e^{-(u+t)}. \quad\dots\dots\dots\dots\dots\dots(1)$$
Next, produce the arc AB through B to the point P, such that the arc BP $=$ S (Fig. 70).

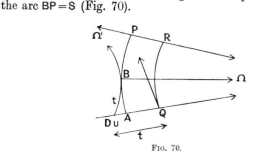

Fig. 70.

Let the tangent at B as before cut the axis through A at D, and let $AD = u$ and $BD = t$.

On $A\Omega$, on the opposite side of A from D, take the point Q, such that $DQ = t$.

Then the perpendicular through Q to the axis is parallel to DB, and, therefore, to $P\Omega'$.

Let the Limiting-Curve through Q cut the axis $P\Omega$ in R.

Since the tangent at Q is parallel to the axis through R, arc $QR = S$.

But $AQ = t - u$.

Therefore
$$S + s = S e^{t-u}. \quad\dots\dots\dots\dots\dots\dots(2)$$
From (1) and (2), we have
$$e^u = \cosh t, \quad\dots\dots\dots\dots\dots\dots(3)$$
and
$$s = S \tanh t. \quad\dots\dots\dots\dots\dots\dots(4)$$

§ 57. The Equation of the Limiting-Curve.

Let Ox and Oy be two lines at right angles, and let P be the point (x, y) on the Limiting-Curve through O, with Ox for axis (Fig. 71).

Draw PM perpendicular to the axis Ox, and let the Concentric Limiting-Curve through M cut the axis through P in N.

Then $OM = PN = x$, $MP = y$.

Let arc $OP = s$, and arc $MN = s'$.

From the construction it follows that $s' < S$.

Now the coordinates of P, x(OM), and y(MP) are, respectively, the u and t of the previous section with reference to the arc s'.

Therefore we have, from § 56 (3),

$$e^x = \cosh y. \quad\dots\dots\dots\dots\dots\dots\dots\dots(1)$$

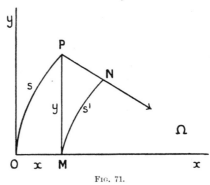

Fig. 71.

This is the equation of the Limiting-Curve through O with its axis coinciding with the axis of x.

Also, we have $s = s'e^x$

$$= Se^x \tanh y, \text{ from § 56 (4),}$$

$$= S \sinh y. \quad\dots\dots\dots\dots\dots\dots(2)$$

§ 58. The Hyperbolic Functions of Complementary Segments.

Let Ox and Oy be two lines at right angles, and let the Limiting-Curve through O with axis Ox have the arc OP = S (Fig. 72).

Let A be a point upon Ox, such that OA = x, and let the Limiting-Curve through A be cut by the axis through P in B. Let arc AB = s.

At A draw the perpendicular to the axis of x. Since it must cut PB, let it intersect it at C.

Produce AC through C to the point D, such that AC = CD.

At D draw DQ perpendicular to CD.

The line DQ must be parallel to CP, since ∠DCP = ∠ACB, and CB is parallel to AΩ.

Therefore Oy, CP, and DQ are parallel.

It follows that the segments OA and AD are complementary,

i.e. $$\Pi(OA) + \Pi(AD) = \frac{\pi}{2}.$$

With the usual notation (cf. § 27) we take x' as the complementary segment to x.

Therefore, if $OA = x, \quad AC = \dfrac{x'}{2}.$

It follows that $Se^{-x} = s = S\tanh\dfrac{x'}{2}.$ (§ 56 (4).)

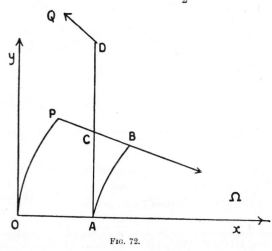

FIG. 72.

Therefore for complementary segments we have

$$e^{-x} = \tanh\frac{x'}{2}.$$

But $\sinh x = \dfrac{e^x - e^{-x}}{2}.$

$\therefore \ \sinh x = \dfrac{1}{2}\left(\coth\dfrac{x'}{2} - \tanh\dfrac{x'}{2}\right) = \dfrac{1}{\sinh x'} = \operatorname{cosech} x'.$

$\therefore \ \cosh x = \sqrt{1 + \sinh^2 x} = \coth x'.$

$\therefore \ \tanh x = \operatorname{sech} x' \ $ and $\ \coth x = \cosh x'.$

Also $\operatorname{sech} x = \tanh x' \ $ and $\ \operatorname{cosech} x = \sinh x'.$

§ 59. The Equations connecting the Sides and Angles of a Right-Angled Triangle.

Let ABC be any right-angled triangle, C being the right angle.

Produce the side AC through C, and draw the parallel BΩ through B to AC.

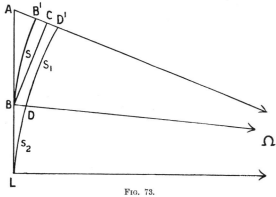

FIG. 73.

Also produce AB through B to L, where AL is the segment l, such that

$$\lambda = \Pi(l). \quad [\lambda = \angle \text{BAC} \quad (\text{cf. Fig. 37}).]$$

Through L draw LΩ parallel to BΩ and AC.

Let the Limiting-Curves through B and L, with centre at Ω, meet the axes at B', D, and D' (Fig. 73).

Let the arcs BB', DD', LD be denoted by s, s_1, s_2, and let the segment BD $= u$.

Then we have

$$\text{S} \sinh a = s = s_1 e^u, \quad [\S \ 57 \ (2).]$$
$$s_1 + s_2 = \text{S} \tanh l, \quad [\S \ 56 \ (4).]$$
$$s_2 = \text{S} \tanh \text{BL} = \text{S} \tanh (l - c),$$
$$e^u = \cosh \text{BL} = \cosh (l - c). \quad [\S \ 56 \ (3).]$$

It follows that

$$\sinh a = \cosh (l - c)\{\tanh l - \tanh (l - c)\}$$
$$= \frac{\sinh l \cosh (l - c) - \cosh l \sinh (l - c)}{\cosh l}$$
$$= \sinh c / \cosh l.$$

Thus $\sinh c = \sinh a \cosh l.$ ....I.

(Hypothenuse, side, and opposite angle.)

From this formula, connecting the hypothenuse, a side, and the opposite angle of any right-angled triangle, we can obtain the relations between all the other elements, by using the associated triangles of § 36.

We know that, starting with a right-angled triangle in which the elements are

$$a, \; b, \; c, \; (\lambda, \; \mu), \quad \text{............................(1)}$$

we obtain successively triangles with the elements

$$m', \; b, \; l, \; \left(\gamma, \; \frac{\pi}{2} - \alpha\right), \quad \text{.....................(2)}$$

$$c', \; m', \; a', \; \left(\lambda, \; \frac{\pi}{2} - \beta\right), \quad \text{.....................(3)}$$

$$l', \; c', \; b', \; \left(\frac{\pi}{2} - \alpha, \; \mu\right), \quad \text{.....................(4)}$$

$$l', \; a, \; m, \; \left(\gamma, \; \frac{\pi}{2} - \beta\right) \quad \text{.....................(5)}$$

From the second triangle

$$m', \; b, \; l, \; \left(\gamma, \; \frac{\pi}{2} - \alpha\right),$$

we have $\sinh l = \sinh m' \cosh c$

$$= \frac{1}{\sinh m} \cosh c, \text{ by § 58.}$$

Therefore $\cosh c = \sinh l \sinh m.$ ....II.

(Hypothenuse and two angles.)

Also, from the same triangle (by I.),

$$\sinh l = \sinh b \cosh a'$$
$$= \sinh b \coth a.$$

Therefore $\tanh a = \dfrac{\sinh b}{\sinh l}.$ ....III)

(Two sides and an angle.)

Now, since $\cosh c = \sinh l \sinh m,$

we have $\cosh c = \dfrac{\sinh b}{\tanh a} \times \dfrac{\sinh a}{\tanh b}.$

Therefore $\cosh c = \cosh a \cosh b.$ ....IV.

(Hypothenuse and two sides.)

Further, $\cosh a = \sinh l \dfrac{\sinh a}{\sinh b}$ (by III.)

$$= \sinh l \dfrac{\cosh m}{\cosh l} \quad \text{(by I.).}$$

Therefore $\cosh a = \tanh l \cosh m.$ ....V.

(Side and two angles.)

Applying (IV.) to the triangle

$$c',\ m',\ a',\ \left(\lambda,\ \frac{\pi}{2} - \beta\right),$$

we have $\cosh a' = \cosh c' \cosh m',$

and this gives $\tanh a = \tanh m \tanh c.$ .. ..VI.

(Hypothenuse, a side, and included angle.)

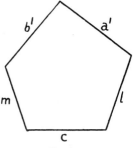

Fig. 74.

These six formulae are all given by a rule similar to Napier's Rules in Spherical Trigonometry .

(i) *Let the letters* a′, l, c, m, b′ *be written one at each of the sides of a pentagon taken in order.* *Then*

cosh of the middle part = the product of the hyperbolic sines of the adjacent parts

and

cosh of the middle part = the product of the hyperbolic cotangents of the opposite parts.

§60. The Equations for an Oblique-Angled Triangle.

In the case of the Oblique-Angled Triangle ABC, the sides opposite the angular points A, B, and C will be denoted by a, b, and c, as usual; but the angles at A, B, and C will be denoted by λ, μ, and ν.

With this notation the distance of parallelism for the angle at A will be l.

We proceed to prove that

I.   **sinh a : sinh b : sinh c = sech l : sech m : sech n.**

This corresponds to the Sine Rule of ordinary Trigonometry.

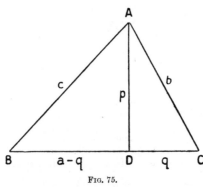

Fig. 75.

Let ABC be all acute angles.

From an angular point, say A, draw the perpendicular AD to the opposite side. We then obtain two right-angled triangles ABD and ACD, as in Fig. 75.

Writing AD $=p$, we have (by §59, I.)

$$\sinh p = \frac{\sinh c}{\cosh m}, \text{ from the triangle ABD,}$$

and $$\sinh p = \frac{\sinh b}{\cosh n}, \text{ from the triangle ACD.}$$

Thus we have

$$\sinh b : \sinh c = \operatorname{sech} m : \operatorname{sech} n.$$

Taking another angular point— say B—and proceeding in the same way, we would have

$$\sinh a : \sinh c = \operatorname{sech} l : \operatorname{sech} n.$$

Therefore

$$\sinh a : \sinh b : \sinh c = \operatorname{sech} l : \operatorname{sech} m : \operatorname{sech} n.$$

If one of the angles is obtuse, we obtain the same result, using the notation $\Pi(-x) = \pi - \Pi(x)$.

For the right-angled triangle, the result follows from § 59, I.

II. We shall now prove the theorem corresponding to the Cosine Rule of ordinary Trigonometry.

We take in the first place the case when B and C are acute angles.

From A draw the perpendicular AD to BC.

Let $AD = p$, $CD = q$, and $BD = a - q$ (Fig. 75).

Then, from the triangle ABD we have

$$\cosh c = \cosh(a - q)\cosh p \quad (\S 59, \text{IV.}),$$

and from the triangle ACD we have

$$\cosh b = \cosh p \cosh q.$$

Also, we have

$$\tanh(a - q) = \tanh c \tanh m \quad (\S 59, \text{VI.}).$$

Therefore $\cosh b = \dfrac{\cosh c \cosh q}{\cosh(a - q)}$

$$= \frac{\cosh c (\cosh a \cosh(a - q) - \sinh a \sinh(a - q))}{\cosh(a - q)}$$

$$= \cosh a \cosh c - \sinh a \cosh c \tanh(a - q)$$

$$= \cosh a \cosh c - \sinh a \sinh c \tanh m.$$

If the angle B is obtuse, so that D falls on CB produced, the same result follows, provided account is taken of the notation $\Pi(-x) = \pi - \Pi(x).$

If the angle B is a right angle, the result follows from § 59, IV.

We are thus brought to the Cosine Formula, which may be put in the form :

$$\cosh a = \cosh b \cosh c - \sinh b \sinh c \tanh l.$$

§ 61. The Measurement of Angles.

Up till this stage, except in §§ 51-2, there has been no need to introduce a unit of angle into our work. The equation $\alpha = \Pi(a)$, connecting the segment and the corresponding angle of parallelism, has had only a geometrical significance. In it α has stood for a certain definite acute angle, which has the property that the perpendicular to one of its bounding lines, at a distance a from the angular point, is parallel to the other bounding line.

When it comes to assigning numerical values to angles, the choice of one number is sufficient, if, in addition, the angle zero is denoted by O. In the Non-Euclidean Trigonometry we shall assign the number $\dfrac{\pi}{2}$ to the right angle. All other angles will have the numerical values proper to them on this scale.

In the rest of this work, when we use the equation $\alpha = \Pi(a)$, both α and a will be numbers, the one the measure of the angle on this scale, the other the measure of the segment on one of the scales agreed upon below (§ 65), in which the unit segment is the distance apart of two concentric Limiting-Curves, when the ratio of the arcs cut off by two of their axes is e or $e^{\frac{1}{k}}$.

It should perhaps be remarked that in dealing with the trigonometrical formulae in the previous sections the measure of the segment, and not the segment itself, is what we have meant to denote by the letters in the different equations.

§ 62. The Trigonometrical Functions of the Angle.

The Trigonometrical Functions

$$\sin \alpha, \ \cos \alpha, \ \tan \alpha, \ \text{etc.},$$

are defined by the equations :

$$\sin \alpha = \frac{e^{ia} - e^{-ia}}{2i}, \qquad \cos \alpha = \frac{e^{ia} + e^{-ia}}{2},$$

$$\tan \alpha = \frac{\sin \alpha}{\cos \alpha}, \qquad \cot \alpha = \frac{1}{\tan \alpha},$$

$$\sec \alpha = \frac{1}{\cos \alpha}, \qquad \operatorname{cosec} \alpha = \frac{1}{\sin \alpha}.$$

The fundamental equation of the Hyperbolic Trigonometry is

$$\tanh a = \cos \alpha,$$

when $\alpha = \Pi(a).$

We proceed to obtain this relation : *

Consider the function $f(\alpha)$ defined by the equation

$$\tanh a = \cos f(\alpha).$$

and let us write $a = \Delta(\alpha)$.

When $\alpha = \dfrac{\pi}{2}$, $a = 0$, $\tanh a = 0$, $\cos f(\alpha) = 0$; i.e. $f\left(\dfrac{\pi}{2}\right) = \dfrac{\pi}{2}$.

When $\alpha = 0$, $a = \infty$, $\tanh a = 1$, $\cos f(\alpha) = 1$; i.e. $f(0) = 0$.

Further, as a increases from 0 to ∞, $f(\alpha)$ diminishes continuously from $\dfrac{\pi}{2}$ to 0.

Next consider a triangle ABC—not right-angled—and let the perpendicular from B cut the base AC at D. Let the elements of the triangle ABD be denoted by $AB = c$, $BD = a$, $DA = b$, $\angle ABD = \mu$, $\angle BAD = \lambda$. Also let the elements of the triangle BDC be denoted by $BC = c_1$, $CD = b_1$, $DB = a_1$, $\angle BCD = \lambda_1$, $\angle DBC = \mu_1$.

As the side BD is common, $a = a_1$.

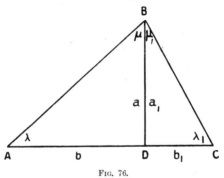

Fig. 76.

Then, from the Cosine Formula, § 60, we have

$$\tanh m = \frac{\cosh c \cosh c_1 - \cosh (b + b_1)}{\sinh c \sinh c_1}.$$

---

* The method of this and the preceding sections is due to Liebmann, "Elementare Ableitung der nichteuklidischen Trigonometrie," *Ber. d. k. sächs. Ges. d. Wiss. Math. Phys. Klasse*, vol. lix. p. 187 (1907), and *Nichteuklidische Geometrie*, 2nd ed. p. 71. Another method, also independent of the geometry of space, is to be found in Gérard's work, and in the paper by Young referred to below, p. 136.

With the notation of this section, we have

$$\cos f(\mu + \mu_1) = \tanh \Delta (\mu + \mu_1)$$

$$= \frac{\cosh c \cosh c_1 - \cosh (b + b_1)}{\sinh c \sinh c_1}$$

$$= \coth c \coth c_1 - \frac{\cosh b \cosh b_1}{\sinh c \sinh c_1} - \frac{\sinh b \sinh b_1}{\sinh c \sinh c_1}.$$

But we know that

$$\tanh a = \tanh c \tanh m, \quad [\S 59, \text{VI.}]$$

i.e.
$$\tanh a = \tanh c \cos f(\mu).$$

Similarly
$$\tanh a_1 = \tanh c_1 \cos f(\mu_1).$$

Therefore $\quad \coth c \coth c_1 = \coth^2 a \cos f(\mu) \cos f(\mu_1).$

Further, from § 59, I., we obtain

$$\frac{\sinh b}{\sinh c} = \frac{1}{\cosh m} = \sin f(\mu),$$

$$\frac{\sinh b_1}{\sinh c_1} = \frac{1}{\cosh m_1} = \sin f(\mu_1).$$

Therefore $\quad \dfrac{\sinh b \sinh b_1}{\sinh c \sinh c_1} = \sin f(\mu) \sin f(\mu_1).$

We are left with the term

$$\frac{\cosh b \cosh b_1}{\sinh c \sinh c_1}.$$

But, from § 59, VI. and IV., we have

$$\frac{\tanh m}{\sinh a} = \frac{\cosh c}{\sinh c \cosh a} = \frac{\cosh b}{\sinh c}.$$

Therefore $\quad \dfrac{\cosh b \cosh b_1}{\sinh c \sinh c_1} = \dfrac{\cos f(\mu) \cos f(\mu_1)}{\sinh^2 a}.$

Thus we obtain

$$\cos f(\mu + \mu_1) = \coth^2 a \cos f(\mu) \cos f(\mu_1)$$

$$- \operatorname{cosech}^2 a \cos f(\mu_1) \cos f(\mu_1) - \sin f(\mu) \sin f(\mu_1)$$

$$= \cos f(\mu) \cos f(\mu_1') - \sin f(\mu) \sin f(\mu_1)$$

$$= \cos [f(\mu) + f(\mu_1)].$$

But when
$$\mu = \mu_1 = \mu + \mu_1 = 0,$$
$$f(\mu) = f(\mu_1) = f(\mu + \mu_1) = 0.$$

Therefore we have
$$f(\mu + \mu_1) = f(\mu) + f(\mu_1).$$

This is a functional equation from which the continuous function $f(\mu)$ is to be derived.

It may be written $f(x + y) = f(x) + f(y),$

with
$$f(0) = 0, \quad f\left(\frac{\pi}{2}\right) = \frac{\pi}{2}.$$

Thus we have
$$\frac{f(x + h) - f(x)}{h} = \frac{f(y + h) - f(y)}{h}.$$

Proceeding to the limit
$$f'(x) = f'(y).$$

Thus $f'(x) = \text{constant}.$

Therefore $f(x) = \mathsf{A}x + \mathsf{B}.$

The values of $f(0)$ and $f\left(\frac{\pi}{2}\right)$ determine A and B, so that we have finally
$$f(x) = x.$$

Thus we are led to the desired equation
$$\mathbf{\tanh a = \cos \alpha.}$$

§ 63. From the result proved in last section,
$$\tanh a = \cos \alpha,$$
it follows immediately that
$$\sinh a = \cot \alpha,$$
$$\cosh a = \operatorname{cosec} \alpha,$$
$$\coth a = \sec \alpha,$$
$$\operatorname{sech} a = \sin \alpha,$$
$$\operatorname{cosech} a = \tan \alpha.$$

If we insert these values in the Trigonometrical Formulae of § 59, we obtain :

$$\sinh a = \sinh c \sin \lambda \quad \text{from} \quad \sinh c = \sinh a \cosh l.$$
$$\sinh b = \tanh a \cot \lambda \quad ,, \quad \sinh b = \tanh a \sinh l.$$
$$\cosh c = \cot \lambda \cot \mu \quad ,, \quad \cosh c = \sinh l \sinh m.$$
$$\cosh c = \cosh a \cosh b \quad ,, \quad \cosh c = \cosh a \cosh b.$$
$$\cos \lambda = \cosh a \sin \mu \quad ,, \quad \cosh a = \tanh l \cosh m.$$
$$\tanh a = \tanh c \cos \mu \quad ,, \quad \tanh a = \tanh m \tanh c.$$

And the formulae of § 60 for the Oblique-Angled Triangle become

$$\sinh a : \sinh b : \sinh c = \sin \lambda : \sin \mu : \sin \nu,$$
$$\cosh a = \cosh b \cosh c - \sinh b \sinh c \cos \lambda.$$

All these results agree with the corresponding formulae in Spherical Trigonometry, when λ, μ, ν *take the place of* A, B, C, *and the Hyperbolic Functions of* a, b, *and* c *take the place of the Circular Functions of* a, b, *and* c.

§ 64. The Angle of Parallelism.

Since

$$\tanh a = \cos \alpha,$$

we have

$$\frac{1 - \cos \alpha}{1 + \cos \alpha} = \frac{1 - \tanh a}{1 + \tanh a}.$$

Therefore

$$\tan^2 \frac{\alpha}{2} = e^{-2a},$$

and

$$\tan \frac{\alpha}{2} = e^{-a}.$$

The angle α is acute, so the positive sign has to be taken in extracting the square root.

This may be written

$$\tan \tfrac{1}{2} \Pi(p) = e^{-p}.*$$

§ 65. The formulae of §§ 56-64 have been deduced on the understanding that the unit of length employed is the distance between concentric Limiting-Curves when the ratio of the arcs cut off by two of their axes is e.

---

* This result is given by Bolyai, *Appendix*, § 29, and by Lobatschewsky in his various books, *e.g. Geometrische Untersuchungen zur Theorie der Parallellinien*, § 36.

If a different unit is adopted, so that the ratio of the arc AB to the arc A_1B_1 is a, any number greater than unity, we have the equation

$$s_x = sa^{-x} \text{ instead of } s_x = se^{-x}.$$

Putting $a = e^{\frac{1}{k}},$

this gives $s_x = se^{-\frac{x}{k}}.$

This parameter k will enter into all the equations of the preceding sections, so that $\sinh \frac{a}{k}$, $\cosh \frac{a}{k}$, etc., will replace $\sinh a$, $\cosh a$, etc.

And the equation for the Angle of Parallelism will be

$$\tan \tfrac{1}{2}\Pi(p) = e^{-\frac{p}{k}}.$$

The Euclidean Geometry now appears as a special case of the Hyperbolic Geometry, for if we let $k \to \infty$, the formulae of this Non-Euclidean Geometry reduce to those of the Euclidean.

In the first place, since

$$\tan \tfrac{1}{2}\Pi(p) = e^{-\frac{p}{k}},$$

the angle of parallelism becomes $\frac{\pi}{2}$ when $k \to \infty$.

Further, the equations connecting the sides and angles of a right-angled triangle, viz.

$$\sinh \frac{a}{k} = \sinh \frac{c}{k} \sin \lambda,$$

$$\sinh \frac{b}{k} = \tanh \frac{a}{k} \cot \lambda,$$

$$\cosh \frac{c}{k} = \cot \lambda \cot \mu,$$

$$\cosh \frac{c}{k} = \cosh \frac{a}{k} \cosh \frac{b}{k},$$

$$\cos \lambda = \cosh \frac{a}{k} \sin \mu,$$

$$\tanh \frac{a}{k} = \tanh \frac{c}{k} \cos \mu,$$

become
$$\sin A = \frac{a}{c},$$
$$\cot A = \frac{b}{a},$$
$$\cot A \cot B = 1,$$
$$a^2 + b^2 = c^2,$$
$$\cos A = \sin B,$$
$$\cos B = \frac{a}{c},$$

when we write A, B for λ and μ.

From the Sine and Cosine Formulae for the Oblique-Angled Triangle (§ 63) we get at once,
$$\sin A : \sin B : \sin C = a : b : c,$$
$$a^2 = b^2 + c^2 - 2bc \cos A.$$

Again, $\frac{a}{k}$, $\frac{b}{k}$, and $\frac{c}{k}$ can be made infinitesimals by letting $a, b,$ and c tend to zero instead of k to infinity. In this case again the Euclidean relations are obtained.

This result can be stated in other terms :

In the immediate neighbourhood of a point on the Hyperbolic Plane, the formulae of the Euclidean Geometry hold true.

Or, again :

The Euclidean Formulae hold true in Infinitesimal Geometry on the Hyperbolic Plane.

These theorems have an important bearing upon the question as to whether the Hyperbolic Geometry can actually represent the external relations of the space in which we live. The experimental fact that, within the limits of error to which all actual observations are subject, the sum of the angles of a triangle is two right angles does not prove that the geometry of our space is the Euclidean Geometry. It might be a Hyperbolic Geometry in which the parameter k was very great.

The Geometry of Bolyai and Lobatschewsky can be made to fit in with the facts of experience by taking k large enough. The Postulate of Euclid reaches the same end by another means. It is a better means, for it gives a simpler geometry.

CHAPTER V.

MEASUREMENTS OF LENGTH AND AREA, WITH THE AID OF THE INFINITESIMAL CALCULUS.

§ **66.** In this Chapter we shall apply the Trigonometrical Formulae found in Chapter IV. to the measurements of Length and Areas of Curves.

The first thing to be done is to obtain the expression for the element of arc of a plane curve.

The Element of Arc in Cartesian Coordinates.

In the Euclidean Plane

$$ds^2 = dx^2 + dy^2.$$

We shall now prove that in the Hyperbolic Plane

$$\mathbf{ds}^2 = \cosh^2 \frac{\mathbf{y}}{\mathbf{k}} \, \mathbf{dx}^2 + \mathbf{dy}^2.$$

Let P, Q be the points (x, y), $(x + \delta x, y + \delta y)$.
Draw PM and QN perpendicular to the axis of x.
Then $OM = x$, $MP = y$, $ON = x + \delta x$, and $NQ = y + \delta y$.
From P draw PH perpendicular to QN.
Let $PQ = \delta s$, $PH = q$, $HQ = p$, and $NH = z$.
Then, in the right-angled triangle PHQ,

$$\delta s^2 = p^2 + q^2,\text{*} \quad \text{to the lowest order.}$$

---

* This follows from § 65, where we have proved that the Euclidean Formulae hold in Infinitesimal Geometry. If we start with

$$\cosh \frac{\delta s}{k} = \cosh \frac{p}{k} \cosh \frac{q}{k},$$

we obtain the same result when we neglect terms above the lowest order.

Also, in the quadrilateral MNHP, the angles at M, N, and H are right angles, and the sides beginning at M are

$$\delta x, \ z, \ q, \ y.$$

These correspond to $a, \ m', \ c, \ l$

in a right-angled triangle.   [Cf. § 35.]

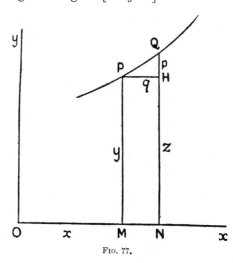

Fig. 77.

Thus we have $\sinh \dfrac{\delta x}{k} = \dfrac{\sinh \dfrac{q}{k}}{\cosh \dfrac{y}{k}}.$ [Cf. § 59, I.]

Therefore $q = \cosh \dfrac{y}{k} \delta x$, to the lowest order.

Also, we have

$$\cosh \frac{\delta x}{k} = \tanh \frac{y}{k} \coth \frac{z}{k}. \quad \text{[Cf. § 59, V., and § 58.]}$$

Therefore y and z differ by a small quantity when δx is small.

Put $z = y + \eta.$

Then we have $\tanh \dfrac{y+\eta}{k} \cosh \dfrac{\delta x}{k} = \tanh \dfrac{y}{k}.$

This gives, to the lowest order,

$$\left(\tanh \frac{y}{k} + \frac{\eta}{k}\right)\left(1 + \frac{\delta x^2}{2k^2}\right) = \tanh \frac{y}{k}\left(1 + \frac{\eta}{k}\tanh \frac{y}{k}\right),$$

i.e.
$$\eta = -\frac{1}{2k}\sinh \frac{y}{k}\cosh \frac{y}{k}\,\delta x^2.$$

Therefore y and z differ by a quantity of the second order when δx is of the first order.

Now
$$p = (y + \delta y) - z.$$

Therefore
$$p = \delta y, \text{ to the first order.}$$

It follows from $\delta s^2 = p^2 + q^2$, that

$$\delta s^2 = \cosh^2 \frac{y}{k}\,\delta x^2 + \delta y^2, \text{ to the lowest order.}$$

Thus we have shown that the element of arc in Cartesian Coordinates is given by

$$\mathbf{ds^2 = \cosh^2 \frac{y}{k}\,dx^2 + dy^2}.$$

§ 67. Element of Arc in Polar Coordinates.

In the Euclidean Plane we have for the element of arc in Polar Coordinates, the equation

$$ds^2 = dr^2 + r^2 d\theta^2.$$

We proceed to find the corresponding formula in the Hyperbolic Plane.

It may be obtained in two ways. It could be deduced from

$$ds^2 = \cosh^2 \frac{y}{k}\,dx^2 + dy^2,$$

by using the relations connecting x, y and r, θ; viz.

$$\left.\begin{array}{c} \cosh \dfrac{r}{k} = \cosh \dfrac{x}{k}\cosh \dfrac{y}{k}, \\[3mm] \tan \theta = \dfrac{\tanh \dfrac{y}{k}}{\sinh \dfrac{x}{k}}. \end{array}\right\} \quad [\text{Cf. § 63.}]$$

It is simpler and more instructive to obtain the result directly.

Let P, Q be the points (r, θ), $(r + \delta r, \theta + \delta \theta)$.

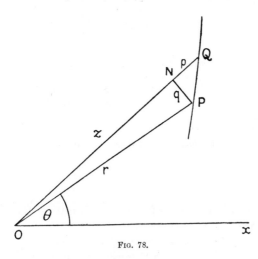

Fig. 78.

Draw PN perpendicular to OQ.

Let $PQ = \delta s$, $PN = q$, $NQ = p$, and $ON = z$.

Then, from the triangle PNQ, we have as before

$$\delta s^2 = p^2 + q^2.$$

Also, from the triangle ONP, we have

$$\sinh \frac{q}{k} = \sinh \frac{r}{k} \sin \delta \theta. \quad [\S\ 63.]$$

Therefore $\quad q = k \sinh \dfrac{r}{k} \delta \theta$, to the lowest order.

Also, we have from the same triangle

$$\cosh \frac{r}{k} = \cosh \frac{z}{k} \cosh \frac{q}{k}.$$

Therefore r and z are nearly equal.

Put $\qquad\qquad\qquad r = z + \xi.$

Then $\qquad \cosh \dfrac{z}{k} + \dfrac{\xi}{k} \sinh \dfrac{z}{k} = \cosh \dfrac{z}{k} \left(1 + \dfrac{q^2}{2k^2} \right),$

to the lowest order.

Thus $\qquad \xi = \dfrac{q^2}{2k} \coth \dfrac{z}{k}$, to the lowest order ;

i.e. r and z differ by a small quantity of the second order, when $\delta\theta$ is of the first order.

But $\qquad\qquad\qquad\qquad p = r + \delta r - z.$

Therefore $\qquad\qquad\qquad p = \delta r,$ to the first order.

It follows that

$$\delta s^2 = \delta r^2 + k^2 \sinh^2 \frac{r}{k} \delta\theta^2, \text{ to the lowest order.}$$

Therefore $\qquad \mathbf{ds^2 = dr^2 + k^2 \sinh^2 \dfrac{r}{k} \, d\theta^2}.$

§ 68. The Element of Arc in Limiting-Curve Co-ordinates.

We shall now describe a system of coordinates peculiar to the Hyperbolic Plane. The position of the point P is given by the Limiting-Curve and axis on which it lies, the Limiting-

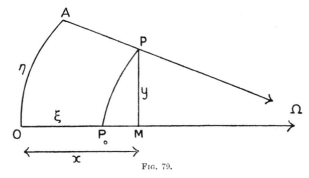

Fig. 79.

Curves being all concentric, their common centre being at infinity on the axis of x.

Let the Limiting-Curve through P cut off a segment of length ξ (OP$_0$) on the axis of x, and let the axis through P

cut off an arc of length η (OA) on the Limiting-Curve through
O. (Fig. 79.)

(ξ, η) are called the Limiting-Curve Coordinates of the
point P.

Now take another point Q with coordinates

$$(\xi + \delta\xi, \ \eta + \delta\eta).$$

Let the Limiting-Curve through Q cut the axis of x (the
axis through O) at Q_0.

Let the Limiting-Curve through P be cut by the axis through
Q at S, and the Limiting-Curve through Q by the axis through
P in R.

Also, let A and B be the points where the Limiting-Curve
through O is cut by the axes through P and Q.

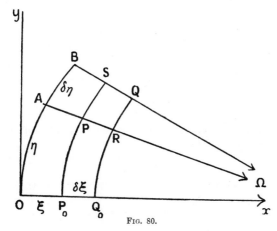

Fig. 80.

Then we have

$$\text{arc OA} = \eta, \quad \text{arc OB} = \eta + \delta\eta,$$

$$\text{OP}_0 = \xi, \qquad \text{OQ}_0 = \xi + \delta\xi.$$

It follows from the properties of Concentric Limiting-
Curves [§ 55], that

$$\text{arc QR} = \delta\eta\, e^{-\frac{\xi + \delta\xi}{k}}.$$

$$\therefore \ \text{arc QR} = \delta\eta\, e^{-\frac{\xi}{k}}, \text{ to the first order.}$$

Further, $\mathsf{PR} = \delta\xi$, and we write $\mathsf{PQ} = \delta s$, as usual.
Now we know that

$$\mathsf{PQ}^2 = \mathsf{PR}^2 + \mathsf{RQ}^2, \text{ to the lowest order.}$$

$$\therefore \quad \delta s^2 = \delta\xi^2 + e^{-\frac{2\xi}{k}} \delta\eta^2, \text{ to the lowest order.}$$

Therefore

$$\mathbf{ds}^2 = \mathbf{d}\xi^2 + \mathbf{e}^{-\frac{2\xi}{k}} \mathbf{d}\eta^2.$$

This result could also have been deduced from that of § 66 by using the equations connecting (x, y) and (ξ, η). [Cf. § 57 and § 69 (3).]

§ 69. We apply these formulae to find the perimeter of a circle, and the lengths of portions of the Equidistant-Curve and the Limiting-Curve.

1. *The Perimeter of a Circle of Radius* a.

In

$$ds^2 = dr^2 + k^2 \sinh^2 \frac{r}{k} d\theta^2,$$

we put

$$r = a \text{ and } dr = 0.$$

Thus the arc from $\theta = 0$ to $\theta = \theta$ is given by

$$s = k \sinh \frac{a}{k} \times \theta.$$

The Perimeter of the Circle follows by putting $\theta = 2\pi$, and is given by the expression

$$\left[2\pi\mathbf{k} \sinh \frac{\mathbf{a}}{\mathbf{k}} \right.$$

2. *The Equidistant-Curve* y = b.

In

$$ds^2 = \cosh^2 \frac{y}{k} dx^2 + dy^2,$$

we put

$$y = b \text{ and } dy = 0.$$

Thus the arc from $x = 0$ to $x = x$ is given by

$$\mathbf{s} = \mathbf{x} \cosh \frac{\mathbf{b}}{\mathbf{k}}.$$

3. *The Limiting-Curve.*

The equation of the Limiting-Curve through the origin, with its centre at infinity on the axis of x, is

$$e^{\frac{x}{k}} = \cosh \frac{y}{k}. \quad [\text{Cf. } \S 57 (1).]$$

In $\qquad ds^2 = \cosh^2 \frac{y}{k}\, dx^2 + dy^2,$

we put $\qquad dx = \tanh \frac{y}{k}\, dy.$

Then $\qquad ds^2 = \left(1 + \sinh^2 \frac{y}{k}\right) dy^2.$

Thus $\qquad ds = \cosh \frac{y}{k}\, dy.$

It follows that $s = k \sinh \dfrac{y}{k}$, when we measure s from the origin.

If we compare this result with §57 (2), we see that the length of the arc of the Limiting-Curve, such that the tangent at one end is parallel to the axis through the other, is unity, when $k = 1$.

§70. The Element of Area.

Let the arc AB be an arc of a Limiting-Curve, centre Ω, such that the tangent at B is parallel to the axis through A.

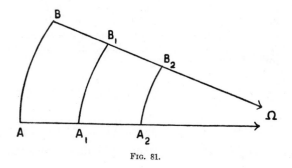

FIG. 81.

Then we know that the length of the arc AB is k.   [§57 (2) and §69 (3).]

Also, if $AA_1 = 1$, the length of the arc $A_1B_1 = ke^{-\frac{1}{k}}$;

    if $A_1A_2 = 1$, the length of the arc $A_2B_2 = ke^{-\frac{2}{k}}$,

and so on.

Let the area of $\mathsf{ABB_1A_1}$ be denoted by Δ_0.

Then (cf. § 48) the area of $\mathsf{A_1B_1B_2A_2}$ will be $\Delta_0 e^{-\frac{1}{k}}$;

that of $\mathsf{A_2B_2B_3A_3}$ will be $\Delta_0 e^{-\frac{2}{k}}$, etc.

Thus the area of $\mathsf{ABB_nA_n}$

$$= \Delta_0 \left(1 + e^{-\frac{1}{k}} + e^{-\frac{2}{k}} + \ldots + e^{-\frac{n-1}{k}} \right)$$

$$= \Delta_0 \left(\frac{1 - e^{-\frac{n}{k}}}{1 - e^{-\frac{1}{k}}} \right).$$

Therefore, as $n \to \infty$, this area approaches a limit, namely

$$\Delta = \frac{\Delta_0}{1 - e^{-\frac{1}{k}}}.$$

This is the area of the region bounded by two axes of a Limiting-Curve and an arc such that the tangent at one end is parallel to the axis through the other end.

The unit of area has not yet been chosen in this discussion. We now fix it so that the area denoted above by Δ will be k^2 the unit of area.

With this measurement

$$\Delta_0 = k^2 \left(1 - e^{-\frac{1}{k}} \right).$$

Also the area of $\mathsf{ABA_nB_n}$ will be $k^2 \left(1 - e^{-\frac{n}{k}} \right)$.

Next, let P be a point on AB, or AB produced, such that the arc $\mathsf{AP} = s$.

Then   area $\mathsf{APP_1A_1}$: area $\mathsf{ABB_1A_1} = s : k$,

and   area $\mathsf{APP_nA_n} = ks \left(1 - e^{-\frac{n}{k}} \right)$.

Taking x, first, a rational number, and then treating the irrational number x as the limit of a sequence of rational numbers, we find from the above that the area bounded by the arcs of two Concentric Limiting-Curves, distant x apart, the larger one being of length s, is equal to

$$ks\left(1 - e^{-\frac{x}{k}}\right).$$

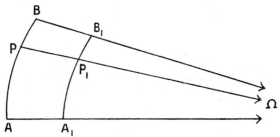

FIG. 82.

From this result the expression for the element of area in Limiting-Curve Coordinates will now be deduced.

Let P, Q, R and S be the points

(ξ, η), $(\xi + \delta\xi, \eta + \delta\eta)$, $(\xi + \delta\xi, \eta)$, and $(\xi, \eta + \delta\eta)$ [cf. Fig. 80].

Then $\quad\quad$ arc PS $= \delta\eta\, e^{-\frac{\xi}{k}}$, $\quad$ [§ 68]

and $\quad\quad\quad\quad$ PR $= \delta\xi$.

Therefore the area PQRS is given by

$$k\, \delta\eta\, e^{-\frac{\xi}{k}}\left(1 - e^{-\frac{\delta\xi}{k}}\right).$$

When $\delta\xi$, $\delta\eta$ are small, this becomes, to the lowest order,

$$e^{-\frac{\xi}{k}}\,\delta\xi\,\delta\eta.$$

Therefore the element of area in Limiting-Curve Coordinates is

$$e^{-\frac{\xi}{k}}\,d\xi\,d\eta.$$

This is equal to the product of the two perpendicular chords PR and PS which bound the infinitesimal element, and with these units the expression for the element of area is the same as that in the Euclidean Plane.

§71. The Element of Area in Cartesian Coordinates.

This result can be obtained from the expression found in §70, by using the methods of the Calculus.

We have
$$\eta = k \tanh \frac{y}{k} \, e^{\frac{x}{k}},$$
$$e^{\frac{x-\xi}{k}} = \cosh \frac{y}{k}.$$

[Cf. §57 and §69 (3).]

These are the equations connecting (x, y) and (ξ, η).

To find the element of area in Cartesian Coordinates (x, y), we need only replace

$$e^{-\frac{\xi}{k}} \, d\xi \, d\eta$$

by

$$e^{-\frac{x}{k}} \cosh \frac{y}{k} \frac{\partial(\xi, \eta)}{\partial(x, y)} \, dx \, dy.$$

After reduction, we obtain

$$\cosh \frac{y}{k} \, dx \, dy.$$

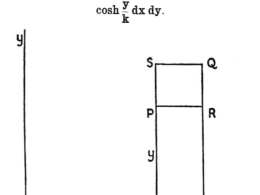

Fig. 83.

The result, however, can be found directly as follows:

Let P, Q be the points (x, y), $(x + \delta x, y + \delta y)$.

Let the Equidistant-Curves through P and Q with Ox as base-line meet the ordinates at R and S (Fig. 83).

The figure PRQS becomes a rectangle in the limit, and we can use the Euclidean expression for its area (cf. §70).

Then $\qquad\qquad$ arc $PR = \cosh\dfrac{y}{k}\,\delta x \quad$ [§ 69 (2)]

and $\qquad\qquad\qquad$ $PS = \delta y.$

Hence the element of area in Cartesian Coordinates is

$$\cosh\frac{y}{k}\,dx\,dy.$$

§ 72. The Element of Area in Polar Coordinates.

As before, the result can be obtained by using the equations

$$\cosh\frac{r}{k} = \cosh\frac{x}{k}\cosh\frac{y}{k},$$

$$\tan\theta = \frac{\tanh\dfrac{y}{k}}{\sinh\dfrac{x}{k}},$$

which connect $(r,\ \theta)$ and $(x,\ y)$.

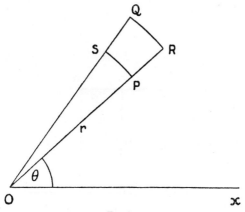

Fig. 84.

But it is simpler to obtain the element of area directly from the geometrical figure :

Let P, Q be the points $(r,\ \theta)$, $(r + \delta r,\ \theta + \delta\theta)$.

Let the circles through P and Q cut the radii at S and R, forming the element PRQS.

Then we have $\qquad$ arc $PS = k \sinh \dfrac{r}{k} \delta\theta$, by § 69 (1),

$$PR = \delta r.$$

The figure PRQS becomes a rectangle in the limit. Therefore *the element of area in Polar Coordinates is*

$$\mathbf{k \sinh \dfrac{r}{k} \, dr \, d\theta.}$$

The area of the circle of radius a is thus given by

$$\int_0^a \int_0^{2\pi} k \sinh \dfrac{r}{k} \, dr \, d\theta,$$

which becomes $\qquad$ $2\pi k^2 \left(\cosh \dfrac{a}{k} - 1 \right),$

or $\qquad$ $4\pi k^2 \sinh^2 \dfrac{a}{2k}.$

§73. The Area of a Triangle and of a Quadrilateral with three Right Angles.

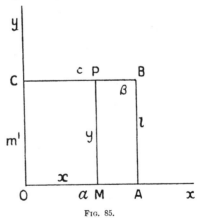

FIG. 85.

Let OABC be a quadrilateral with the sides a, m', c, l, as in Fig. 85, and the angles at O, A, C right angles; A lying on the axis of x and C on the axis of y.

Let P be any point on CB, and PM the perpendicular from P to OA.

Then, from the associated right-angled triangle for the quadrilateral OMPC, we have

$$\tanh\frac{y}{k}\cosh\frac{m}{k}=\cosh\frac{x}{k}. \quad (\S\,59,\text{ V.})$$

But the area of the quadrilateral OABC is given by

$$\int_0^a\int_0^y\cosh\frac{y}{k}\,dx\,dy.$$

Denote this by S.

Integrating, we have

$$S = k\int_0^a\sinh\frac{y}{k}\,dx$$

$$= k\int_0^a\frac{\cosh\frac{x}{k}}{\sqrt{\sinh^2\frac{m}{k}-\sinh^2\frac{x}{k}}}\,dx$$

$$= k^2\sin^{-1}\frac{\sinh\frac{a}{k}}{\sinh\frac{m}{k}}\,;$$

$$\therefore\ \sin\frac{S}{k^2}=\frac{\sinh\frac{a}{k}}{\sinh\frac{m}{k}}.$$

But, from the associated right-angled triangle, we have

$$\tanh\frac{b}{k}=\frac{\sinh\frac{a}{k}}{\sinh\frac{m}{k}}. \quad (\S\,59,\text{ III.})$$

And $\qquad\qquad \tanh\frac{b}{k}=\cos\beta. \quad (\S\,62.)$

Therefore $$\sin \frac{S}{k^2} = \cos \beta.$$

Therefore $$S = k^2\left(\frac{\pi}{2} - \beta\right).$$

Thus the area of a quadrilateral with three right angles and an acute angle β is equal to

$$k^2\left(\frac{\pi}{2} - \beta\right)$$

on this scale.

But a triangle ABC (Fig. 86) is equal in area to Saccheri's Quadrilateral BCC′B′, in which the angles at B and C are each equal to half the sum of the angles of the triangle.

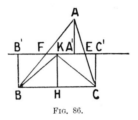

FIG. 86.

The triangle is thus equal in area to twice the quadrilateral with three right angles, and an acute angle equal to $\frac{1}{3}$(A + B + C).

Using the result just found, the area of the triangle ABC on this scale of measurement is

$$k^2(\pi - 2\beta),$$

where $$2\beta = A + B + C.$$

In other words, the area of the triangle is the product of k^2 and its defect.

Comparing this with § 52, we see why the particular unit of area was chosen in § 70.

CHAPTER VI.

THE ELLIPTIC PLANE GEOMETRY.

§ 74. In Hilbert's Parallel Postulate, through any point **A** outside any line b, *two* parallels a_1 and a_2 can be drawn to the line, and these separate the lines in the plane of the parallels which cut b from the lines which do not cut it.

On the Euclidean Hypothesis, the two rays a_1 and a_2 together form one and the same line, and there is but *one* parallel to any line from a point outside it.

There is still another case to be examined, namely that in which all the rays through **A** cut the line b. In this case there is *no* parallel through a point outside a line to that line.

We shall see that this corresponds to the Hypothesis of the Obtuse Angle of Saccheri, in accordance with which the sum of the angles of a triangle exceeds two right angles. Saccheri and Legendre were able to rule this case out as untrue ; but their argument depended upon the assumption that a straight line was infinite in length. Riemann was the first to recognise that a system of geometry compatible with the Hypothesis of the Obtuse Angle became possible when, for the hypothesis that the straight line is *infinite,* was substituted the more general one that it is *endless* or *unbounded.* (Cf. §§ 19, 20.)

The geometry built up on the assumption that a straight line is *unbounded,* but not *infinite,* and that *no* parallel can be drawn to a straight line from a point outside it will now be treated in the same manner in which the Hyperbolic Geometry was discussed.

§ 75. We proceed to the development of Plane Geometry when the assumptions

      (i) *All straight lines intersect each other,*

      (ii) *The straight line is not infinite,*

take the place of the Parallel Hypothesis of Euclid and his implicit assumption that the line is infinite.

Let A and B be any two points on a given line L.

The perpendiculars at A and B to the line must intersect, by assumption (i).

Let them meet at the point O.

Since ∠OAB = ∠OBA, we have OA = OB.

At O make ∠BOQ = ∠AOB (Fig. 87), and produce OQ to cut the line L at P.

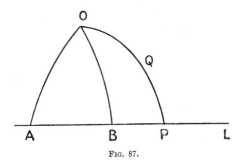

Fig. 87.

Then AB = BP and ∠OPA is a right angle.

By repeating this construction, we show that if P is a point on AB produced through B, such that AP = m . AB, the line OP is perpendicular to L and equal to OA and OB. The same holds for points on AB produced through A, such that BP = m . AB. In each case m is supposed to be a positive integer.

Now, let C be a point on AB, such that AB = m . AC, m being a positive integer. The perpendicular at C to L must pass through the point O, since if it met OA at O' the above argument shows that O'B must be perpendicular to L and coincide with OB.

It follows that if P is any point on the line L, such that AP = $\dfrac{m}{n}$. AB, m and n being any two positive integers, OP is perpendicular to the line L and equal to OA and OB.

The case when the ratio AP : AB is incommensurable would be deduced from the above by proceeding to the limit.

Now, all points on the line are included in this argument, so that the perpendiculars at all points of the line L pass through the same point.

Now, let L' be another line and A', B' two points upon it, such that the segment AB = A'B'.

The perpendiculars at A', B' meet in a point, which we shall call O'.

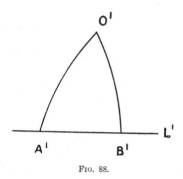

Fᴵɢ. 88.

The triangles AOB and A'O'B' have a side of the one equal to a side of the other, and the two angles adjacent to the sides are equal, each to each.

It follows that O'A' = OA.

Thus we have shown that *the perpendiculars at all points on any line meet at a point which is at a constant distance from the line.*

The point will be called the Pole of the Line.

§ 76. Now, in Fig. 89, produce OA to O_1, where $O_1A = OA$. Join O_1B.

Then, from the triangles OAB and O_1AB, it follows that $\angle O_1BA = \angle OBA =$ a right angle.

Thus OB and O_1B are in a straight line.

Also, AO_1 produced must intersect AB at a point C, such that O_1C is perpendicular to AB, and OC will be also perpendicular to AB.

Thus OAO_1 produced returns to O, and the line is *endless* or *unbounded.*

Its length is four times the distance of the pole of the line from the given line.

We shall denote the constant distance OA by 𝔏, so that with this notation the length of the line is 4𝔏.

Thus two other assumptions of the ordinary geometry are contradicted in this geometry :

Two straight lines enclose a space ;
Two points do not always determine a straight line.

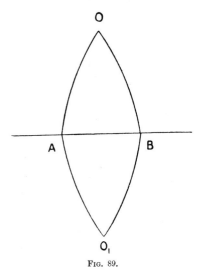

Fig. 89.

Through the two poles of a line an infinite number of lines can be drawn, just as through the two ends of a diameter of a sphere an infinite number of great circles can be drawn.

It is now clear that the argument which Euclid employs in I. 16 is not valid in this geometry. The exterior angle of a triangle is greater than either of the interior and opposite angles only when the corresponding median is inferior to 𝔏. If this median is equal to 𝔏, the exterior angle is equal to the interior angle considered ; if it is greater than 𝔏, the exterior angle is less than the interior angle considered.

Also, as I. 16 was essential to the proof of I. 27, it is now evident why in this geometry that theorem does not hold. Of course, if I. 16 did hold, there would have to be at least one parallel to a line through any point outside it. In a limited region of the plane, I. 16 does hold, and theorems dependent upon it are true in such a region.

The plane of this geometry has properties completely analogous to those possessed by the surface of a sphere. The great circles of the sphere correspond to the straight lines of the plane. Like the line, they are endless. Any two points on the surface of the sphere determine a great circle, provided the points are not the opposite ends of a diameter. The great circles through any point on the sphere intersect all other great circles.

We shall find that this analogy can be carried further. The sum of the angles of a spherical triangle is greater than two right angles. The sum of the angles of a triangle in this plane is greater than two right angles. The Spherical Excess measures the area of spherical triangles. With suitable units the area of plane triangles is equal to their excess. Indeed the formulae of this Plane Trigonometry, as we shall show later, are identical with the formulae of ordinary Spherical Trigonometry.*

§ 77. It must be remarked, however, that in the argument of § 76 it is assumed that the point O_1 is a different point from O. If the two points coincide, the plane of this geometry has a wholly different character. The length of a straight line is now $2\mathfrak{L}$ instead of $4\mathfrak{L}$. If two points P, Q are given on the plane, and any arbitrary straight line, we can pass from P to Q by a path which does not leave the plane, and does not cut the line. In other words, the plane is not divided by its lines into two parts.

The essential difference between the two planes is that in the one the plane has the character of a *two-sided* surface, and in the other it has the character of a *one-sided* surface.† The first plane—that which we have been examining—is usually called the spherical plane (or *double* elliptic plane) ; the second plane is usually called the elliptic (or *single* elliptic) plane.

The geometries which can be developed on both of these planes are referred to as Riemann's (Non-Euclidean) Geometries. It seems probable that the Spherical Plane was the only

---

* Spherical Geometry can be built up independently of the Parallel Postulate, so it is not necessary to say ordinary Spherical Trigonometry when referring to it.

† Cf. Bonola, *loc. cit.* § 75.

form in his mind. The Single Elliptic Plane and its importance in the higher treatment of the Non-Euclidean Geometries were first brought to light by Klein.

§ 78. We shall now show that this geometry corresponds to Saccheri's Hypothesis of the Obtuse Angle, so that the sum of the angles of a triangle is always greater than two right angles.

The following theorem enables us to put the proof concisely :

1. *In any triangle* ABC *in which the angle* C *is a right angle, the angle* A *is less than, equal to, or greater than a right angle, according as the segment* BC *is less than, equal to, or greater than* 𝔏.

Let P be the pole of the side AC.

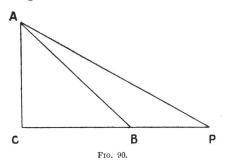

Fig. 90.

Then P lies upon BC, and PC = 𝔏.
Join AP.
Then ∠ PAC = a right angle.

If CB > CP, then ∠ BAC > ∠ PAC ; *i.e.* ∠ BAC > a right angle.
If CB = CP, then ∠ BAC = ∠ PAC ; *i.e.* ∠ BAC = a right angle.
If CB < CP, then ∠ BAC < ∠ PAC ; *i.e.* ∠ BAC < a right angle.

The converse also holds.

Now consider any right-angled triangle ABC in which C is the right angle.

If either of the sides AC or BC is greater than or equal to 𝔏, the sum of the angles is greater than two right angles by the above theorem.

If both sides are less than 𝔏, from D, the middle point of the hypothenuse, draw DE perpendicular to the side BC.

Let P be the pole of DE.

Produce ED to F, so that ED = DF.
Join AF and PF.
Then the triangles ADF and DEB are congruent, and AF, FP lie in one straight line.

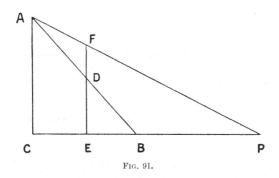

Fig. 91.

But we know that ∠ PAC > a right angle, since CP is greater than 𝔏.
Therefore the sum of the angles at A and B in the right-angled triangle ACB is greater than a right angle in this case as well as in the others.

Thus we have proved that

2. *In any right-angled triangle the sum of the angles is greater than two right angles.*

Finally, let ABC be any triangle in which none of the angles are right angles.
We need only consider the case when two of the angles are acute.
Let ∠ ABC and ∠ ACB be acute.
From A draw AD perpendicular to BC ; D must lie on the segment BC.
Then, from (2),

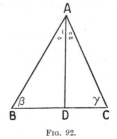

Fig. 92.

∠ ABD + ∠ BAD > a right angle

and ∠ DAC + ∠ ACD > a right angle.

It follows that the sum of the angles of the triangle ABC is greater than two right angles.

Thus we have proved that

3. *The sum of the angles of any triangle is greater than two right angles.*

The amount by which the sum of the angles of a triangle exceeds two right angles is called its **Excess.**

§ 79. Saccheri's Quadrilateral, and the Quadrilateral with three Right Angles and one Obtuse Angle.

Let AC and BD be equal perpendiculars to the segment AB. The quadrilateral ABDC we have called Saccheri's Quadrilateral.

Let E, F be the middle points of AB and CD.

We know that E F is perpendicular to both AB and CD ; and that the angles ACD and BDC are equal.

But the sum of the angles of a quadrilateral must be greater than four right angles, since it is made up of two triangles.

It follows that the angles at C and D are obtuse.

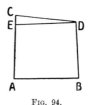

Fig. 93.   Fig. 94.

Thus the *Elliptic Geometry corresponds to Saccheri's Hypothesis of the Obtuse Angle.*

Now let ABDC (Fig. 94) be a quadrilateral in which the angles at A, B, and D are right angles.

The angle at C must be obtuse by § 78.

Each of the two sides containing the obtuse angle in a quadrilateral with three right angles is less than the side opposite to it.

To prove this, we proceed as follows :

If AC is not less than BD, it must be either greater than it or equal to it.

But we know that if AC = BD, ∠ ACD = ∠ BDC, which is impossible, as one is obtuse and the other a right angle.

If AC > BD, cut off AE = BD, and join ED.

Then we know that   ∠ AED = ∠ EDB.

But ∠EDB is acute, so that both must be acute, which is impossible.

Therefore AC must be less than BD.

Again, starting with AB and CD, which are both perpendicular to BD, we find that CD is less than AB, so our theorem is proved.

We shall not proceed further with the formal development of this geometry. There is no Theory of Parallels, for parallel lines do not exist in it. There is only one kind of circle, the locus of corresponding points upon a pencil of straight lines. The measurement of areas follows on the same lines as in the Hyperbolic Geometry.

Two triangles which have the same excess have equal areas, and conversely.

The area of a triangle is proportional to its excess.

CHAPTER VII.

THE ELLIPTIC PLANE TRIGONOMETRY.

§ 80. The following treatment of the Elliptic Trigonometry is due to Gérard and Mansion. Gérard discussed the Hyperbolic Trigonometry on these lines.* Mansion showed that the method discovered by Gérard was applicable also to the Elliptic case.†

The notation to be employed has first to be explained.

Let OA and OA' be two lines meeting at O at right angles. Let OL be a third line making an acute angle with OA and OA'.

Let P be any point upon the line OL, such that OP < 𝕷.

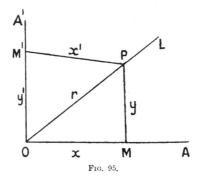

Fig. 95.

Let PM and PM' be the perpendiculars to OA and OA'.

We denote OM, MP, and OP by x, y, and r; and OM' and M'P by y' and x'.

---

* Gérard, *Sur la Géométrie non euclidienne* (Paris, 1892). Cf. also Young, "On the Analytical Basis of Non-Euclidian Geometry," *Amer. Journ. of Math.*, vol. xxxiii. p. 249 (1911); and Coolidge, *Non-Euclidean Geometry*, ch. iv. (Oxford, 1909).

† Mansion, *Principes Fondamentaux de la Géométrie non euclidienne de Riemann* (Paris, 1895).

§ 81.   I.   *If* P, Q *are any two points on* OL, *such that*

$$OP < OQ < \mathfrak{L},$$

and Pp, Qq *are perpendicular to* OA, *then* $\angle OPp < \angle OQq.$

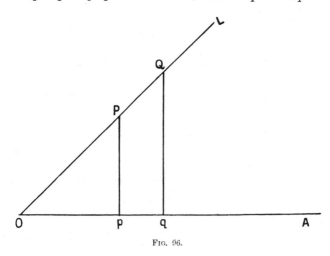

Fɪɢ. 96.

We know that $\angle p$PQ $+ \angle$ PQ$q > 2$ right angles.

Also $\angle$ OP$p + \angle p$PQ $= 2$ right angles.

Therefore $\angle$ OP$p < \angle$ PQ$q.$

If S is the point on OL, such that OS $= \mathfrak{L}$ and Ss is perpendicular to OA, we know that $\angle$ OSs $=$ a right angle.
It follows that $\angle$ OP$p < \angle$ OQ$q <$ a right angle.

II.   *From* O *to* S, y *continually increases.*

Let P and Q be any two points upon OL, such that

$$OP < OQ < \mathfrak{L}.$$

Then we know that if P$p =$ Qq, we must have $\angle p$PQ $= \angle$ PQq, which is impossible by (I.).

Again, if P$p >$ Qq, cut off pP$' = q$Q, and join P$'$Q.   (Fig. 97.)

Then $\angle p$P$'$Q $= \angle$ P$'$Q$q.$

But $\angle$ PQ$q <$ a right angle.

Therefore $\angle p\mathsf{P}'\mathsf{Q}$ and $\angle \mathsf{P}'\mathsf{Q}q$ are equal acute angles, which is impossible.

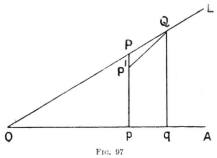

Fig. 97

Thus, as the point P moves along OL from O towards S, y continually increases.

III. *From* O *to* S, *the ratio* $\dfrac{x}{r}$ *continually increases.*

First, consider points upon OL corresponding to equal segments on OA.

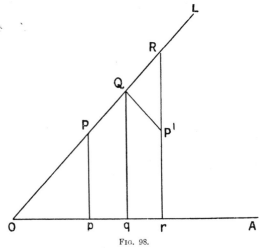

Fig. 98.

Let P, Q, R be three such points, so that
$$pq = qr.$$

Then we know that $p\mathsf{P} < q\mathsf{Q} < r\mathsf{R}$.

From $r\mathsf{R}$ cut off $r\mathsf{P}' = p\mathsf{P}$, and join QP'.

Then we have $\mathsf{PQ} = \mathsf{QP}'$ and $\angle\,\mathsf{Q}\mathsf{P}p = \angle\,\mathsf{Q}\mathsf{P}'r$.

Therefore $\angle\,\mathsf{QRP}' > \angle\,\mathsf{QP'R}$ and $\mathsf{QR} < \mathsf{QP}'$.

Thus, if $pq = qr$, $\mathsf{PQ} > \mathsf{QR}$.

Therefore, for equal increments of x, we have decreasing increments of r.

It follows from this that if P and Q are any two points upon OL, such that $\mathsf{OP} < \mathsf{OQ} < \mathcal{L}$, and OM, ON are commensurable,

$$\frac{\mathsf{OM}}{\mathsf{OP}} < \frac{\mathsf{ON}}{\mathsf{OQ}}.$$

When OM and ON are incommensurable, we reach the same conclusion by proceeding to the limit.

Thus, from O to S, the ratio $\dfrac{x}{r}$ continually increases.

IV. *From* O *to* S, *the ratio* $\dfrac{y}{r}$ *decreases.*

First we consider points upon OL at equal distances along that line.

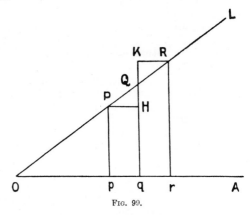

Fig. 99.

Let P, Q, and R be three such points, so that

$$\mathsf{PQ} = \mathsf{QR}.$$

From P and R draw PH and RK perpendicular to $\mathsf{Q}q$.

Then we know that $\mathsf{P}p < \mathsf{H}q$ and $\mathsf{R}r < \mathsf{K}q$ (§ 79).

But $\mathsf{QH} = \mathsf{QK}$. Therefore $\mathsf{Q}q - \mathsf{H}q = \mathsf{K}q - \mathsf{Q}q$.

It follows from the above that $\mathsf{Q}q - \mathsf{P}p > \mathsf{R}r - \mathsf{Q}q$.

Therefore, for equal increments of r we have diminishing increments of y.

It follows from this that if P and Q are any two points upon OL, such that $\mathsf{OP} < \mathsf{OQ} < \mathsf{L}$, and OP, OQ are commensurable,

$$\frac{\mathsf{P}p}{\mathsf{OP}} > \frac{\mathsf{Q}q}{\mathsf{OQ}}.$$

When OP and OQ are incommensurable, we obtain the same result by proceeding to the limit.

Thus, as P moves along OL from O towards S, the ratio $\frac{y}{r}$ continually decreases.

V. *When* r *tends to zero, the ratio* x : r *tends towards a finite limit from above, and the ratio* y : r *tends towards a finite limit from below.*

From (III.) we know that $x : r$ continually decreases as r tends to zero, so that this ratio has a limit, finite or zero.

From (IV.) we know that $y : r$ continually increases as r tends to zero, so that this ratio either has a finite limit, not zero, or becomes infinite.

But from the quadrilateral whose sides are (x, y, x', y') we have $x > x'$. (Fig. 95.) Thus $x : r > x' : r$.

But, by (IV.), $x' : r$ either has a finite limit, not zero, or becomes infinite, as r tends to zero.

Therefore the limit of $x : r$ cannot be zero, and must be some finite number. Also $x : r$ approaches this limit from above.

But it follows from the preceding argument that $y' : r$ has a finite limit, not zero.

Also we know that $y < y'$, and thus $y : r < y' : r$.

It follows that $y : r$ has a finite limit, not zero, and it approaches this from below.

These two limits $\operatorname*{Lt}_{r \to 0}\left(\frac{y}{r}\right)$, $\operatorname*{Lt}_{r \to 0}\left(\frac{x}{r}\right)$ are chosen as the sine and cosine of the acute angle which OL makes with OA,* and the other ratios follow in the usual way.

---

* These limits are functions of the angle. It can be shown that they are continuous, and that with a proper unit of angle they are given by the usual exponential expressions. Cf. Coolidge, *loc. cit.* p. 53.

§ 82. We turn now to the quadrilateral with three right angles and one obtuse angle.

Let OABb be such a quadrilateral, the angles at O, B, and b being right angles.

Produce Ob, and cut off $bc = Ob$ and $cd = bc$.

Draw the perpendiculars to Ob produced at the points c and d ; and from A the perpendiculars to the lines just drawn.

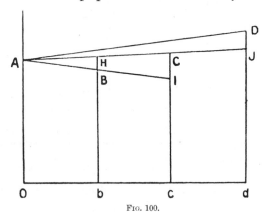

Fig. 100.

We thus obtain three quadrilaterals OABb, OACc, OADd, of this nature, standing on the bases Ob, Oc, and Od.

It is easy to show that the obtuse angles of these quadrilaterals increase as the bases increase.

Let bB produced meet AC at H, AB produced meet Cc at I, and AC produced meet Dd at J.

Then we have AB = BI, AB < AH, and AI > AC.

It follows that AB > AC – AB.

Also we have HC = CJ and AD < AJ.

Therefore AC – AH = AJ – AC, and finally AC – AB > AD – AC.

Thus AB > AC – AB > AD – AC.

§ 83. We return to the notation of § 80 and the figure OMPM′, in which the angles at O, M, and M′ are right angles, and the sides OM, MP, PM′, and OM′ are denoted by x, y, x', and y' respectively.

We shall now prove the following theorem :

In the quadrilateral with three right angles (x, y, x', y'), *in which the sides* x′, y *include the obtuse angle, if* y′ *is kept fixed and* x *tends to zero, the ratio* x′ : x *tends to a finite limit* $\phi(y')$ *from above, and this ratio is less than* $\phi(y)$.

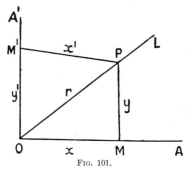

FIG. 101.

As in § 81 we find that $x' : x$ continually decreases as x tends to zero. It must have a limit, which may be zero or some number less than unity.

Produce MP, and draw M′Q perpendicular to MP.

From § 82 we know that as x decreases, the ratio $\dfrac{M'Q}{x}$ increases.

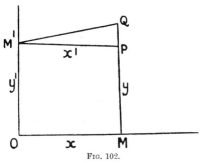

FIG. 102.

It must therefore have a finite limit, not zero, or become infinite.

But $\dfrac{M'Q}{x} < \dfrac{M'P}{x}$, since M′Q < M′P.

Thus $\underset{x \to 0}{\mathrm{Lt}} \left(\dfrac{x'}{x} \right)$ cannot be zero.

This function is associated with the segment M'O, denoted by y', and will be written as $\phi(y')$.

Now we have seen that

$$\phi(y') > \mathsf{M'Q} : x.$$

But in the quadrilateral OM'PM, the side PM plays the same part as OM' in the quadrilateral OM'QM.

Thus $\phi(y) > \mathsf{M'P} : x.$

Thus we have $\phi(y') < \dfrac{x'}{x} < \phi(y).$

Since $x' < x$, the function $\phi(y')$ is less than unity, except for $y' = 0$, when it becomes equal to unity.

§ 84. We shall now show that the function defined in the previous section is continuous.

Let OS and Os be two lines meeting at O, such that

$$\mathsf{OS} = \mathsf{O}s = \mathfrak{L} \text{ and } \angle \mathsf{SO}s \text{ is acute.}$$

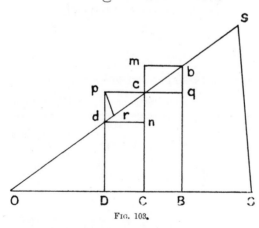

Fig. 103.

Then the angles at S and s are both right angles.

Let $\mathsf{SB} = x - y$, $\mathsf{SC} = x$, and $\mathsf{SD} = x + y$.

Let the perpendiculars at B, C, and D to OS, meet Os at b, c, and d.

Through b and d draw bm and dn perpendicular to Cc.

From § 81 (III.), applied to the acute angles dcn and bcm, we have $cb < cd$, $cm : cb < cC : cO$, and $cn : cd < cC : cO$.

From the second of these relations we have

$$\frac{Cm}{Ss} - \frac{Cc}{Ss} < \frac{Cc}{Ss}\frac{cb}{cO},$$

i.e.
$$\left(\frac{Bb}{Ss} : \frac{Bb}{Cm}\right) - \frac{Cc}{Ss} < \frac{Cc}{Ss}\frac{cb}{cO}. \quad\ldots\ldots\ldots\ldots\ldots(\alpha)$$

Then, by § 83, if Ss, and thus Bb and Cm tend to zero, we have

$$Lt \frac{Bb}{Ss} = \phi(x - y),$$

$$Lt \frac{Bb}{Cm} = \phi(y),$$

$$Lt \frac{Cc}{Ss} = \phi(x).$$

Further, $Lt\, cb = CB = y$ and $Lt\, cO = CO = \mathfrak{L} - x.$

Therefore, from (α), we have

$$\frac{\phi(x - y)}{\phi(y)} - \phi(x) \lesseqgtr \frac{y}{\mathfrak{L} - x}\,\phi(x),$$

i.e.
$$\phi(x - y) - \phi(x)\,\phi(y) \lesseqgtr \frac{y}{\mathfrak{L} - x}\,\phi(x)\,\phi(y). \quad\ldots\ldots\ldots(\beta)$$

Again, from the inequality $\dfrac{cn}{cd} < \dfrac{cC}{cO}$, we have in the same way

$$\phi(x)\,\phi(y) - \phi(x + y) \lesseqgtr \frac{y}{\mathfrak{L} - x}\,\phi(x)\,\phi(y). \quad\ldots\ldots\ldots(\gamma)$$

Adding (β) and (γ), we have

$$\phi(x - y) - \phi(x + y) \lesseqgtr \frac{2y}{\mathfrak{L} - x}\,\phi(x)\,\phi(y) < \frac{2y}{\mathfrak{L} - x},$$

since $\phi(x)$, $\phi(y)$ are each less than unity. It follows that $\phi(x)$ is a continuous function of x.

§ 85. We shall now show that

$$\phi(\mathbf{x} + \mathbf{y}) + \phi(\mathbf{x} - \mathbf{y}) = 2\phi(\mathbf{x})\phi(\mathbf{y}).$$

With the figure of § 84, let the perpendicular at c to Cc meet Dd and Bb in p and q. From cd cut off $cr = cb$, and join pr.

Then we have $cp = cq$ and $pr = qb$.

We shall presently suppose Ss to become infinitesimal. In this case the angles at p and q differ infinitesimally from right angles, and $\angle dpr$ becomes infinitesimal.

It follows that dr is infinitesimal as compared with pd; [*] and that if Ss is an infinitesimal of the first order, dr is at least of the second order.

But $dp - qb = dp - pr < dr$.

And $dp - qb = (Dp - Dd) - (Bb - Bq)$.

Therefore we have

$$\mathrm{Lt}\left(\frac{Dp}{Cc} \cdot \frac{Cc}{Ss} - \frac{Dd}{Ss} - \frac{Bb}{Ss} + \frac{Bq}{Cc} \cdot \frac{Cc}{Ss}\right) = 0.$$

But

$$\mathrm{Lt}\left(\frac{Dp}{Cc}\right) = \phi(y) = \mathrm{Lt}\left(\frac{Bq}{Cc}\right).$$

And

$$\mathrm{Lt}\left(\frac{Cc}{Ss}\right) = \phi(x), \qquad \mathrm{Lt}\left(\frac{Dd}{Ss}\right) = \phi(x+y),$$

and

$$\mathrm{Lt}\left(\frac{Bb}{Ss}\right) = \phi(x-y).$$

Thus we have

$$\phi(x + y) + \phi(x - y) = 2\phi(x)\phi(y).$$

§ 86. We proceed to the equation

$$\phi(x + y) + \phi(x - y) = 2\phi(x)\phi(y).$$

We are given that $\phi(x)$ is a continuous function, which is equal to unity when $x = 0$, and when $x > 0$, $\phi(x) < 1$.

Let x_1 be a value of x in the interval to which the equation applies.

Then we can find k, so that $\phi(x_1) = \cos\dfrac{x_1}{k}$.

---

[*] Cf. Coolidge, *loc. cit.* p. 49.

The function $\cos x$ has here a purely analytical meaning, being defined by the equation

$$\cos x = 1 - \frac{x^2}{2!} + \frac{x^4}{4!} - \dots \, .$$

It follows that
$$\phi(\, x_1) = \cos \frac{2x_1}{k},$$

$$\phi(nx_1) = \cos \frac{nx_1}{k},$$

$$\phi\left(\frac{nx_1}{2^m}\right) = \cos \left(\frac{nx_1}{2^m k}\right).$$

Now let x be any other value of x in the interval. If it happens that this value is included in the set

$$nx_1 \text{ or } \frac{nx_1}{2^m},$$

we know that $\phi(x) = \cos \left(\frac{x}{k}\right)$, by the above.

But if it is not included in these forms, we can still find positive integers m, n by going on far enough in the scale, such that

$$\left(x - \frac{nx_1}{2^m}\right) < \epsilon,$$

where ϵ is any positive number as small as we please.

But $\phi(x)$ and $\cos \frac{x}{k}$ are continuous functions.

It follows that
$$\phi(x) = \cos \frac{x}{k}.$$

This value of k will be related to the measure of the line OS, denoted by $\mathfrak{L}$ in the previous sections.

§ 87. We have now to deal with a rather complicated figure. From it we shall obtain the fundamental equation of this Trigonometry for the Right-Angled Triangle ABC, in which C is the right angle, viz.

$$\cos \frac{c}{k} = \cos \frac{a}{k} \cos \frac{b}{k}. \quad \dots \dots \dots \dots \dots (1)$$

Let ABC be a right-angled triangle, in which C is the right angle.

From a point b upon AB produced draw bc perpendicular to AC,

Move the triangle bcA along AC till c coincides with C and bc takes up the position b'C.

We thus have the triangle $b'a'$C congruent with bAc.

In the same way move the triangle bcA along BA until b coincides with B and the triangle takes up the position B$a''c''$.

Through the middle point I of a'A draw IL perpendicular to BA.

Then LI produced will be perpendicular to $b'a'$.

We thus obtain the common perpendicular to $b'a'$ and BA, the line KIL.

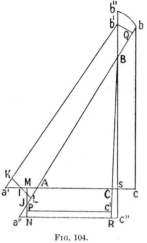

In the same way we obtain the common perpendicular MJN to AC and $a''c''$ through the middle point J of Aa''.

Finally, we draw b'Q perpendicular to AB and bb'' perpendicular to BC.

Fig. 104.

We have seen that as Bb tends to zero, we have

$$\text{Lt}\,\frac{bb''}{Bb} = \text{Lt}\,\frac{b'Q}{b'B} \quad\dots\dots\dots\dots\dots\dots\text{(i)}$$

In the same way $\text{Lt}\,\dfrac{MJ}{JA} = \text{Lt}\,\dfrac{IL}{IA}.$

Thus $\text{Lt}\,\dfrac{MN}{Aa''} = \text{Lt}\,\dfrac{KL}{Aa'}. \quad\dots\dots\dots\dots\dots\text{(ii)}$

Dividing (i) by (ii) and remembering that Aa'' = Bb and Aa' = Cc, we have

$$\text{Lt}\,\frac{bb''}{MN} = \text{Lt}\,\frac{b'Q}{KL}\,.\,\text{Lt}\,\frac{Cc}{Bb'},$$

which may be written

$$\text{Lt}\,\frac{b'Q}{KL} = \text{Lt}\,\frac{bb''}{Cc}\,.\,\text{Lt}\,\frac{Bb'}{MN}. \quad\dots\dots\dots\dots\text{(iii)}$$

We shall now show that this equation is the same as

$$\phi(\text{AB}) = \phi(\text{BC})\,\phi(\text{CA}).$$

From § 83, we have

$$\phi(\mathsf{LQ}) < \frac{b'\mathsf{Q}}{\mathsf{KL}} < \phi(\mathsf{K}b').$$

Now, when Bb tends to zero, LQ and Kb' tend to BA, and from § 84, $\phi(\mathsf{LQ})$ and $\phi(\mathsf{K}b')$ tend to $\phi(\mathsf{AB})$.

Thus, $$\mathrm{Lt}\,\frac{b'\mathsf{Q}}{\mathsf{KL}} = \phi(\mathsf{AB}). \quad\ldots\ldots\ldots\ldots\ldots\ldots(\mathrm{iv})$$

In the same way we have

$$\mathrm{Lt}\left(\frac{bb''}{\mathsf{C}c}\right) = \phi(\mathsf{BC}). \quad\ldots\ldots\ldots\ldots\ldots\ldots(\mathrm{v})$$

There remains the limit of $\dfrac{\mathsf{B}b'}{\mathsf{MN}}$.

Let s be the point at which Bc'' meets AC.
We know from § 81 (I.), that s lies between C and c, and we have B$s >$ BC.
Then, since Cb' = Bc'', we have B$b' > sc''$.

Therefore $$\frac{\mathsf{B}b'}{\mathsf{MN}} > \frac{sc''}{\mathsf{M}n} > \phi(\mathsf{N}c'').$$

Produce BC till it meets $a''c''$ in R.
We have BR $>$ Bc'', so that BR $>$ Cb'.
From BR cut off Bc' = Cb'.
Draw c'P perpendicular to MN.
Then we have

$$\frac{\mathsf{B}b'}{\mathsf{MN}} < \frac{\mathsf{B}b'}{\mathsf{MP}} = \frac{\mathsf{C}c'}{\mathsf{MP}} < \phi(\mathsf{P}c') < \phi(\mathsf{CM} - \mathsf{PM} - \mathsf{C}c').$$

Thus $$\phi(\mathsf{CM} - \mathsf{PM} - \mathsf{C}c') > \frac{\mathsf{B}b'}{\mathsf{MN}} > \phi(\mathsf{N}c'').$$

Proceeding to the limit,

$$\phi(\mathsf{AC}) = \mathrm{Lt}\left(\frac{\mathsf{B}b'}{\mathsf{MN}}\right). \quad\ldots\ldots\ldots\ldots\ldots\ldots(\mathrm{vi})$$

From (iii)-(vi), it follows that $\phi(\mathsf{AB}) = \phi(\mathsf{BC})\phi(\mathsf{CA})$, or with the usual notation from § 86,

$$\cos\frac{\mathsf{c}}{\mathsf{k}} = \cos\frac{\mathsf{a}}{\mathsf{k}}\cos\frac{\mathsf{b}}{\mathsf{k}}.$$

NOTE.   At several points in this argument we have assumed that the segments concerned are less than $\mathfrak{L}$.

Once the fundamental theorem has been proved for triangles in which this condition is satisfied, it can be extended by analysis to all other cases.

§ 88.   The remaining formulae are easily obtained :

To prove $\qquad \tan \dfrac{b}{k} = \cos \text{A} \tan \dfrac{c}{k}.$ .... (2)

Let ABC be any right-angled triangle, with C a right angle.

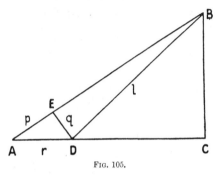

FIG. 105.

Take any point D on AC, and join BD.
Draw DE perpendicular to AB.
Let $\text{AE} = p$, $\text{ED} = q$, $\text{AD} = r$, and $\text{BD} = l$.
Then, from the triangle DBC, we have

$$\cos \frac{l}{k} = \cos \frac{a}{k} \cos \left(\frac{b - r}{k} \right)$$

$$= \cos \frac{a}{k} \cos \frac{b}{k} \cos \frac{r}{k} + \cos \frac{a}{k} \sin \frac{b}{k} \sin \frac{r}{k}$$

$$= \cos \frac{c}{k} \cos \frac{r}{k} + \cos \frac{a}{k} \sin \frac{b}{k} \sin \frac{r}{k}.$$

Also, from the triangle BDE, we have in the same way

$$\cos \frac{l}{k} = \cos \frac{c}{k} \cos \frac{r}{k} + \cos \frac{q}{k} \sin \frac{p}{k} \sin \frac{c}{k}.$$

Therefore $\quad \cos \dfrac{a}{k} \sin \dfrac{b}{k} \sin \dfrac{r}{k} = \cos \dfrac{q}{k} \sin \dfrac{p}{k} \sin \dfrac{c}{k}.$

Using the equations $\cos \dfrac{c}{k} = \cos \dfrac{a}{k} \cos \dfrac{b}{k}$,

$$\cos \frac{r}{k} = \cos \frac{p}{k} \cos \frac{q}{k},$$

this gives

$$\frac{\tan \dfrac{b}{k}}{\tan \dfrac{c}{k}} = \frac{\tan \dfrac{p}{k}}{\tan \dfrac{r}{k}}.$$

This result holds however small r may be.

But we have seen that when $r \to 0$, $\dfrac{x}{r}$ has a definite limit other than zero, and that this limit is taken as the cosine of the angle.   (§ 81.)

Therefore

$$\cos \mathsf{A} = \underset{r \to 0}{\mathrm{Lt}} \; \frac{\tan \dfrac{p}{k}}{\tan \dfrac{r}{k}}$$

$$= \frac{\tan \dfrac{b}{k}}{\tan \dfrac{c}{k}}.$$

§ 89. To prove that

$$\sin \mathsf{A} = \frac{\sin \dfrac{a}{k}}{\sin \dfrac{c}{k}}. \quad \dots\dots\dots\dots\dots\dots(3)$$

We have seen that as $r \to 0$, the ratio $\dfrac{y}{r}$ tends to a definite limit, other than zero, and that this limit is taken as the sine of the angle.

Now from the equation

$$\cos \frac{c}{k} = \cos \frac{a}{k} \cos \frac{b}{k},$$

we find that when a, b, and c are small,

$c^2 = a^2 + b^2$, to the lowest order.

It follows that $\sin^2 \mathsf{A} + \cos^2 \mathsf{A} = 1$.

But, from § 88, we have

$$\cos A = \frac{\tan \dfrac{b}{k}}{\tan \dfrac{c}{k}}.$$

Therefore

$$\sin^2 A = 1 - \frac{\tan^2 \dfrac{b}{k}}{\tan^2 \dfrac{c}{k}}$$

$$= \frac{\sin^2 \dfrac{c}{k} - \tan^2 \dfrac{b}{k} \cos^2 \dfrac{c}{k}}{\sin^2 \dfrac{c}{k}}$$

$$= \frac{1 - \sec^2 \dfrac{b}{k} \cos^2 \dfrac{c}{k}}{\sin^2 \dfrac{c}{k}}$$

$$= \frac{1 - \cos^2 \dfrac{a}{k}}{\sin^2 \dfrac{c}{k}}$$

$$= \frac{\sin^2 \dfrac{a}{k}}{\sin^2 \dfrac{c}{k}}.$$

Therefore

$$\sin A = \frac{\sin \dfrac{a}{k}}{\sin \dfrac{c}{k}}.$$

The remaining formulae,

$$\cos A = \cos \frac{a}{k} \sin B, \quad\dots\dots\dots\dots\dots\dots(4)$$

$$\sin \frac{b}{k} = \tan \frac{a}{k} \cot A, \quad\dots\dots\dots\dots\dots(5)$$

$$\cos \frac{c}{k} = \cot A \cot B, \quad\dots\dots\dots\dots\dots(6)$$

can be easily deduced from those already obtained.

The six equations (1)–(6) are the equations of ordinary Spherical Trigonometry, when $\frac{a}{k}$, $\frac{b}{k}$, and $\frac{c}{k}$ are substituted for a, b, c.

§ 90. The Trigonometry of the Oblique-Angled Triangle follows from that of the Right-Angled Triangle, the definitions of the sine and cosine being extended to obtuse angles. The formulae will be identical with those of ordinary Spherical Trigonometry, with the parameter k introduced.

The elements of arc and area can also be deduced as in Chapter V. In this case we shall have

$$ds^2 = \cos^2 \frac{y}{k} \, dx^2 + dy^2,$$

$$ds^2 = dr^2 + k^2 \sin^2 \frac{r}{k} \, d\theta^2,$$

$$d\mathsf{A} = \cos \frac{y}{k} \, dx \, dy,$$

$$d\mathsf{A} = k \sin \frac{r}{k} \, dr \, d\theta.$$

Also the Euclidean Formulae hold true in Infinitesimal Geometry on the Elliptic Plane.

CHAPTER VIII.

THE CONSISTENCY OF THE NON-EUCLIDEAN GEOMETRIES AND THE IMPOSSIBILITY OF PROVING THE PARALLEL POSTULATE.

§ 91. As we have already seen, the discovery of the Non-Euclidean Geometries arose from the attempts to prove Euclid's Parallel Postulate. Bolyai and Lobatschewsky did a double service to Geometry. They showed why these attempts had failed, and why they must always fail ; for they succeeded in building up a geometry as logical and consistent as the Euclidean Geometry, upon the same foundations, except that for the Parallel Postulate of Euclid, another incompatible with it was substituted. They differed from almost all their predecessors in their belief that, proceeding on these lines, they would not meet any contradiction ; and they held that the system of geometry built upon their Parallel Postulate was a fit subject of study for its own sake.

The question naturally arises : How can one be certain that these Non-Euclidean Geometries are logical and consistent systems ? How can we be sure that continued study would not after all reveal some contradiction, some inconsistency ? Saccheri thought he had found such in the Hyperbolic Geometry ; but he was mistaken. Even Bolyai, many years after the publication of the *Appendix*, was for a time of the opinion that he had come upon a contradiction, and that the sought-for proof of the Euclidean Hypothesis was in his hands. He, too, was mistaken.

Of course, it is not sufficient simply to point to the fact that these geometries—developed into a large body of doctrine as they have been—do not offer in any of their propositions the contradiction which the earlier workers in those fields were convinced they must contain. We must be sure that, proceeding further on these lines, such contradiction could never be discovered. If we can prove this to be the case, then we know that Euclid's Parallel Postulate cannot be demonstrated.

§ 92. There are several ways by which it is possible to establish the fact that the Hyperbolic and Elliptic Geometries are as logical and consistent as the Euclidean Geometry.*

Lobatschewsky, and to some extent Bolyai, relied upon the formulae of the Hyperbolic Plane Trigonometry. These are identical with the formulae of Spherical Trigonometry, if the radius of the sphere is imaginary. If the ordinary Spherical Trigonometry offers no contradiction, their geometry could not do so. However, this proof is not complete in itself, for it leaves aside the domain of Solid Geometry, and does not establish the impossibility of the difficulty appearing in that field. (Cf. Chapter II. §§ 15, 17.)

The most important of all the proofs of the consistency of the Non-Euclidean Geometries is that due to Cayley and Klein. In it one passes beyond the elementary regions within the confines of which this book is meant to remain. Other proofs are analytical. The assumptions of geometry are translated into the domain of number. Any inconsistency would then appear in the arithmetical form of the assumptions or in the deductions from them. This form of proof also seems to lie outside the province of this book.

Finally, there are a number of geometrical proofs, depending upon concrete interpretations of the Non-Euclidean Geometries in the Euclidean. The earliest of these—due to Beltrami, and dealing with the Hyperbolic Geometry—requires a knowledge of the Geometry of Surfaces. But an elementary representation of the Hyperbolic Plane and Space in the Euclidean was given by Poincaré.

" Let us consider," he says, " a certain plane, which I shall call the fundamental plane, and let us construct a kind of dictionary by making a double series of terms written in two columns, and corresponding each to each, just as in ordinary dictionaries the words in two languages which have the same signification correspond to one another :

Space.   -   -   The portion of space situated above the fundamental plane.

---

* For a discussion on more advanced lines, cf. Sommerville's *Non-Euclidean Geometry*, ch. v. and vi. (London, 1914).

Plane. - -	Sphere cutting orthogonally the fundamental plane.
Line. - - -	Circle cutting orthogonally the fundamental plane.
Sphere. - -	Sphere.
Circle. - -	Circle.
Angle. - -	Angle.
Distance between two points.	The logarithm of the anharmonic ratio of these two points and of the intersections of the fundamental plane with the circle passing through these points and cutting it orthogonally.
Etc.	Etc.

" Let us take Lobatschewsky's theorems and translate them by the aid of this dictionary, as we would translate a German text with the aid of a German-French dictionary. *We shall then obtain the theorems of ordinary geometry.* For instance, Lobatschewsky's theorem : ' The sum of the angles of a triangle is less than two right angles ' may be translated thus : ' If a curvilinear triangle has for its sides arcs of circles which cut orthogonally the fundamental plane, the sum of the angles of this curvilinear triangle will be less than two right angles.' Thus, however far the consequences of Lobatschewsky's hypotheses are carried, they will never lead to a contradiction ; in fact, if two of Lobatschewsky's theorems were contradictory, the translation of these two theorems made by the aid of our dictionary would be contradictory also. But these translations are theorems of ordinary geometry, and no one doubts that ordinary geometry is exempt from contradiction." *

§ 93. To Poincaré is also due another representation of the Hyperbolic Geometry, which includes that given in the preceding section as a special case. We shall discuss this representation at some length, as also a corresponding one for the Elliptic Geometry, since from these we can obtain in a simple and elementary manner the proof of the impossibility of

---

* Poincaré, *La Science et l'Hypothèse.* English translation by Greenstreet, p. 41 *et seq.*

proving the Parallel Postulate and of the logical consistency both of the Hyperbolic and Elliptic Geometries. In this discussion the "dictionary method" of § 92 will be more fully explained.

We shall consider three families of circles in a plane— extending the argument to spheres later. These are the family of circles passing through a fixed point; the family of circles cutting a fixed circle orthogonally; and the family of circles cutting a fixed circle diametrally (i.e. the common chord of the fixed circle and any of the variable circles is to be a diameter of the fixed circle). Denoting the fixed point by O, and taking the fixed circle as a circle with centre O and radius k, the first family of circles has *power* zero with regard to O; the second, *power* k^2; and the third, *power* $-k^2$. We shall see that the geometries of these three families of circles agree with the Euclidean, Hyperbolic, and Elliptic Geometries, respectively.

§ 94. The System of Circles through a Fixed Point.

If we invert from a point O the lines lying in a plane through O we obtain a set of circles passing through that point. To every circle there corresponds a straight line, and to every straight line a circle. The circles intersect at the same angles as the corresponding lines. The properties of the family of circles could be deduced from the properties of the set of lines, and every proposition concerning points and lines in the one system could be interpreted as a proposition concerning points and circles in the other.

There is another method of dealing with the geometry of this family of circles. We shall describe it briefly, as it will make the argument in the case of the other families, which represent the Non-Euclidean Geometries, easier.

If two points A and B are given, these, with the point O, fully determine a circle passing through the point O. We shall call these circles *nominal lines*.* We shall refer to the points in the plane of the circles as *nominal points*, the point O being supposed excluded from the domain of the *nominal*

---

* In another place, cf. Bonola, *loc. cit.*, English translation, Appendix V., and *Proc. Edin. Math. Soc.*, Vol. 28, p. 95 (1910), I have used the terms *ideal points, ideal lines,* etc. For these I now substitute *nominal points, nominal lines,* etc., owing to possible confusion with the *ideal* points, *ideal* lines, etc., of §§ 37, 38.

points. We define the angle between two *nominal lines* as the angle between the circles with which the *nominal lines* coincide at their common point.

With these definitions, two different *nominal points* A, B in this Nominal Geometry always determine a *nominal line* AB, just as two different ordinary points always determine a straight line AB.

The *nominal points* and *lines* also satisfy the " axioms of order," * which express the idea of between-ness, when the point O is excluded from the domain of the nominal points. If this point were not excluded, we could not say that of any three nominal points on a nominal line, there is always one, and only one, which lies between the other two.

Proceeding to the question of parallels, we define *parallel nominal lines* as follows :

The nominal line through a nominal point parallel to a given nominal line is the circle of the system which passes through the given point and touches at O *the circle coinciding with the given nominal line.*

Referring to Fig. 106 we see that in the pencil of nominal lines through A there is one nominal line which does not cut BC, namely, the circle of the system which touches OBC at O.

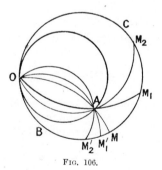

Fɪɢ. 106.

This nominal line does not cut the nominal line BC, for the point O is excluded from the domain of the nominal points. It is at right angles to AM, the nominal line through A perpendicular to the nominal line BC. Every nominal line through

---

* Cf. Hilbert, *loc. cit.* § 3.

A making with AM an angle less than a right angle will cut BC on the side of OAM in which the acute angle lies.

Therefore in the geometry of these nominal points and lines the Euclidean Parallel Postulate holds.

§ 95. Before we can deal with the metrical properties of this geometry, we require a measure of length. *We define the nominal length of a nominal segment as the length of the rectilinear segment to which it corresponds.* *

From this definition it is not difficult to show that *the nominal length of a nominal segment is unaltered by inversion with regard to a circle of the system; and that inversion with regard to such a circle is equivalent to reflection of the nominal points and lines in the nominal line which coincides with the circle of inversion.*

Now, if we invert successively with regard to two circles of the system (*i.e.* if we reflect in two nominal lines one after the other), we obtain what corresponds to a displacement in two dimensions. A nominal triangle ABC takes up the position A′B′C′ after the first reflection ; and from A′B′C′ it passes to the position A″B″C″ in the second. The sides and angles of A″B″C″ (in our nominal measurement) are the same as the sides and angles of the nominal triangle ABC, and the point C″ lies on the same side of A″B″ as the point C does of AB.

Further, we can always fix upon two inversions which will change a given nominal segment AB into a new position such that A comes to A′, and AB lies along a given nominal line through A′. We need only invert first with regard to the circle which " bisects " the nominal line AA′ at right angles. This brings AB into a position A′B″, say. Then, if we invert with regard to the circle of the system which bisects the angle between A′B″ and the given nominal line through A′, the segment AB is brought into the required position.

The method of superposition is thus available in the geometry of the nominal points and lines. Euclid's argument can be " translated " directly into the new geometry. We have only to use the words nominal points, nominal lines, nominal parallels, etc., instead of the ordinary points, lines, parallels, etc., and we obtain from the ordinary geometry the corresponding propositions in the geometry of this family of circles.

It should perhaps be pointed out that the nominal circle with centre A is an ordinary circle. For the orthogonal

---

* See p. 175.

trajectories of the circles of the system through A (*i.e.* of the nominal lines through A) is the family of coaxal circles with O and A as Limiting Points. The nominal lengths of the nominal segments from A to the points where one of these circles cuts the pencil of lines will be the same.

§ **96.** The argument sketched in the preceding sections can be extended to Solid Geometry. Instead of the system of circles lying in one plane and all passing through the point O, we have now to deal with the system of spheres all passing through the point O.

The *nominal point* is the same as the ordinary point, but the point O is excluded from the domain of the nominal points.

The nominal line through two nominal points is the circle passing through O and these two points.

The nominal plane through three nominal points is the sphere passing through O and these three points.

The nominal line through a point A parallel to a nominal line BC *is the circle through* A *which lies on the sphere through* O, A, B *and* C, *and touches the circle* OBC *at the point* O.

It is clear that a nominal line is determined by two different nominal points, just as a straight line is determined by two different ordinary points. The nominal plane is determined by three different nominal points, not on a nominal line, just as an ordinary plane is determined by three different ordinary points not on a straight line. If two points of a nominal line lie on a nominal plane, then all the points of that line lie on that plane. The intersection of two nominal planes is a nominal line, etc.

The measurement of angles in the new geometry is the same as that in the ordinary geometry ; the angle between two nominal lines is defined as the angle between the circles with which these lines coincide at their intersection. The measurement of length is as before. Inversion in a sphere through O is equivalent to reflection in the nominal plane coinciding with that sphere. Displacements, being point-transformations according to which every point of the domain is transformed into a point of the domain, in such a way that nominal lines remain nominal lines, and nominal lengths and angles are unaltered, will be given by an even number of inversions in the spheres of the system.

Thus, the geometry of these nominal points, lines, and planes is identical with the ordinary Euclidean Geometry. Its elements satisfy the same laws ; every proposition valid in the one is also valid in the other ; and from the theorems of the Euclidean Geometry those of the Nominal Geometry can be inferred, and *vice versa*.

The plane geometry of the nominal points and lines described in the preceding sections is a special case of the more general plane geometry based upon the definitions of this section.

§ 97. The System of Circles orthogonal to a Fixed Circle.

We proceed to discuss the geometry of the system of circles orthogonal to a fixed circle, centre O and radius k. We shall call this circle the fundamental circle. Then the system of circles has *power* k^2 with respect to O.

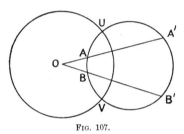

Fig. 107.

Let A and B be any two points within the fundamental circle and A′, B′ the inverse points with respect to that circle. Then A, A′, B, B′ are concyclic, and the circle which passes through them cuts the fundamental circle orthogonally. There is one and only one circle orthogonal to the fundamental circle which passes through two different points within that circle.

In discussing the properties of the family of circles orthogonal to the fundamental circle, we shall call the points *within* that circle *nominal points*. The points on the circumference of the fundamental circle are excluded from the domain of the *nominal points*.*

---

* In this discussion the *nominal points*, etc., are defined somewhat differently from the *ideal points*, etc., in the paper referred to on p. 156.

We define the nominal line through any two nominal points as the circle which passes through these two points and cuts the fundamental circle orthogonally.

Two different nominal points A, B always determine a nominal line AB, just as two different ordinary points A, B always determine a straight line AB. The nominal points and lines also obey the "axioms of order."

We define the angle between two intersecting nominal lines as the angle between the tangents at the common point, within the fundamental circle, of the circles with which the nominal lines coincide.

We have now to consider in what way it will be proper to define *parallel nominal lines.*

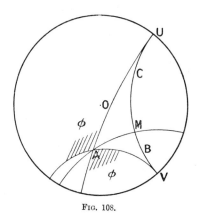

FIG. 108.

Let AM (Fig. 108) be the *nominal line* through A perpendicular to the *nominal line* BC ; in other words, the circle of the system which passes through A and cuts the circle of the system through BC orthogonally. Imagine AM to rotate about A so that these nominal lines through A cut the nominal line through BC at a gradually smaller angle. The circles through A which touch the circle through BC at the points U and V, where it meets the fundamental circle, are nominal lines. They separate the lines of the pencil of nominal lines through A, which cut BC from those which do not cut it. All the lines in the angle ϕ shaded in the figure do not cut the line BC ; all those in the angle ψ, unshaded, do cut this nominal line.

This property is what is assumed in the Parallel Postulate on which the Hyperbolic Geometry is based. We are therefore led to define parallel nominal lines in the plane geometry we are investigating as follows :

The nominal lines through a nominal point parallel to a nominal line are the two circles of the system passing through the given point which touch the circle with which the given nominal line coincides at the points where it cuts the fundamental circle.

Thus we have in this geometry two parallels—a right-handed parallel and a left-handed parallel—and these separate the lines of the pencil which intersect the given line from those which do not intersect it.

§ 98. At this stage we can say that any of the theorems of the Hyperbolic Geometry which involve only angle properties will hold in the geometry of the circles, and *vice versa.* Those involving metrical properties of lines we cannot discuss until the *nominal length* of a *nominal segment* has been defined.

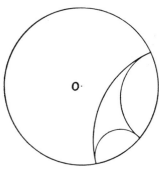

Fig. 109.

For example, it is obvious that *there are nominal triangles whose angles are all zero* (Fig. 109). The sides of these triangles are parallel in pairs, and we regard parallel lines as containing an angle zero.

Further, *we can prove that the sum of the angles in any nominal triangle is less than two right angles,* by inversion, as follows :

Let C_1, C_2, C_3, be three circles of the system—*i.e.* three nominal lines forming a nominal triangle, say PQR. We suppose these circles completed, and we deal with the whole

circumference of each. Invert the circles from the point of
intersection R' of C_1 and C_2, which lies outside the fundamental
circle. Then the nominal lines C_1 and C_2 become two straight
lines C_1' and C_2', through the inverse of R. Also the fundamental circle C inverts into a circle C', cutting C_1' and C_2' at
right angles, so that its centre is at the point of intersection
of these two lines. Again the circle C_3 inverts into a circle C_3',
cutting C' orthogonally. Hence its centre lies outside C'.

We thus obtain a curvilinear triangle in which the sum of
the angles is less than two right angles ; and since the angles
in this triangle are equal to those in the nominal triangle, our
result is proved.

Finally, *it can be shown that there is always one and only one
circle of the system which will cut two not-intersecting circles
of the system orthogonally.* In other words, *two not-intersecting
nominal lines have a common perpendicular.*

All these results we have established in the Hyperbolic
Geometry. They could be accepted in the geometry of the
circles for that reason.

§ **99.** As to the measurement of length, we define the *nominal
length* of a *nominal segment* as follows :

The nominal length of any nominal segment AB *is equal to*

$$\log\left(\frac{AV}{AU}\Big/\frac{BV}{BU}\right),$$

where U *and* V *are the points where the circle which coincides
with the nominal line* AB *cuts the fundamental circle.* (Cf.
Fig. 107.)

With this definition the nominal length of AB is the same
as that of BA. Also the nominal length of the complete line
is infinite. If C is any point on the nominal segment AB
between A and B, the nominal length of AB is the same as the
sum of the nominal lengths of AC and CB.

Let us consider what effect inversion with regard to a circle
of the system has upon the nominal points and lines.

Let A be a nominal point and A' the inverse of this point
in the fundamental circle.

Let the circle of inversion meet the fundamental circle in C,
and let its centre be D (Fig. 110).

Suppose A and A' invert into B and B'.

Since the circle AA'C touches the circle of inversion at C, its inverse also touches that circle at C. But the points A, A', B, B' are concyclic, and the radical axes of the three circles AA'C, BB'C and AA'B'B are concurrent.

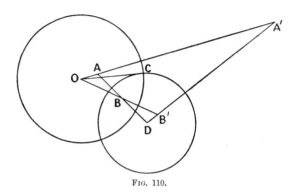

Fig. 110.

Therefore BB' passes through O and OB . OB'=OC². Thus the circle AA'B'B is orthogonal to the fundamental circle and also to the circle of inversion.

It follows that *if any nominal point A is changed by inversion with regard to a circle of the system into the point B, the nominal line AB is perpendicular to the nominal line with which the circle of inversion coincides.*

We shall now prove that it is " bisected " by that nominal line. Let the circle through A, A', B and B' meet the circle of inversion at M and the fundamental circle at U and V (Fig. 111). It is clear that U and V are inverse points with regard to the circle of inversion.

Then we have
$$\frac{BV}{AU}=\frac{CV}{CA}, \quad \frac{AV}{BU}=\frac{CV}{CB}.$$

$$\therefore \frac{AV}{AU} \cdot \frac{BV}{BU}=\frac{CV^2}{CA \cdot CB}=\frac{CV^2}{CM^2}=\left(\frac{MV}{MU}\right)^2.$$

$$\therefore \frac{AV}{AU}\bigg/\frac{MV}{MU}=\frac{MV}{MU}\bigg/\frac{BV}{BU}.$$

Thus the nominal length of AM is equal to the nominal length of BM.

Therefore we have the following result :

Inversion with regard to any circle of the system changes any point A *into a point* B, *such that the nominal line* AB *is perpendicular to and " bisected " by the nominal line with which the circle of inversion coincides.*

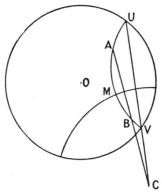

Fɪɢ. 111.

In other words,

Any nominal point takes up the position of its image in the nominal line coinciding with the circle of inversion.

We shall now examine what effect such an inversion has upon a nominal line.

Since a circle orthogonal to the fundamental circle inverts into a circle also orthogonal to the fundamental circle, any nominal line AB inverts into a nominal line *ab*, and the points U and V for AB invert into the points *u* and *v* for *ab* (Fig. 112).

When the circle of inversion and the nominal line AB intersect, the lines AB and *ab* meet on the circle of inversion. Denoting this point by M, it is easy to show that the nominal lengths of AM and BM are respectively equal to the nominal lengths of *a*M and *b*M. It follows that the nominal length of the segment AB is unaltered by inversion with regard to any circle of the system.

The same result can be obtained immediately from the corresponding figure when the nominal line AB does not cut the circle of inversion.

The preceding results may be summed up as follows :

Inversion with regard to any circle of the system has the same effect upon the nominal points and lines as reflection in the nominal line with which the circle of inversion coincides.

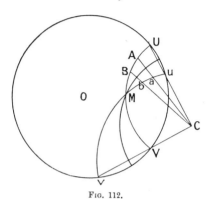

F<small>IG</small>. 112.

The argument of § 95 can now be applied to the geometry of this family of circles. Successive inversion with regard to two circles of the system corresponds to a displacement in two dimensions. We can always fix upon two circles of the system which will change a nominal segment AB into a new position, such that A coincides with P and AB lies along a given nominal line through P. The method of superposition is thus available in this geometry, and any theorems in the Hyperbolic Geometry involving congruence of linear segments can be at once " translated " into it.

§ 100. We notice that the definition of the nominal length of a segment fixes the *nominal unit of length*. We may take this unit segment on one of the diameters of the fundamental circle, since these lines are also nominal lines of the system. Let it be the segment OP (Fig. 113).

Then we must have

$$\log \left(\frac{OV}{OU} \Big/ \frac{PV}{PU} \right) = 1 ;$$

that is, $\log \left(\frac{PU}{PV} \right) = 1 ;$ that is, $\frac{PU}{PV} = e.$

Thus the point P divides the diameter in the ratio $e : 1$.

The unit segment is thus fixed for any position in the domain of the nominal points, since the segment OP can be " moved "

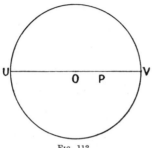

Fig. 113.

so that one of its ends coincides with any given nominal point.

A different expression for the nominal length, viz.,

$$k \log \left(\frac{AV}{AU} \middle/ \frac{BV}{BU}\right),$$

would simply mean an alteration in this unit, and taking logarithms to the base a instead of e would have the same effect.

§ 101. We are now able to establish some further theorems of Hyperbolic Geometry, using the metrical properties of this Nominal Geometry.

In the first place we can say that *Similar Triangles are impossible.* For if there were two nominal triangles with the same angles and not congruent, we could " move " the second so that its vertex would coincide with the corresponding angular point of the first, and its sides would lie along the same nominal lines as the sides of the first. We would thus obtain a "quadrilateral " whose angles would be together equal to four right angles ; and this is impossible, since we have seen that the sum of the angles in these nominal triangles is always less than two right angles.

We also see that parallel lines are asymptotic ; that is, they continually approach each other. This follows from the figure for nominal parallels and the definition of nominal length.

Further, it is obvious that as the point A moves away along the perpendicular MA to the line BC (Fig. 108), the angle of parallelism diminishes from $\frac{\pi}{2}$ to zero in the limit.

We shall now prove that the angle of parallelism, $\Pi(p)$, for the segment p, is given by

$$e^{-p} = \tan\left(\frac{\Pi(p)}{2}\right).$$

Consider a nominal line and a parallel to it through a point A.

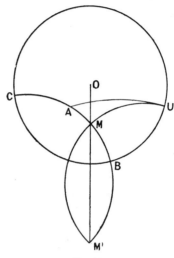

Fig. 114.

Let AM (Fig. 114) be the perpendicular to the given line MU and AU the parallel.

Let the figure be inverted from the point M′, the radius of inversion being the tangent from M′ to the fundamental circle.

Then we obtain a new figure (Fig. 115) in which the corresponding nominal lengths are the same, since the circle of inversion is a circle of the system. The lines AM and MU become straight lines through the centre of the fundamental circle, which is the inverse of the point M. Also, the circle AU becomes the circle au, touching the radius mu at u, and cutting ma at an angle $\Pi(p)$. These radii mu, mb are also nominal lines of the system.

Let the nominal length of AM be p.

Then we have
$$p = \log\left(\frac{AB}{AC} \Big/ \frac{MB}{MC}\right),$$

$$= \log\left(\frac{ab}{ac} \Big/ \frac{mb}{mc}\right) = \log\left(\frac{ab}{ac}\right).$$

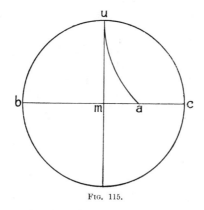

Fig. 115.

But from the geometry of Fig. 115, remembering that au cuts bc at the angle $\Pi(p)$, we have
$$ac = k\left\{1 - \tan\left(\frac{\pi}{4} - \frac{\Pi(p)}{2}\right)\right\},$$
$$ab = k\left\{1 + \tan\left(\frac{\pi}{4} - \frac{\Pi(p)}{2}\right)\right\},$$
where k is the radius of the fundamental circle.

Therefore
$$p = \log \cot\left(\frac{\Pi(p)}{2}\right)$$

and
$$e^{-p} = \tan\left(\frac{\Pi(p)}{2}\right).$$

Finally, in this geometry there will be three kinds of circles. There will be (i) the circle with its centre at a finite distance;

(ii) the limiting-curve, with its centre at infinity, or at a point where two parallels meet; and (iii) the equidistant-curve, with its centre at the ideal * point of intersection of two lines which have a common perpendicular.

All these curves are ordinary circles, but they do not belong to the system of circles orthogonal to the fundamental circle.

As to the first, the nominal lines through a point A are all cut orthogonally by the circles of the coaxal system with A and its inverse point A′ as Limiting Points. Thus these circles are the circles of this nominal geometry with A as their centre. They would be traced out by the end of a nominal segment through A, when it is reflected in the nominal lines of the pencil.

As to the second, the circles which touch the fundamental circle at a point U cut all the circles of the system which pass through U orthogonally. They are orthogonal to the pencil of parallel nominal lines meeting at infinity in U.

Thus these circles are the circles of this nominal geometry with their centre at the point at infinity common to a pencil of parallel nominal lines. They would be obtained when the reflection takes place in the lines of this pencil.

As to the third, all circles through U, V cut all the nominal lines perpendicular to the line AB (cf. Fig. 111) orthogonally. Thus these circles are the circles of the nominal geometry with their centre at the *ideal* point common to this pencil of not-intersecting nominal lines. They would be obtained when the reflection takes place in the lines of this pencil.

These three circles correspond to the ordinary circle, the Limiting-Curve and the Equidistant-Curve of the Hyperbolic Geometry.

§ 102. The Impossibility of proving Euclid's Parallel Postulate.

We can now assert that it is impossible for any inconsistency to exist in this Hyperbolic Geometry. If such a contradiction entered into this plane geometry, it would also occur in the interpretation of the result in the nominal geometry. Thus a contradiction would also be found in the Euclidean Geometry. We can therefore state that it is impossible that any logical

---

* Cf. § 37.

inconsistency could arise in the Hyperbolic Plane Geometry, provided no logical inconsistency can arise in the Euclidean Plane Geometry. It could still be argued that such a contradiction might be found in the Hyperbolic Solid Geometry. An answer to such an objection is forthcoming at once. The geometry of the system of circles, all orthogonal to a fixed circle, can be readily extended into a three-dimensional system. The *nominal points* are the points inside a fixed sphere, excluding the points on the surface of the sphere from their domain. The *nominal lines* are the circles through two nominal points cutting the fixed sphere orthogonally. The *nominal planes* are the spheres through three nominal points cutting the fixed sphere orthogonally. The ordinary plane enters as a particular case of these nominal planes, and so the plane geometry just discussed is a special case of a plane geometry of this system. With suitable definitions of nominal lengths, nominal parallels, etc., we have a solid geometry exactly analogous to the Hyperbolic Solid Geometry. It follows that no logical inconsistency could arise in the Hyperbolic Solid Geometry, since, if such did occur, it would also be found in the interpretation of the result in this Nominal Geometry, and therefore it would enter into the Euclidean Geometry.

By this result our argument is complete. However far the Hyperbolic Geometry is developed, no contradictory results could be obtained. This system is thus logically possible, and the axioms upon which it is founded are not contradictory. Hence it is impossible to prove Euclid's Parallel Postulate, since its proof would involve the denial of the Parallel Postulate of Bolyai and Lobatschewsky.

§ 103. The System of Circles cutting a Fixed Circle diametrally.

We shall now discuss the geometry of the system of circles cutting a fixed circle, centre O and radius k, diametrally. The points in which any circle of the system cuts the fixed circle are to be at the extremities of some diameter. We shall call the fixed circle, as before, the fundamental circle. The system of circles with which we are to deal has power $-k^2$ with respect to O.

Let A and B be any two points within the fundamental circle, and A′, B′ the points on OA and OB, such that OA . OA′ $= -k^2$ and OB . OB′ $= -k^2$.

Then A, A′, B, B′ are concyclic, and the circle which passes through them cuts the fundamental circle diametrally (Fig. 116). There is one, and only one, circle cutting the fundamental circle diametrally, which passes through two different points within the fundamental circle.

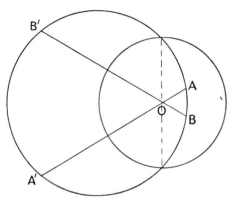

FIG. 116.

In discussing the properties of the family of circles cutting the fundamental circle diametrally, two methods can be followed. We can restrict the *nominal points* of the geometry to the points within and upon the fundamental circle. In this case we regard the points on the circumference at the extremities of a diameter as one and the same nominal point. In the other case, we extend the field of nominal points outside the circle to infinity, and the points on the circumference do not require special treatment.

These two alternatives, we shall see below, correspond to the two forms of the Elliptic Geometry, in one of which every straight line intersects every other straight line in one point, while in the other form, straight lines have always two points of intersection. *The nominal lines are the circles which cut the fundamental circle diametrally.*

When the field of nominal points is restricted to points within or upon the fundamental circle, *any two different nominal points* A, B *determine a nominal line* AB. Also *any two nominal lines must intersect at a single nominal point.*

When the domain of the nominal points is both within and without the fundamental circle, two nominal points do not always determine uniquely a nominal line. If the points A and B are upon the circumference of the circle at opposite ends of a diameter, a pencil of nominal lines passes through A and B. Again, if the points A and B lie on a line through O and OA . OB $= -k^2$, the same remark holds true.

Further, with the same choice of nominal points, every nominal line intersects every other nominal line in two nominal points.

The simplest way of discussing the properties of the system of circles with which we are dealing, is to make use of the fact that they can be obtained by projecting the great circles of a sphere stereographically from a point on the surface of the sphere on the tangent plane at the point diametrally opposite. If the centre of projection is a pole of the sphere, the equator projects into the fundamental circle, and one hemisphere projects into points outside this circle, the other into points within it. This projection is a conformal one, and the angle at which two great circles intersect is the same as the angle at which the corresponding circles in the plane cut each other.

We define the angle between two nominal lines as the angle between the circles with which they coincide.

We are now able to prove some of the theorems of this Nominal Geometry.

Since all the great circles perpendicular to a given great circle intersect at the poles of that circle, it follows that *all the nominal lines perpendicular to a given nominal line intersect at one point, in the case when the nominal points are within or upon the circumference of the fundamental circle ; in two points, when this field is both within and without.* (Cf. §§ 75-77.)

The point of intersection is spoken of as *a pole*, or *the pole*, of the line.

Again, in a right-angled spherical triangle ABC, in which C is the right angle, the angle at A $\gtreqless$ a right angle, according as the pole of AC lies on CB produced, or coincides with B, or lies between C and B.

When translated into the language of the nominal geometry, we have the theorem which corresponds to § 78 (1).

Further, the sum of the angles of a spherical triangle is greater than two right angles. It follows, since the projection is conformal, that *the sum of the angles of a nominal triangle in this geometry is greater than two right angles.* (Cf. § 78 (3).)

However, the metrical properties of this geometry cannot be treated so easily as were the corresponding properties in the geometry of the system of circles cutting the fundamental circle orthogonally. The same argument to a certain extent applies, but in the definition of nominal lengths the intersections with an imaginary circle have to be taken. It should be added that in the extension to solid geometry the system of spheres cutting a fixed sphere diametrally has to be employed.

The fuller discussion of this nominal geometry will not be undertaken here. If it is desired to establish the fact that no contradiction could appear in the Elliptic Geometry, however far that geometry were developed, there are simpler methods available than this one. The case of the Hyperbolic Geometry was discussed in detail, because it offered so elementary a demonstration of the impossibility of proving the Parallel Postulate of Euclid.

§ 104. We have already quoted some remarks of Bolyai's on the question of whether the Euclidean or the Non-Euclidean Geometry is the true geometry.* We shall conclude this presentation of our subject with two quotations from modern geometers on the same topic :

"What then," says Poincaré, "are we to think of the question : Is Euclidean Geometry true ? It has no meaning. We might as well ask if the metric system is true, and if the old weights and measures are false ; if Cartesian coordinates are true and polar coordinates false. One geometry cannot be more true than another ; it can only be more convenient. Now, Euclidean Geometry is, and will remain, the most convenient : first, because it is the simplest, and it is so not only because of our mental habits or because of the kind of intuition that we have of Euclidean space ; it is the simplest in itself, just as a polynomial of the first degree is simpler than a polynomial of the second degree ; secondly, because it sufficiently agrees with the properties of natural solids, those bodies which we compare and measure by means of our senses.†

---

* Cf. § 15.

† Poincaré, *La Science et l'Hypothèse.* English translation, p. 50.

And another French geometer writes :

" We are then entitled to say that the geometry which most closely resembles reality is the Euclidean Geometry, or at least one which differs very little from it ; . . . the error is too small to be apparent in the domain of our observations and with the aid of the instruments at our disposal.

" In a word, not only have we theoretically to adopt the Euclidean Geometry, but in addition this geometry is physically true." *

The matter can be put in another way. The question whether the Euclidean Geometry is the true geometry has no place in Geometry—the Pure Science. It has a place in Geometry—the Applied Science. The answer to the question —if an answer can be given—lies with the experimenter. But his reply is inconclusive. All that he can tell us is that the sum of the angles of any triangle that he has observed— however great the triangle may have been—is equal to two right angles, subject to the possible errors of observation. To say that it is exactly two right angles is beyond his power.

One interesting point must be mentioned in conclusion. In the Theory of Relativity, it is the Non-Euclidean Geometry of Bolyai and Lobatschewsky which, in some ways at least, is the more convenient. Gauss's jesting remark that he would be rather glad if the Euclidean Geometry were not the true geometry, because then we would have an absolute measure of length, finds an echo in the writings of those who in these last years have developed this new theory.†

---

* Hadamard, *Leçons de Géométrie élementaire*, vol. i. p. 286 (Paris, 1898).

† Cf. the letter to Taurinus, quoted on p. 24. Also the letter to Gerling given in Gauss, *Werke*, vol. viii. p. 169.

A similar remark is to be found in Lambert's *Theorie der Parallel-Linien*, § 80 ; see Engel u. Stäckel, *loc. cit.* p. 200.

** The correspondence between the nominal segment and rectilinear segment referred to in the definition of nominal length (§ 95) is indicated at the beginning of § 94. The definition thus gives the nominal length of the nominal segment AB as proportional to $\dfrac{AB}{OA \cdot OB}$. The discussion of this case will be found in full in the places indicated in the footnote on p. 156.

INDEX OF NAMES OF AUTHORS.

Numbers refer to pages.

SUBJECT INDEX.

Numbers refer to pages.

Absolute Science of Space, 27-29.
Absolute unit of length, 17, 25.
Absolute units as compared with
relative, 17, 90.
Angle of parallelism, 41, 50, 109.
Associated Right-angled Triangles
63-66.

Circle, Arc of, 118.
Area of, 124.
of infinite radius (see Limiting-
Curve), 80.
Three kinds of, in Hyperbolic
Geometry, 83, 170.
One kind of, in Elliptic Geo-
metry, 135.
Complementary segments, 51.
Hyperbolic functions of, 98-99.
Congruence, Axioms of, 2, 5.
of infinite areas, 17.
Consistency of the Non-Euclidean
Geometries, Ch. VIII.
Correspondence between right-
angled triangle and quadri-
lateral with three right angles,
59-63.
Courbe-limits (see Limiting-Curve),
80.

Defect of triangle, 54.
of polygon, 89.
Direction of parallelism, 45.
Direction-theory of parallels, 11.
Displacement equivalent to two
reflections or inversions in the
nominal geometry, 158, 159,
166.

Element of arc, in Elliptic Geometry, 152.
in Hyperbolic Geometry, Cartesian Coordinates, 112-114.
in Limiting-Curve Coordinates,
117-118.
in Polar Coordinates, 114-116.
Element of area, in Elliptic Geo-
metry, 152.
in Hyperbolic Geometry, in Cartesian Coordinates, 122-123.
in Limiting-Curve Coordi-
nates, 119-121.
in Polar Coordinates, 123-124.
Equidistant-Curve, 82.
Base-line of, 83.
Concave to base-line, 83.
Arc of, 118.
Equivalent polygons, 84.
Equivalent triangles, 85.
Theorems on, 85-88.
Euclid's unexpressed axioms, 3, 4.
Parallel Postulate or Parallel
Hypothesis, 2.
Postulates I.-II., 3.
Postulate III., 5, 74.
Excess of a triangle, 134.
Exterior angle, Theorem of (I. 16),
3, 130, 131.
in triangle with one angular
point at infinity, 48.

Geometry, Absolute, 29.
Astral, 22.
Elliptic, 39, 131.
Euclidean, 2.
Hyperbolic, 39.

A HISTORY

LOGARITHMIC SLIDE RULE

AND ALLIED INSTRUMENTS

BY

FLORIAN CAJORI, PH.D.
Professor of Mathematics, and Dean of the School of Engineering,
Colorado College

PREFACE

OF the machines for minimizing mental labor in computation, no device has been of greater general interest than the Slide Rule. Few instruments offer a more attractive field for historical study. Its development has reached into many directions and has attracted men of varied gifts. Among these are not only writers on arithmetic, carpenters, and excise officers, but also such practical engineers as Coggeshall, E. Thacher, Beauchamp Tower; such chemists as Wollaston and Regnault; such physicists as J. H. Lambert, Thomas Young, J. D. Everett; such advanced mathematicians as Segner, Perry, Mannheim, Mehmke, and the great Sir Isaac Newton.

And yet the history of this instrument has been neglected to such an extent that gross inaccuracies occur in standard publications, particularly in regard to its early history. Charles Hutton and De Morgan do not agree as to the inventor of the instrument. Hutton ascribes the invention to Edmund Wingate,[1] but fails to support his assertion by reference to, or quotation from, any of Wingate's publications. De Morgan denies the claims made for Wingate,[2] but had not seen

---

[1] Hutton's *Mathematical Tables*, London, 1811, *Introduction*, p. 36, also his *Philosophical and Mathematical Dictionary*, Art. " Gunter's Line."

[2] Article " Slide Rule " in the *Penny Cyclopaedia*, 1842, same article in the *English Cyclopædia*, Arts and Sciences.

all of Wingate's works; he claims the invention for William Oughtred, and his conclusion is affirmed in as recent publications as the *International Cyclopaedia,* New York, 1892, and the *Slide Rule Notes,* by H. C. Dunlop and C. S. Jackson, London, 1901. In the present monograph we aim to settle this question. It will be shown, moreover, that the invention of the "runner" and the suggestion of the possibility of utilizing the slide rule in the solution of numerical equations are of much earlier date than has been supposed by some writers. We shall also show that the device of inverting a logarithmic line is much older than is commonly believed. A fuller statement than is found elsewhere will be given here of the improvements in the slide rule made in England previous to the year 1800, and an effort will be made to determine more precisely how extensively this instrument was put to practical use at that early time. So far as space permits, we shall indicate the many-sided developments, in the design of slide rules, made during the last one hundred years. Slide rules have been adapted to almost every branch of the arts in which calculation is required. This fact becomes very evident, if one examines the list of slide rules, given near the end of this volume.

By reference to the "Bibliography of the Slide Rule" in the Alphabetical Index the reader will find the principal books which have been written on this instrument.

I have been assisted in the reading of the proofs by Mr. Albert Russell Ellingwood, a student in Colorado College. I extend to him my thanks for this help.

FLORIAN CAJORI.

SCHOOL OF ENGINEERING, COLORADO COLLEGE,
Colorado Springs, Colo., 1909.

CONTENTS

LIST OF ILLUSTRATIONS

HISTORY OF THE LOGARITHMIC SLIDE RULE

THE INVENTION OF LOGARITHMS AND OF THE LOGARITHMIC LINE OF NUMBERS

THE miraculous powers of modern computation are largely due to the invention of logarithms. We owe this to John Napier (1550–1617), Baron of Merchiston, in Scotland, who gave it to the world in 1614. It met with immediate appreciation both in England and on the European continent. And only a few years later, in 1620, was made a second invention which was a necessary prelude to the invention of the slide rule. In that year Edmund Gunter (1581–1626), professor of astronomy in Gresham College, London, designed the logarithmic "line of numbers," which is simply a straight line, with the digits 1, 2, 3, . . . , 10 arranged upon it from one extremity to the other, in such a way that the distance on the line from the end marked 1, to the figure 2, is to the distance from 1 to any other number, as the logarithm of 2 is to the logarithm of that other number. In other words, distances along the line were not taken proportional to the numbers on it, but to the logarithms of those numbers. Gunter mounted this line, together with other lines giving the logarithms of trigonometric functions, upon a ruler or scale, commonly called "Gunter's scale" (see Fig. 1), by means of which questions in navigation could be resolved with the aid of a pair of compasses. These compasses were used in adding or subtracting distances on the scale, by which, according to the properties of logarithms, products or quotients of numbers could be found. Gunter described his logarithmic "line of numbers" in his *Canon Triangulorum*, London, 1620, as well as in his *Description and Use of the Sector, Cross-Staff and other Instruments*, London, 1624.

GUNTER'S SCALE AND THE SLIDE RULE OFTEN
CONFOUNDED

In former years the invention of the slide rule was frequently, but erroneously, attributed to Gunter. Thus, E. Stone, in his *New Mathematical Dictionary*, London, 1726 and 1743, says in the article "Sliding Rules," "they are very ingeniously contrived and applied by Gunter, Partridge, Cogshall, Everard, Hunt, and others, who have written particular Treatises about their Use and Application." These very same words are found, according to De Morgan, in Harris' *Lexicon Technicum*, 1716.[1] In Charles Hutton's *Mathematical Dictionary*, 1815, we read "they are variously contrived and applied by different authors, particularly Gunter, Partridge, Hunt, Everard and Coggleshall." A similar statement is made in the eighth edition of the *Encyclopaedia Britannica*, 1860. Now, as we have seen, Gunter certainly constructed the first logarithmic line and scale. But this scale, as invented by Gunter, has no sliding parts and is, therefore, not a sliding rule. Confusion has prevailed as to the distinction between Gunter's line and the slide rule. Stone, in both editions of his *Dictionary* (1726, 1743), describes Gunter's line as follows: "It is only the Logarithms laid off upon straight Lines;

[1] In 1726 Stone evidently drew from a different source of information than in 1723, when he published in London Bion's *Construction and Principal Uses of Mathematical Instruments* and added descriptions of English instruments. In 1723 he speaks of both "Mr. Windgate" and "Mr. Oughtred," but in 1726 their names are omitted.

3

and its Use is for performing Operations of Arithmetick, by Means of a Pair of Compasses, or even without, by sliding two of these Lines of Numbers by each other." In another place (Art. "Sliding Rule") of his *Dictionary* he says: "Sliding Rules, or Scales, are Instruments to be used without Compasses, in Gauging, measuring, etc., having their Lines fitted so as to answer Proportions by Inspection; they are very ingeniously contrived and applied by Gunter, Partridge, Cogshall, Everard, Hunt and others. . . ." In the final article of the 1743 edition of the *Dictionary*, an article which, he says, is "to be added to the Head of Roots of Equations," he uses the terms "Gunter's Lines" and "Sliding Rule" interchangeably. Thus, he uses the name "Gunter's Lines" to apply to both instruments, but in one article he restricts the name "sliding rules" to instruments "used without compasses," though he still retains Gunter in the list of designers of sliding rules. Since both instruments went in those days often under the same name ("Gunter's Lines"), it is easy to see how the inventor of the Gunter's line proper (without sliding parts) passed also as the inventor of the slide rule. It is not unusual to find the slide rule described under the name of Gunter's line in much later publications. This was done, for instance, by *Appleton's Dictionary of . . . Engineering*, Vol. I., New York, in 1868.

Gunters Scale

Fig. 1.—Gunter's Scale.

From a drawing in Edmund Stone's edition of M. Bion's *Construction and Principal Uses of Mathematical Instruments*, London, 1723. Usually, Gunter's Scale was two feet long and had on it the following logarithmic lines: *S. R.* (sines of the rhumbs), *T. R.* (tangents of the rhumbs), *Numb.* (numbers), *Sines, V. Sine* (versed sine), *Tangents, Merid.* (meridian line), *E. P.* (equal parts).

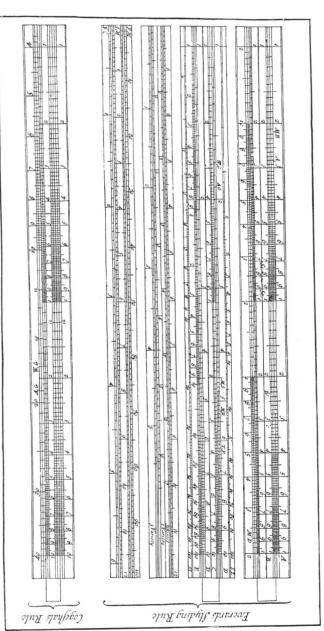

Fig. 2.—Everard's Slide Rule for Gauging.

Fig. 3.—Coggeshall's Slide Rule.

From a drawing in E. Stone's edition of M. Bion's *Construction and Principal Uses of Mathematical Instruments.* London, 1723.

CONFLICTING STATEMENTS ON THE INVENTION OF THE SLIDE RULE

De Morgan, in his article "Slide Rule" in the *Penny Cyclopaedia*, 1842, reprinted in the *English Cyclopaedia* (Arts and Sciences), ascribes the invention of the slide rule to William Oughtred (1574–1660), a famous English mathematician, and denies that Edmund Wingate (1593–1656) ever wrote on the slide rule. He repeats this assertion relating to Wingate in his biographical sketch of Wingate, inserted in the *Penny Cyclopaedia* and also in his work, entitled *Arithmetical Books from the Invention of Printing to the Present Time*, London, 1847, p. 42. It will soon appear that De Morgan is ill informed on this subject, although his criticism of a passage in Ward's *Lives of the Professors of Gresham College*, 1740, is well taken. Ward claims that Edmund Wingate introduced the slide rule into France in 1624. What he at that time really did introduce was Gunter's scale, as appears from the examination of his book, published in Paris in 1624 under the title, *L'usage de la régle de proportion en l'arithmétique et géométrie*. We shall see that Wingate invented the slide rule a few years later.

In his *Mathematical Tables*, Hutton expresses himself on Gunter's logarithmic lines as follows (p. 36): "In 1627 they were drawn by Wingate, on two separate rulers sliding against each other, to save the use of compasses in resolving proportions. They were also, in 1627, applied to concentric circles, by Oughtred." Hutton makes the same statement in his *Mathematical Dic-*

tionary, London, 1815, article "Gunter's Line," but nowhere gives his authority for it.   A. Favaro, in an article on the history of the slide rule which we shall have occasion to quote very often,[1] cites the following work of Wingate which De Morgan had not seen: *Of Natural and Artificial Arithmetic*, London, 1630.   R. Mehmke, in his article in the *Encyklopädie der Mathematischen Wissenschaften*, Vol. I, Leipzig, 1898–1904, p. 1054, simply refers to Favaro's paper.

[1] A. Favaro, in *Veneto Istituto Atti* (5) 5, 1878–79, p. 500, abbreviated in Favaro's *Leçons de statique graphique*, 2ième partie, *calcul graphique*, Paris, 1885, translated into French by P. Terrier.

DISENTANGLEMENT OF THE MAIN FACTS

None of the writers on the history of the slide rule has had the opportunity to examine all of Wingate's works bearing on Gunter's scale and the slide rule. This inaccessibility of original sources of information has led to statements that are incomplete and in some cases erroneous. But it so happens that now every one of the early books of Wingate has been examined by one authority or another who has been writing on the history of the slide rule. By collecting the findings of these authorities we are able to draw conclusions which, we believe, are final. Did Wingate invent the straight-edge slide rule? If so, when and where did he first publish his invention?

In some of the most recent books it is stated that Wingate published a description of the slide rule in France in a work bearing the title, *L'Usage de la régle de proportion en l'arithmétique et géométrie*, Paris, 1624. But they give no indication of having had the opportunity themselves to examine Wingate's text.[1] That Wingate published *on the slide rule* in 1624 is an error, writers such as De Morgan[2] and Benoit,[3] who had access to the 1624 publication noted above, and actually examined it, agree that Wingate in 1624 described Gunter's scale only.

English editions of this work of 1624 appeared in London

---

[1] Such statements are found in Maurice d'Ocagne, *Calcul simplifié*, 2e éd., Paris, 1905, p. 113, and in E. Hammer, *Der logarithmische Rechenschieber*, 4te Aufl., Stuttgart, 1908, p. 5.

[2] Art. "Slide Rule" in the *Penny Cyclopaedia*.

[3] *Régle à Calcul expliquée*, Paris, 1853, p. VI.

under the title, *The Use of the Rule of Proportion*, in 1626, 1628, 1645, 1658, 1683.[1] The interesting question arises, did the 1626 English edition describe the slide rule? There is no copy of this edition in the British Museum. De Morgan does not refer to it. But the aforementioned French writer on the slide rule, M. P.-M.-N. Benoit, does. Benoit asserts [2] that in the English translation (London, 1626) of Wingate's French work (Paris, 1624) there is explained the use of two logarithmically divided scales, made to slide against each other. But Benoit says nothing to indicate that he speaks from actual inspection of the 1626 edition. On the very same page where he refers to it, he is very careful to add foot-notes regarding the 1624 edition and some other rare books, and to state where copies of them can be found. But no foot-note or reference is given for the 1626 edition. We shall give reasons for our belief that Benoit is in error when he says that the 1626 edition contained an account of the slide rule. Our reasons are as follows:

In Allibone's *Dictionary of Authors*, it is stated that the Paris publication of 1624 came out "in English 1626, 1628, with additions 1645, with an appendix 1658." Hence it would appear that the 1626 edition had no additions or changes. More conclusive are the assertions of De Morgan,[3] and of a present official of the British Museum, both of whom saw the edition of 1645 and found nothing on the slide rule in it. If the 1645 edition is silent on this instrument, it is safe to assume that the 1626 edition is silent too.

---

[1] *Dictionary of National Biography*, Art. "Wingate, Edmund."

[2] *Bull. de la société d'encouragement pour l'industrie nationale* Vol. 52, 1853, p. 586. The historical part of this article is copied from Benoit's work *La régle à calcul expliquée*, Paris, 1853, p. VI.

[3] *Arithmetical Books*, p. 42.

Wingate published in 1626 in Paris a work, entitled, *Arithmétique logarithmique*, 1626. This has been examined by De Morgan[1] and Favaro,[2] and does not contain the slide rule.

The present writer secured a reader to examine the copies of Wingate's books that are in the British Museum. In the report of this examination, mention was made of a booklet to which none of the writers on the history of the slide rule had alluded, namely, Wingate's *Construction and Use of the Line of Proportion*, London, 1628. It contains the description of a "double scale," called a "line of proportion." Wingate says in the preface: "I have invented this tabular scale, or line of proportion . . . ." It looked as if this "line of proportion" might be a slide rule. To ascertain the exact facts, the present writer had a copy made and sent to him of the entire booklet and of the diagram in it. The perusal of this showed that the "line of proportion" is not a slide rule at all, but merely a tabular scale in which numbers are indicated by spaces on one side of a straight line, somewhat as millimeters are marked on a meter stick, while on the other side of the line there are spaces which indicate the mantissas of the common logarithms of those numbers. On this scale one can read off the logarithm of a given number, or ascertain the number from a given logarithm. The instrument has no sliding parts and is merely a scale which takes the place of a small table of logarithms.

The 1628 publication just mentioned indicates that Wingate was not inclined to rest satisfied with the mechanical devices for simplifying computation, known as Gunter's scale, but endeavored to invent new scales of

[1] Arts. "Tables" and "Wingate" in the *Penny Cyclopaedia.*
[2] *Veneto Istituto Atti* (5) 5, 1878–9, p. 500.

his own. And it appears that his next book, *Of Natural and Artificial Arithmetic*, London, 1630, actually contains the description of the slide rule. This work is not in the British Museum and we have not been able to procure a copy of it. But Favaro,[1] we take it, examined the book, as appears from the following passage in Favaro's article: " Wingate (1593–1656), who was instrumental, in a way, to make public a discovery of Gunter [2] and in making known logarithmic arithmetic in France,[3] especially for dispensing with the use of the compasses, arranged the logarithmical divisions on two rulers, which he made slide, one along the other, and he then developed with all particulars this proposal of his." [4]

If we examine the list of Wingate's publications, as given in Sidney Lee's *Dictionary of National Biography*, or in Allibone's *Dictionary of Authors*, we shall see that we have now considered every book published by Wingate on or before 1632, and we have found that the last is the only one which, on being *actually examined* by an authority, was seen to contain a description of the slide rule. The conclusion is, therefore, forced upon us, that the earliest publication in which Wingate wrote on the slide rule is the book, *Of Natural and Artificial Arithmetic*, London, 1630.

But the fact that Wingate did not write on the slide rule in 1624, 1626 or 1628, and that his earliest description of this instrument bears the date of 1630, does not lose him the priority of invention, for we shall see that his only competitor for this honor was Oughtred, an

---

[1] *Op. cit.*, p. 500.

[2] *Construction, description et usàge de la régle de proportion.* Paris, 1624.

[3] *Arithmétique logarithmique*, Paris, 1626.

[4] *Of Natural and Artificial Arithmetic*, London, 1630.

account of whose inventions was not published until 1632.

We proceed to show that Oughtred was an independent inventor of the rectilinear slide rule and the first one to propose the circular type. As De Morgan informs us,[1] Oughtred showed his notes and instruments to his pupil, William Forster, teacher of mathematics in London, who obtained his consent to translate and publish the description of the instruments, and the directions for using them. This was done in a work bearing the title *The Circles of Proportion and the Horizontal Instrument*, London, 1632. In 1633 followed an *Addition*, etc., with an appendix under the title *The Declaration of the Two Rulers for Calculation*. As already stated, Hutton says Oughtred applied logarithms to concentric circles as early as 1627, but Hutton does not give his authority. Benoit likewise mentions 1627, but gives no reference. De Morgan quotes the following interesting extract from Forster's dedication to Sir Kenelm Digby:

"Being in the time of the long vacation 1630, in the Country, at the house of the Reverend, and my most worthy friend and Teacher, Mr. William Oughtred (to whose instruction I owe both my initiation, and whole progresse in these Sciences), I upon occasion of speech told him of a Ruler of Numbers, Sines, and Tangents, which one had bespoken to be made (such as is usually called Mr. Gunter's Ruler) 6 feet long, to be used with a payre of beame-compasses. He answered that was a poore invention, and the performance very troublesome: But, said he, seeing you are taken with such mechanicall wayes of Instruments, I will show you what devises I have had by mee these many yeares. And first, hee brought to mee two Rulers of that sort, to be used by

---

[1] Art. "Slide Rule" in the *Penny Cyclopaedia* and in the *English Cyclopaedia* (Arts and Sciences).

applying one to the other, without any compasses: and after that he shewed mee those lines cast into a circle or Ring, with another moveable circle upon it. I seeing the great expeditenesse of both those wayes, but especially of the latter, wherein it farre excelleth any other Instrument which hath bin knowne; told him, I wondered that he could so many yeares conceale such usefull inventions, not onely from the world, but from my selfe, to whom in other parts and mysteries of Art he had bin so liberall. He answered, That the true way of Art is not by Instruments, but by Demonstration: and that it is a preposterous course of vulgar Teachers, to begin with Instruments and not with the Sciences, and so instead of Artists to make their Schollers only doers of tricks, and as it were Juglers: to the despite of Art, losse of precious time, and betraying of willing and industrious wits unto ignorance, and idlenesse. That the use of Instruments is indeed excellent, if a man be an Artist; but contemptible, being set and opposed to Art. And lastly, that he meant to commend to me the skill of Instruments, but first he would have me well instructed in the Sciences. He also showed me many notes, and Rules for the use of those circles, and of his Horizontall Instrument (which he had projected about 30 yeares before) the most part written in Latine. All which I obtained of him leave to translate into English, and make publique, for the use, and benefit of such as were studious, and lovers of these excellent Sciences."

The following quotation shows the connection between workers on the theory of logarithms and Oughtred:[1]

"Lord Napier, in 1614, publishing at Edinburgh his 'Mirifici logarithmorum canonis Descriptio' . . . , it presently fell into the hands of Mr. Briggs, then geometry reader of Gresham College in London, and that gentleman, forming a design to perfect Lord Napier's plan,

[1] *A New and General Biographical Dictionary . . . new edition in* **12** *vols.*, London, 1784; quoted in *Nature* Vol. 40, 1889, p. 458.

consulted Oughtred upon it, who probably wrote his
'Treatise of Trigonometry' about the same time, since
it is evidently formed upon the plan of Lord Napier's
'Canon.' In prosecuting the same subject, he invented,
not many years after, an instrument, called 'The Circles
of Proportion.' . . . All such questions in arithmetic,
geometry, astronomy, and navigation, as depended upon
simple and compound proportion, might be wrought by
it; and it was the first sliding rule that was projected for
those uses, as well as that of gauging."

It may be added that Oughtred cheerfully acknowl-
edges his indebtedness to Gunter for the invention of
the logarithmic line.

According to De Morgan,[1] Oughtred used in his circular rule two pointing radii which were attached to the
centre of one circle, on which a number of concentric
circles were drawn, each charged with a logarithmic
scale. "These pointers would either move around together, united by friction, or open and shut by the application of pressure: they were in fact a pair of compasses,
laid flat on the circle, with their pivot at its centre.
Calling these pointers antecedent and consequent, to
multiply A and B, the consequent arm must be brought
to point to 1, and the antecedent arm then made to point
to A. If the pointers be then moved together until the
consequent arm points to B, the antecedent arm will
point to the product of A and B." Thus, in Oughtred's
instrument the sliding parts were not circles, but the
pointers, pivoted at the centre. He appropriated two
of his concentric circles to the logarithms of sines.

De Morgan states that Oughtred gave his right in the
invention (as soon as it was settled that it be published)
to Elias Allen, a well-known instrument maker, near St.

---

[1] Art. "Slide Rule" in the *Penny Cyclopaedia.*

Clement's church, in the Strand; that in walking to and fro from this shop, he communicated his invention to one Richard Delamain, a mathematical teacher whom he used to assist in his studies. This Delamain not only tried to appropriate the invention to himself, but wrote a pamphlet of no small scurrility against Oughtred, which the latter answered in an *Apologeticall Epistle* fully as vituperative; which epistle was printed at the end of W. Forster's translation. De Morgan states further, that Forster's work was republished in 1660 by A. H. (Arthur Haughton, another pupil of Oughtred), with Oughtred's consent, but the dedication and epistle were omitted.

The conclusions which we have reached thus far may be summarized as follows: *Edmund Gunter invented a logarithmic line called "Gunter's line," but not the slide rule; the straight edge slide rule was first invented by Edmund Wingate and explained by him in several publications, the earliest of which appeared in 1630. Such a slide rule was also given to the world in 1632 by William Oughtred, in a work prepared for the press by William Forster. Oughtred was the first to design a circular slide rule.*

DEVELOPMENT DURING THE SECOND HALF OF THE SEVENTEENTH CENTURY

Hutton informs his readers that a Mr. Milburne of Yorkshire designed the spiral form of slide rule about 1650.[1] Favaro quotes other writers who make similar statements.[2] We have not been able to secure more detailed information relating to Milburne.

According to Wolf [3] a slide rule was put forth about the middle of the 17th century by Horner, in which the straight edge was replaced by several shorter rules, which folded upon each other. This device never became popular, perhaps because it could not be accurately constructed and manipulated.

Stone [4] declares that "Mr. Brown" projected Gunter's line "into a kind of spiral of 5, 10, or 20 Turns, more or less," and used "flat compasses, or an opening index." Stone in 1723 describes quite fully the spiral and the circular form of instrument,[5] but says nothing which would indicate that these forms had attained popularity in his day.

[1] *Hutton Math. Tables*, 1811, p. 36, and Art. "Gunter's Line," in his *Philos. & Math. Dic.*, London, 1815.

[2] Favaro *op. cit.* p. 501, with a reference to G. S. Klügel's *Mathematisches Wörterbuch*, I. Abtheilung, 3. Theil, Leipzig, 1808, p. 587, also to M. P.-M.-N. Benoit's *La règle à calcul expliquée*, Paris, 1853; p. VII; to Ernest Sedlaczek's *Ueber Visir- und Recheninstrumente*, Wien, 1856, p. 3.

[3] R. Wolf, *Geschichte der Astronomie*, München, 1877, p. 354.

[4] *Mathematical Instruments*, etc., London, 1723, p. 16.

[5] *Idem*, pp. 40, 41.

Perhaps the "Mr. Brown" referred to by Stone is the same as the one named by Pepys in his diary. Under the date of August 10, 1664, he says: "Abroad to find out one to engrave my tables upon my new sliding-rule with silver plates, it being so small that Brown, who made it, cannot get one to do it. So I got Cocker, the famous writing master, to do it, and I set an hour beside him to see him design it all, and strange it is to see him, with his natural eyes, to cut so small at his first designing it, and read it all over, without any missing, when, for my life, I could not, with my best skill, read one word or letter of it." To this entry Pepys adds, the next day: "Comes Cocker with my rule, which he hath engraved to admiration for goodness and smallness of work. It cost me 14s. the doing." Was Pepys' slide rule logarithmic? His diary leaves us in doubt.

More successful than Brown, Horner and Milburne, as a designer of slide rules, was Seth Partridge, whose instruments were constructed in London by Walter Haynes. Partridge describes himself as a surveyor, but his time was mostly occupied in teaching mathematics.[1] In 1657 he completed a small mathematical work entitled, *The Description and Use of an Instrument called the Double Scale of Proportion*, but it does not seem to have been published until 1672.[2] Other editions followed in 1685 and 1692, but were merely reprints of the first edition, except for the title-page. We have not seen any of these editions. De Morgan says that the rules of Partridge "were separate and made to keep together in sliding by the hand; perhaps Partridge considered the invention his own, in right of one ruler sliding between

[1] *Dictionary of National Biography.*
[2] In *Allibone's Dictionary* the date is given 1671.

two others kept together by bits of brass." To Partridge we owe, then, the invention of the slide. He did not mention in his book the names of earlier writers on the slide rule.

We have only meagre biographical data for Hunt and Everard, whose names are associated with the history of the slide rule.

W. Hunt's slide rule is referred to by Leadbetter [1] in the discussion of the area of a circular segment. "Upon Hunt's Sliding rule," he says, "there is a line of segments, by which the area of a segment of a circle may be found, as he [Hunt] shews in his *Mathematical Companion*, pages 168 and 169." Some idea of the adaptation of Hunt's instrument is obtained from the complete title of his book: "A Mathematical Companion, or the Description and Use of a New Sliding-Rule, by which many Useful and Necessary Questions in Arithmetick, Interest, Planometry, Astronomy, Fortification, Dialling, etc., may be speedily resolved, without the help of Pen or Compass, . . . 1697." Stone in 1743 mentions the following writers on gauging: Hunt, Everard, Doubarty, Shettleworth.

Leadbetter [2] says that the slide rule "was first invented by Thomas Everard, Esq., in the Year of our Lord 1683, and made by Isaac Carvar of Horsteydown, near London. . . . Everard was then Officer in the Excise at Southampton." Everard wrote a work on *Gauging*, which appears to have been widely used, as Leadbetter refers to the 9th and 10th edition of it. Everard's slide rule was described in this work, but I have not been able to secure a copy of the book. Leadbetter does not mention Wingate and Oughtred, and

[1] Leadbetter, *Royal Gauger*, 4th ed. London, 1755, p. 80.
[2] *The Royal Gauger*, 4th ed., London, 1755, p. 27.

erroneously attributes the invention of the instrument to Everard.

Thomas Everard must have had some standing as a mechanic and scientist, for we are informed by Leadbetter [1] that "in February 1696, when a Bill was depending in Parliament for laying a Duty on Malt, Mr. George Tollet, Mr. Phil. Shales, Mr. Tho. Jett, and Mr. Tho. Everard, in the Presence of several Members of the House of Commons, did make an experiment in order to find the true Content of the said Standard Bushel."

Everard's sliding rule was used mainly for gauging. In Edmund Stone's translation from the French of Bion's work on mathematical instruments,[2] this rule is described as follows:

"This instrument is commonly made of Box, exactly a Foot long, one Inch broad, and about six Tenths of an Inch thick. It consists of Three Parts, viz. A Rule, and two small Scales or Sliding-Pieces to Slide in it; one on one Side and the other on the other: So that when both the Sliding-Pieces are drawn out to their full Extent, the whole will be three Foot long." (See Fig. 2).

"On the first broad Face of this Instrument are four Lines of Numbers; the first Line of Numbers consists of two Radius's, and is numbered 1, 2, 3, 4, 5, 6, 7, 8, 9, 1, and then 2, 3, 4, 5, etc., to 10. On this Line are placed four Brass Center Pins, the first in the first Radius, at 2150.42, and the third likewise at the same Number taken in the second Radius, having MB set to them; signifying, that the aforesaid Number represents the Cubic Inches in a Malt Bushel: the second and fourth Center Pins are set at the Numbers 282 on each Radius;

[1] Leadbetter, *op. cit.*, p. 122.

[2] *The Construction and Principal Uses of Mathematical Instruments, transl. from the French of M. Bion . . . by Edmund Stone,* London, 1723, p. 22.

they have the letter A set to them, signifying that the aforesaid Number 282 is the Cubic Inches in an Ale-Gallon. . . . The second and third Lines of Numbers which are on the Sliding-Piece . . . are exactly the same with the first Line of Numbers: They are both, for Distinction, called B. The little black Dot, that is hard by the Division 7, on the first Radius, having Si set after it, is put directly over .707, which is the Side of a Square inscribed in a Circle, whose Diameter is unity. The black Dot hard by 9, after which is writ Se, is set directly over .886, which is the Side of a Square equal to the Area of a Circle, whose Diameter is Unity. The black Dot that is nigh W, is set directly over 231, which is the Number of Cubic Inches in a Wine Gallon. Lastly, the black Dot by C, is set directly over 3.14, which is the Circumference of a Circle, whose Diameter is Unity. The fourth Line on the first Face, is a broken Line of Numbers of two Radius's, numbered 2, 10, 9, 8, 7, 6, 5, 4, 3, 2, 1, 9, 8, 7, 6, 5, 4, 3, the Number 1 is set against MB on the first Radius. This Line of Numbers hath MD set to it, signifying Malt Depth.''

Here we have pointed out an important innovation, to which attention has not been called by writers on the history of the slide rule, namely, the inversion of a logarithmic line—an idea usually attributed to Pearson, who wrote about a century later. The difference between the inversion as made by Everard and that of Pearson is that the former inverted a fixed line, while the latter (for certain operations) inverted the slider.

The second broad face has a slider graduated with a line C of double radius and a line D of single radius. There is also a fixed line D with four gauge-points, and a line E of triple radius. These lines are brought into service in problems involving square or cube root. Finally, there are on this face two lines of segments for finding the ullage of a cask. If the axis of the cask is horizontal, the line marked SL (=segments lying) is used. When the axis is vertical, the line marked *SS* (=segments standing) is used.

None of the lines on the two narrow faces is logarithmic and there is no slider there.

A slide rule, designed for the measurement of timber, stonework, and vessels, bears the name of Henry Coggeshall. The name of this writer has been variously given as Coggeshall, Cogshall, and Coggleshall. His earliest slide rule was described by him in 1677 in a pamphlet entitled *Timber Measure by a Line of more Ease, Dispatch and Exactness than any other way now in use, by a Double Scale. . . ., London, 1677.* "He soon after improved the rule, and revised the little work in which the mode of using it was set forth, republishing it in 1682, with the heading *A Treatise of Measuring by a Two-foot Rule, which slides to a Foot.* A third, considerably modified edition, appeared in 1722. It was designated *The Art of Practical Measuring easily performed by a Two-foot Rule which slides to a Foot.*"[1] The instruments of Coggeshall seem to have met with great favor. A fourth edition of this last book, revised by John Ham, was brought out in 1729; a seventh edition in 1767. The Coggeshall slide rule was popular in England as late as the beginning of the 19th century, and was used in 1874 and even later. It has received various modifications in construction. In Stone's translation of Bion, p. 26, it is described thus: "This Rule is framed three Ways; for some have the two Rulers composing them sliding by one another, like Glaziers Rules; and sometimes there is a Groove made in one Side of a Two Foot Joint-Rule, in which a thin sliding Piece being put, the Lines put upon this Rule, are placed upon the said

[1] *Dictionary of National Biography.*

Side. And lastly, one Part sliding in a Groove made along the Middle of the other, the length of each of which is a Foot." (See Fig. 3.) The last form has a disposition of the logarithmic lines, which for over a century and a half enjoyed wide popularity. "Upon the sliding Side of the Rule are four Lines of Numbers; three are double Lines, or Lines of Numbers to two Radius's, and one a single broken Line of Numbers."

It is not generally known that Sir Isaac Newton ever referred to the Slide rule or discovered how it could be used in the solution of numerical equations. For that reason the following translation of an extract from a letter of Oldenburg to Leibnitz, dated June 24, 1675, may not be without interest: [1]

"Mr. Newton, with the help of logarithms graduated upon scales by placing them parallel at equal distances or with the help of concentric circles graduated in the same way, finds the roots of equations. Three rules suffice for cubics, four for biquadratics. In the arrangement of these rules, all the respective coefficients lie in the same straight line. From a point of which line, as far removed from the first rule as the graduated scales are from one another, in turn, a straight line is drawn over them, so as to agree with the conditions conforming with the nature of the equation; in one of

---

[1] *Isaaci Newtoni Opera* (Ed. S. Horsley) Tom. IV, Londini, 1782, p. 520: "Dominus Newtonus, beneficio logarithmorum graduatorum in scalis, παραλλήλως locandis ad distantias aequales, vel circulorum concentricorum eo modo graduatorum adminiculo, invenit radices aequationum. Tres regulae rem conficiunt pro cubicis, quatuor pro biquadraticis. In harum dispositione respectivae coefficientes omnes jacent in eâdem lineâ rectâ; à cujus puncto, tam remoto à primâ regulâ ac scalae graduatae sunt ab invicem, linea recta iis superextenditur, unà cum praescriptis conformibus genio aequationis; quâ in regularum unâ datur-potestas pura radicis quaesitae."

these rules is given the pure power of the required root."

If our interpretation of this passage is correct, it means, in case of a cubic equation $x^3 + ax^2 + bx = c$, that three rules, A, B, D, logarithmically graduated, must be placed parallel and equidistant. On rule A find the number equal to the *numerical* value $|a|$ of the coefficient a of the equation; on rule B find $|b|$, and on rule D find 1. Then arrange these three numbers on the rules in a straight line BD. Select the point E on this line, so that $BE = BA$. Through E pass a line ED' and turn it about E until the numbers at B', A' and D', with their proper algebraic signs attached, are seen to be together equal to the absolute term c. Then the number on the scale at D' is equal to $|x^3|$, and x can be found.

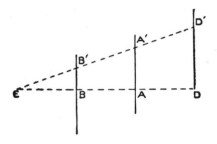

The reason for this is readily seen. Remembering that the length of that part of the rule B, which extends below the point B, is equal to log $|b|$, and assuming $BB' = $ log $|x|$, it follows that the part of the rule below B' is equal to log $|b|$ + log $|x|$ = log $|bx|$. Since $AA' = 2$ log $|x|$, it is seen that the part of the rule A, below the point A', is log $|ax^2|$. Similarly, DD' is equal to 3 log $|x|$ or log $|x^3|$, and $|x|$ can be found by moving the scale B

up until its lower end reaches B. The number at B' will then give the numerical value of the root.

The practical operation of this scheme would call for the use of a device to enable one to read corresponding numbers on scales that are not contiguous. Such a device would fulfil some of the functions of what is now called the "runner." We must therefore look upon Newton as the first to have thought of such an attachment to the slide rule. Sixty-eight years later, Newton's mode of solving equations mechanically is explained more fully and with some restrictions, rendering the process more practical, by E. Stone in the second edition of his *Dictionary* (1743).

De Morgan says that slide rules were little used and little known till the end of the 17th century. He bases this conclusion on the fact that "Leybourn, himself a fancier of instruments, and an improver (as he supposed) of the sector, has 30 folio pages of what he calls instrumental arithmetic in his 'Cursus Mathematicus' (1690), but not one word of any sliding-rule, though he puts fixed lines of squares and cubes against his line of numbers in his version of Gunter's scale."[1]

On the European continent such an instrument was hardly known to exist. The only German writer to be mentioned is Biler, who in 1696 brought out a publication under the title: *Descriptio instrumenti mathematici universalis, quo mediante omnes proportiones sine circino atque calculo methodo facillima inveniuntur.*[2] He called his instrument the *instrumentum mathematicum universale*. The instrument is semicircular in form and differs from that of Oughtred also in dispensing with the sliding

[1] Art. "Slide Rule" in the *Penny Cyclopaedia*.
[2] See Johann Bernoulli III., in his article "Logarithmiques" in the *Encyclopédie méthodique* (*mathématiques*).

indices and using instead the sliding concentric semi-circles.[1] Biler does not state the source whence he obtained his idea of the instrument. A few years later (1699), Michael Scheffelt brought out in Ulm a book, describing an instrument called by him *pes mechanicus*, which was not a slide rule, but employed logarithmic lines of numbers, together with a pair of compasses, as in Gunter's scale.

While in France, Gunter's line was made known by Edmund Wingate as early as 1324, and was again described by Henrion in a work, *Logocanon ou règle proportionnelle* (Paris, 1626), we have not been able to secure evidence that would show familiarity with the slide rule before about 1700.

---

[1] *Favaro, op. cit.,* p. 502; Leupold, *Theatrum Arithmetico-Geometricum,* Lipsiae, 1727, p. 77.

[2] *Pes mechanicus artificialis d. i. neu erfundener Maassstab, mi welchem alle Proportionen der ganzen Mathematik ohne mühsames Rechnen u. s. w. können gefunden werden. Ulm,* 1699.

DEVELOPMENT IN ENGLAND DURING THE
EIGHTEENTH CENTURY

We have seen that in 1726 E. Stone inserted an article of a dozen lines in his *New Mathematical Dictionary* on the slide rule. That this instrument came to be used more extensively in the eighteenth century appears also from the attention given to it by Robert Shirtcliffe in his book *Theory and Practice of Gauging*, London, 1740. On page 27 he says: "Since, as we observed before, the Practice of Gauging almost entirely depends on the Knowledge of the Sliding Rule, it must be of great Importance to the Gentlemen of the Excise to be acquainted, not only with the Method of Operation thereon, but the Reason thereof." He gives drawings of slide rules and devotes twenty-eight pages to explanations of them. The second edition of Stone's *Dictionary* gives evidence of wider interest in this instrument. In the article at the end of the book, to which we referred on p. 4, he speaks of the solution of numerical equations and remarks: "I shall only mention a way of Sir Isaac Newton's of finding the Roots of Numerical Equations by means of Gunter's Lines sliding by one another." We have already explained Newton's scheme. In Stone's description, all coefficients of the equation $x^n + ax^{n-1} + \ldots + mx = n$ are assumed to be positive; the logarithmic lines are not graduated alike, and the moveable straight line determining the positions for x^n, ax^{n-1}, $\ldots$ mx does not turn about a fixed point, but moves parallel to itself. The function of a "runner" becomes more con-

spicuous here. As Stone's *Dictionary* of 1743 is not
generally accessible, it may be worth while to quote
here in full the part of the article which relates to the
use of the slide rule:

"Take as many Gunter's Lines, (upon narrow Rules)
all of the same Length, sliding in Dove-tail Cavities,
made in a broad oblong Piece of Wood, or Metal, as the
Equation whose Roots you want the Dimensions of,
having a Slider carrying a Thread or Hair backward or
forwards at right Angles over all these Lines, and let
these Gunter's consist of two single ones, and a double,
triple, quadruple, etc., one fitted to them; that is, let
there be a fixed single one a top, and the first sliding
one next that, let be a single one, equal to it, each Number from 1 to 10.   Let the second sliding one be a double
Line of Numbers, number'd 1, 2, 3, 4, 5, 6, 7, 8, 9, to
10, in the Middle, and from 1 in the Middle to 1, 2, 3,
etc., to 10, at the End.   Let the third sliding one be a
triple Line of Numbers, numbered 1, 2, 3, 4, 5, 6, 7,
8, 9, 1, and again 2, 3, 4, etc., to 10, and again 2, 3,
4, etc., to 100 at the End.   The Distance from 1 to 1,
1 to 10 and 10 to 100, being the same; let the fourth
sliding one be numbered 1, 2, 3, 4, 5, 6, 7, 8, 9, 1; and
again 2, 3, 4, etc., to 10; and again 2, 3, 4, etc., to 100;
and again 2, 3, 4, etc., 1000.   The distance from 1 to 1,
1 to 10, 10 to 100, and 100 to 1000, being the same,
and so on.

"This being done, take the Coefficient prefixed to
the single Value of the unknown Quantity upon the
fixed single Line of Numbers; the Coefficient of the
Square of the unknown Quantity, upon the double Line
of Numbers; the Coefficient of the Cube of the unknown
Quantity, upon the triple Line of Numbers; the Coefficient of the Biquadrate of the unknown Quantity, upon
the Quadruple Line of Numbers, and so on. And the
Coefficient of the first or highest Term (being always
Unity) take upon that Line of Numbers expressed by
its Dimension, that is, if a square, upon the double
Line; a Cube, upon the triple Line, etc. I say, when

this is done, slide all these Lines of Numbers so, that these Coefficients be all in a right Line directly over one another, and keeping the Rulers in this Situation, slide the Thread or Hair in such manner, that the Sum of all the Numbers upon the fixed single Line, the double Line, the triple Line, etc., which the Thread or Hair cuts, be equal to the Known Term of the Equation, which may be readily enough done with a little practice; and then the number under the Thread upon that Line of Numbers of the same name with the highest Power of the unknown Quantity of the Equation, will be the pure Power of the unknown Quantity, whose Root may be had by bringing Unity on the single Sliding-Line directly over Unity upon this Line. After this, if you divide the Equation by this Root, you will have another, one Dimension less; and thus you may proceed to find a Root of this last Equation; which done, if it be divided by this last Root, you will get an Equation two Dimensions less, and by a Repetition of the Operation you will get a third Root, and so a fourth, fifth, etc., if the given Equation has so many, and if any of the intermediate Terms are wanting, the Gunter's express'd by the Dimensions of those Terms, must be omitted.

"But this method only gives the Roots of Equations the Signs of all the terms whereof, except the known one, are Affirmative; that is, of such that have all Negative Roots, but one, which last, the said Method finds. Therefore when an Equation is given, to find its Roots after this manner, whose Signs have other dispositions, it must be first changed into another Equation, whose Signs are all Affirmative; but that of the known Term, which may be done by putting some unknown Quantity y Plus or Minus, some given Number or Fraction, for the Value of the unknown Quantity x in the proposed Equation.[1]

"*Note*, instead of streight Parallel Sliding Rules, you

---

[1] The transformation of equations herein referred to is more fully discussed by Lagrange in Note XII of his Work, entitled *De la résolution des équations numériques de tous les degrés*, the first edition of which appeared in Paris in the year VI (1798).

Fig. 4.—Everard's Slide

Taken from C. Leadbetter

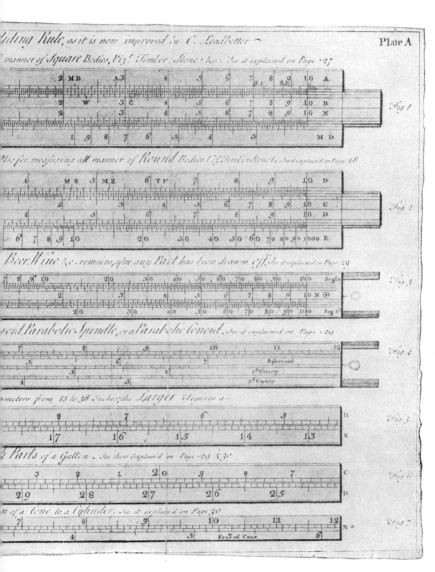

Plate A

Fig. 1

Fig. 2

Fig. 3

Fig. 4

Fig. 5

Fig. 6

Fig. 7

ODIFIED BY C. LEADBETTER.

4th edition, London, 1755.

may have so many Gunter's Lines graduated upon Concentrik Circles, each moving under one another, by which Contrivance, you will have as large Divisions for your Logarithm within the Compass of one Foot, as you have upon a streight Ruler of more than three Feet in length. Although perhaps by these Sliding-Rules, you cannot get all the Signs of the Roots exactly, for want of sufficient Subdivisions of the Gunter's Lines, yet if we can get two or three of the first Figures, it will be of good use to find the Roots by Approximation."

The reason for the process described in this passage is readily comprehended. No doubt the necessity of transforming a given equation into a new one, which has all the coefficients of the unknown quantity positive, operated against the general adoption of the process. We have no evidence that slide rules for this special application were ever constructed, or that the real roots of equations were actually determined in this way.

The slide rules which were used most at this time were those of Coggeshall and Everard. Various little modifications in the design and construction of these rules were made from time to time. Thus the instrument described in Coggeshall's *Art of Practical Measuring* of 1722 (third edition) indicates some alterations of Coggeshall's rule described earlier. There are lines on both sides of the flat faces. The new arrangement was probably due to John Warner, a London dealer in instruments; for Coggeshall says, that Warner added "a curious Scheme of both Sides of the Rule, and of the Scale." On one face are two identical logarithmic lines, each with two radii 1–10, 2–10. On the other flat face one line has a double radius like the lines just mentioned, while the second line has a single radius 1–10 and is called the "square line" or the "Girt line." Each face carries, in addition, two lines indicating feet and inches, with decimal subdivisions thereof. On page 50 he speaks also of a logarithmic "cube line" which may be added to the rule.

The 1722 edition of Coggeshall's book mentions Thomas Wright, "mathematical instrument maker to his Royal Highness, the Prince of Wales," as selling slide rules in Fleet Street, London.

Charles Leadbetter [1] made alterations in Everard's rule. He describes a slide rule as "an Improvement on Everard's mentioned by me in the 9th and 10 editions of *Everard's Gauging.*" Like Everard, Leadbetter was a government officer, having "had the Credit of an Employment under the Honourable the Commissioners of his Majesty's Royal Revenue of Excise." Leadbetter gives a plate (see Fig. 4) with "a view of the several lines and gauge-points upon Everard's Sliding Rule, as it is now improved by C. Leadbetter." The improvements did not involve radical changes. The lines *A, B, C, D, E, MD, SL, SS* are the same as in the older Everard rule. But the lines *SL* and *SS* are no longer on a broader face; they are now on one of the narrow faces. Between them is a third slider, narrower than the other two sliders. The older Everard rule has only two sliders. This new slider carries a line of numbers of double radius, marked *N*. Another innovation are lines of inches and other lines, placed upon the back sides of the three sliders. For ullaging, Shirtcliffe, in his *Theory and Practice of Gauging* (London, 1740), suggests a new line *SR*, and remarks at the end of his book that persons desiring such a rule may have it "made by the ingenious mathematical instrument makers, Mr. John Coggs and Mr. William Wyeth, near St. Dunstan's Church in

---

[1] *Royal Gauger*, 4th ed., London, 1755, p. 27.

Fleetstreet," London. We give one example of the use of the Everard rule: To find the number of bushels of malt in an enclosed space of the shape of a parallelopipedon, set the length of the enclosure on B to the breadth on MD, then against the height on A is the content in bushels on B. In other words, this solves the expression $lbh \div 2150.42$.

Another modification of Everard's rule was made by a Mr. J. Vero, and is referred to by Leadbetter in the following passage: [1] "Mr. Vero, sometime a collector of the Excise, made an Alteration in Everard's Sliding Rule, so that the whole Length of one Foot contained but one single Radius of the Line of Numbers, and both Sliders do work together on one Side of the Rule in every operation; by which contrivance the Divisions in this Rule are twice as large as on those first made by Mr. Everard." Mr. Vero was the author of a work entitled *Excise and Malt-Examiners' Assistant, useful also for Supervisors and Officers*.[2]

As to the accuracy of computations with the slide rule, there exists diversity of opinion among men of that time. John Ward[3] prefers to gauge a vessel "by the Pen only, viz., without the help of those Lines of Numbers upon sliding Rules, so much Applauded, and but too much Practised, which at best do but help to guess at the Truth, and may justly be called an Idle,

[1] Leadbetter *op. cit.*, p. 29. In Hawney's *Complete Measurer*, Baltimore, 1813, p. 247, a slide rule answering this description is given as "invented by Mr. Verie, collector of the excise," this rule being "that which is most used in the excise." The first edition of Hawney's book appeared in London in 1717. Are Vero and Verie the same person?

[2] Leadbetter, *op. cit.*, p. 44.

[3] *The Young Mathematician's Guide . . ., with an Appendix on Practical Gauging*, London, 1707, p. 427.

Ignorant Way of doing Business, if compared with that of the Pen." Later he explains [1] that he means "only Pocket Rules, viz., such as are of Nine Inches or a Foot Long. . . . But when the rules are made Two, or Three Foot long (I had one of Six Foot) then they may be of some Use, especially in Small Numbers. . . . I must not omit to Recommend a Five Foot Rule, Composed of Six Parts or Legs (viz., Ten Inches each Part) with Brass Joynts, put together with Steel Screws (which I Contrived and Made many Years ago) the Last Leg (viz., one of the Extream Legs) having a Sliding Part put to it . . . very Accurately made by Mr. John Rowley" of Fleet Street, London. A more favorable judgment than that of John Ward was passed by Leadbetter who assures us that computations could be made "as near as is ever required in Practice in the Excise." [2] John Farey, an English engineer, wrote in 1827 [3] that the early slide rules were crudely and inaccurately constructed, but that since 1775 Watt and Boulton in their shops, located at Soho, near Birmingham, used a slide rule of higher type, designed especially for engineers. For their computations in the design of steam engines and other machinery, James Watt himself is reported to have used this instrument. Who the manufacturer of these so-called "Soho rules" was is uncertain, but it has been surmised that it was the work of William Jones (1775–1852), a very skilled mechanic of the time.[4]

[1] *The Young Mathematician's Guide* . . . , *with an Appendix on Practical Gauging*, London, 1707, pp. 450, 451.

[2] Leadbetter, *op. cit.*, p. V.

[3] John Farey, *Treatise on the Steam Engine*, London, 1827, Chap. VII, pp. 531 and 536, referred to in *Zeitsch. f. Math. u. Phys.*, Bd. 48, 1903, p. 134.

[4] *Dingler's Polytech. Journal*, Vol. 32 (1829) p. 455, quoted in *Zeitschr. f. Math. und Phys.*, Vol. 48, 1903, p. 317, 318.

To be noted is a treatise on the slide rule, by Flower, which appeared in London in 1768. Another name, associated with the history of Gunter's scale and the slide rule, is John Robertson (1712–1776), who was at one time master of the Royal Mathematical School at Christ's Hospital, later Headmaster of the Royal Academy at Portsmouth and finally Librarian of the Royal Society of London. In 1775 he published in London a *Treatise on Mathematical Instruments.*[1] He modified Gunter's scale, for the purposes of navigation, in such a way as to practically make a slide rule out of it. An account thereof was published after his death by his friend, William Mountaine, in a booklet bearing the title *A Description of the Lines drawn on Gunter's Scale, as improved by Mr. John Robertson,* London, 1778. He was not the first, however, to advance this idea. In 1723 E. Stone [2] says that the lines on Gunter's scale "are also put upon rulers to slide by each other, and are therefore called Sliding Gunters."

Robertson's improved Gunters were mechanically executed under his own inspection by Messrs. Nairne and Blunt, mathematical instrument makers in Cornhill, London. The use of compasses was avoided "by having a proper sliding scale." "If, by choice, . . . any Person wishes to use Compasses, as on the common Gunter, the same may be done here, . . . but it should be observed, that the Compasses have very fine Points, and even then, with the greatest Care, they are apt to indent, and otherwise deface the Sub-divisions." [3] Like Stone, Mountaine called the new instrument the "sliding

---

[1] Favaro, *op. cit.,* p. 504.

[2] *Construction and Prin. Uses of Math'l. Instr's.,* London, 1723, p. 42.

[3] *W. Mountaine, op. cit.,* p. 3.

Gunter," to distinguish it from the "common Gunter."

A feature of great interest in Robertson's rule is the use of an "index," now usually called a "runner." It will be remembered that the use of a runner was suggested by Newton and Stone, but here we see it for the first time actually constructed. The rule was 30 in. long and 2 in. broad, and contained natural numbers on one face, logarithmic scales on the other. There were twelve logarithmic lines on one face, 9 of them fixed and three sliding together, as follows: The fixed lines 1, 2, 3, 4 were, respectively, lines of sine rhumbs, tangent rhumbs, versed sines, sines; the sliding lines 5, 6, 7 were lines of sines, numbers, tangents; the fixed lines 8, 9, 10, 11, 12 were lines of tangents, numbers, meridian degrees to 50, meridian degrees 50 to 74, degrees of longitude.[1] "Along this Face an Index or thin Piece of Brass, about an inch broad, is contrived to slide, which going across the Edge of the Scale at right Angles thereto, will shew on the several Lines the Divisions which are opposite to one another; although the Lines are not contiguous." Here is the runner, usually supposed to be a 19th century invention, in practical operation at a much earlier period. The following details of construction may be of interest:[1]

"The Apparatus at the Right-hand consists of a Brass Box and two Screws; the Slider passes freely through the Box when the perpendicular Screw is eased, and may be readily set by Hand to the Terms given; yet to be more accurate, and to keep the Slider in its true Position, move the perpendicular Screw, which, by a Sub-spring will fix the Slider in the Box, and then by the

[1] Mountaine *op. cit.*, p. 3.

Motion of the Horizontal Screw, the greatest Degree of Accuracy possible may be obtained."

This complicated slide rule was never used extensively, and Gunter's scale, with compasses, continued to be the favorite instrument on shipboard.

Allusions have been made to the theory of gauge-points, the idea of the inversion of a logarithmic line and the invention of the runner. This has been in connection with rectilinear slide rules. Thus far, we have said nothing concerning curvilinear slide rules during the eighteenth century. Stone, in 1723, describes both the circular and spiral forms.[1] That the circular type was actually manufactured about this time is evident from the examination of a book by Benjamin Scott, entitled, *The Description and Use of an Universal and Perpetual Mathematical Instrument*, London, 1733. Scott was an instrument maker in the Strand (London); he "Makes and Sells all Sorts of Mathematical Instruments in Silver, Brass, Ivory, and Wood, . . . all Sorts of Sliding-Rules, Parallel-Rules, best Black-Lead Pencils." His "universal and perpetual instrument" was a circular slide rule, over 18 inches in diameter and consisting of 20 circles. "In the first circle is graduated the Line of Numbers;" it is 58.43 inches in circumference. "By this Line is performed Multiplication, Division, the Rule of Proportion, and Extraction of Roots." Everard's sliding rules, says Scott, "fall infinitely short of the Line of Numbers in this Instrument, because of its great Length." Scott's instrument resembles closely Oughtred's design, but Scott mentions no forerunners in this work.

---

[1] Stone's ed. of Bion's *Mathematical Instruments*, London, 1723, pp. 40, 41.

A few years later we encounter a designer and maker of spiral slide rules, in the person of George Adams, the manufacturer of mechanical instruments for King George III. Adams designed spiral rules in 1748.[1] He engraved upon a brass plate, 12 inches in diameter, ten spiral windings. No statement has been handed down as to Adam's indebtedness to earlier workers in his field.

We come now to an English scientist who has given more systematic, painstaking and thoroughgoing study to the various forms that slide rules may take, than has any other worker of the eighteenth century. His suggestions met with no response in his day, but the ideas which he advanced are embodied in many instruments designed during the nineteenth century. We refer to William Nicholson (1753–1815), well known as the editor of *Nicholson's Journal*. He prepared an article,[2] in which different types of rules are described and the important problem is taken up, to increase the accuracy of the slide rule without increasing the dimensions of the instrument. According to his first design, a long logarithmic line was to be broken up into sections of convenient length and these placed parallel to each other on the face of the rule. Nicholson took ten such parallel lines, equivalent to a double line of numbers upwards to 20 feet in length. In place of a slider he used a beam compass, of the shape of the capital E, the middle cross piece of which was movable. With the aid of this compass it is possible to operate with these ten parallel lines and secure results of the accuracy of those gotten from a single line of twenty times the length.

Another rule was designed by Nicholson, "equivalent to that of $28\frac{1}{2}$ in. in length, published by the late Mr.

[1] *Nicholson's Journal*, Vol. I, 1797, p. 375.
[2] *Philosophical Transactions* (London), 1787, Pt. II, p. 246–252

Robertson. It is, however, but $\frac{1}{4}$ of the length and contains only $\frac{1}{4}$ of the quantity of division." In the slider GH, Fig. 5, "is a movable piece AB, across which a fine line is drawn; and there are also lines CD, EF, drawn across the slider, at a distance from each other equal to the length of the rule. The line CD or EF is to be placed at the consequent, and the line in the piece AB at the antecedent; then, if the piece AB be placed at any other antecedent, the same line CD or EF will indicate its consequent in the same ratio taken the same way; that is, if the antecedent and the consequent lie on the same side of the slider, all other antecedents and consequents in that ratio will lie in the same manner, and the contrary if they do not, etc. But if the consequent line fall without the rule, the other fixed line on the slider will show the consequent; but on the contrary side of the slider to that where it would else have been seen by means of the first consequent line."

The preference is given by Nicholson to the type consisting of concentric circles. (See Fig. 6.) Nicholson was not aware that Benjamin Scott had described an instrument of this kind as early as 1733, nor did he know at that time of the spiral instrument of George Adams and of the earlier work of Biler and Clairaut on the Continent. Later Nicholson learned that he had been anticipated by Adams and Clairaut,[1] but the circular slide rules of Oughtred, Biler and Scott were apparently never brought to his knowledge.

Nicholson's very remarkable improvements received very little attention. We have not been able to learn that any of his rules were actually constructed and sold. In 1797 he wrote an article on "A method of dis-

---

[1] *Nicholson's Journal* Vol. V., p. 40.

FIG. 5.—ONE OF NICHOLSON'S SLIDE RULES OF 1787.

From the *Philosophical Transactions* (London), Vol. 77 (1787), p. 246.   To solve $m : n = p : x$, put CD or EF
at n and the runner AB at m.   Then, by moving the slide, bring AB to p, and CD or EF gives x.
Notice that p and x lie on the same side or on opposite sides of the slide, according as m and n lie on
the same side or on opposite sides of the slide.

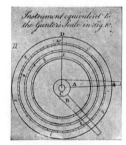

FIG. 6.—NICHOLSON'S CIRCULAR
SLIDE RULE OF 1787.

From the *Philosophical Transactions*
(London), Vol. 77 (1787), p. 246.
To solve $m : n = p : x$, place one leg
at m, the other at n, and fix them
to that angle.   Then move first leg
to p, and the second leg indicates x.

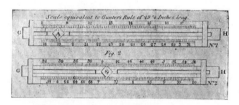

FIG. 7.—ONE OF NICHOLSON'S SLIDE RULES OF 1797.

From Nicholson's *Journal of Natural Philosophy, Chemistry, and
the Arts*, London, Vol. I (1797), p. 372.   No. 1 is the upper
side of the instrument, No. 2 is the under side.   By spreading the logarithmic line over both sides, the rule could be
made shorter without sacrifice of accuracy.   To solve $m : n =
p : x$, put CD or EF at n and AB at m.   Then move the slide
until AB is at p; CD or EF indicates x.   The relative position
of p and x is the same as the relative position of m and n.

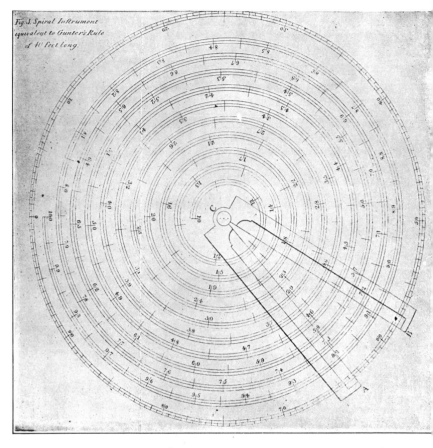

FIG. 8.—NICHOLSON'S SPIRAL SLIDE RULE OF 1797.

From Nicholson's *Journal,* London, Vol. I (1797), p. 372. To solve $m : n = p : x$ move one thread to m, the other to n, and fix them to that angle. Then move the first thread to p, and the second thread indicates x.

posing Gunter's line of numbers, by which the divisions are enlarged and other advantages obtained," [1] in which he remarked that ten years ago he had communicated to the Royal Society a method of extending the range of the rule which he "still considers less generally known than its utility may perhaps claim." By a yet different disposition of Gunter's lines he now gets a slide rule "equivalent to that of $29\frac{1}{2}$ lines in length, published by the late Mr. Robertson. It is, however, but $\frac{1}{8}$ the part of the length and contains only $\frac{1}{4}$ of the quantity of division." (See Fig. 7.)

"The Sketch No. 1 represents one face or side of the instrument, and No. 2 represents the opposite face. Each contains one fourth part of the lines of numbers. When it is used, the slider must be set so that the line on the piece AB may be placed at the antecedent, and one of the end marks CD, or EF, may be opposite the consequent. After this adjustment of the slider, the whole may be moved at pleasure, till the piece AB is set at any other required antecedent; and then the same line CD, or EF, as before, will indicate the consequent at the same distance or position as before. But if the consequent mark of the slider should fall without the rule, the other line will indicate the required consequent upon the rule, though at the distance of one line on the rule farther off in position than the other consequent mark would else have shown it."

Fig. 8. shows a spiral slide rule, designed by Nicholson in 1797.

The English astronomer, William Pearson (1767–1847) of Lincoln, made the suggestion that the tongue of the slide rule be inserted wrong side foremost, for certain

[1] *Nicholson's Journal*, Vol. I., 1802, p. 372–5, reprinted from issue of 1797.

computations.[1] This feature was not altogether novel. Logarithmic lines on the fixed part of the rule had been inverted long before this in the Everard rules, described by Stone, Leadbetter, and Shirtcliffe. The new feature lay in showing that the slider could be used when inverted, as well as in its ordinary position, and that this inversion is particularly convenient in computing reciprocal proportion and furnishes "a short and easy method of multiplying, dividing, . . . squaring and extracting the square root, at one position of the inverted slider, whereby the eye is directed to only one point of view for the result, after the slider is fixed." It accomplished this without the additional complexity of a new line D, found at that time on some rules for rootextraction. Later, some of the English rules had one of the two scales upon the slider inverted, a suggestion said to have been first made by William Hyde Wollaston,[2] while the Frenchman, A. Beghin placed an inverted scale as a third scale upon the slider.[2]

Mr. Pearson adds in his article the significant remark, that he entertains no hope that this suggestion will be adopted in practice, for mechanics do not like innovations, as is evident from the fact that twenty of the oldfashioned Coggeshall's rules are sold to every one of the more recent and improved designs.

An interesting, but difficult, question to settle is the extent to which the slide rule was actually used in England during the eighteenth century. As late as 1842 De Morgan complained that this instrument was greatly undervalued, that nine Englishmen out of ten would not know what the instrument was for, if they saw it, and that not one in a hundred would be able to work a simple

[1] *Nicholson's Journal*, Vol. I., 1797, p. 450.

[2] *Encyklopädie d. Math. Wiss.*, Vol. I, 1898–1904, Leipzig, p. 1057.

question by means of it.[1]   But granted that only one in five hundred knew how to use the slide rule, would that not be a large proportion, considering how few people are called upon, day after day, month after month, to carry on arithmetical computations which require much more than addition or subtraction?

About the only way of estimating the extent to which the instrument was used is by the frequency of references to the slide rule and of directions for the use of it.

Robert Shirtcliffe's *Theory and Practice of Gauging*, London, 1740, gives, as we have seen, about thirty pages to the explanation of the slide rule and remarks (p. 27) that since the practice of gauging almost entirely depends on the knowledge of the slide rule, it must be of great importance to the gentlemen of the excise to be acquainted, not only with the method of operation thereon, but the reason thereof.   There are many proofs to show that the slide rule was used extensively in practical gauging, though probably not used by all excise officers.   "As some writers have attempted to persuade the Publick," writes Leadbetter,[2] "that Tables ready calculated are far more exact and ready in Practical Gauging, than the Sliding Rule, it may not be here amiss to observe, that if Tables happen to be false printed . . . the Officer must act at random, not knowing whether he is right or wrong; whereas, by the Sliding Rule, 'tis impossible he should ever err; for the Use of that instrument being but once well understood, . . . the Officer, with the greatest Dispatch and Certainty, may . . . come to the exactness of the tenth Part of a Unit, which is as near as is ever required in Practice in the Excise."   More remarkable yet is the frequency that

[1] Article "Slide Rule" in the *Penny Cyclopaedia.*
[2] Leadbetter, *op. cit.*, p. IV, V.

instructions for the use of the slide rule are found in the popular works on practical arithmetic which touch upon mensuration, published not only in England, but also in North America. Thus "George Fisher" (Mrs. Slack), in her *Arithmetic*, London, 1794, p. 239, as also John Mair, the Scotch writer on arithmetic (1794), and the American arithmetician Nicolas Pike (1788) give rules for the use of the instrument. John Macgregor [1] remarks that "this rule is so well known, that it is unnecessary to give a tedious description" of it.

Certain it is that the slide rule was used much more in England, during the eighteenth century, than in Germany or France. As to other European countries, we have not been able to secure evidence that the instrument was even known to exist. The Italian Professor, Antonio Favaro, has written the fullest history of the slide rule known to us,[2] but not a single Italian author or mechanic of the seventeenth or eighteenth century is brought forward by him. One circumstance which facilitated the wider use of the slide rule in England is the greater attention given in elementary instruction there to the subject of decimal fractions. Decimal arithmetic was emphasized much more in Great Britain than in Germany or France. A knowledge of it is a prerequisite for computation with the slide rule. As Leadbetter says: [3] "Because the Sliding Rule is calculated for Decimal Fractions, it is requisite the Learner be made acquainted therewith before he proceeds to use of the Rule itself."

[1] *A Complete Treatise on Practical Mathematics*, Edinburgh, 1792, p. 353.

[2] Favaro, *op. cit.*, 1879.

[3] Leadbetter, *op. cit.*, p. 1.

DEVELOPMENT IN GERMANY DURING THE EIGHTEENTH CENTURY

It has been pointed out earlier in this history that the first German writer interested in the slide rule was Biler (1696), but there is no indication that the slide rule actually acquired a foothold in Germany at that time. Over a quarter of a century later Jacob Leupold (1674-1727) prepared a mathematical work,[1] which was issued immediately after his death, in which reference is made not only to Biler's, but also to a rectilinear instrument resembling modern slide rules. "Wer der Inventor davon sey," says he, "kann ich nicht sagen . . . ich auch dergleichen Linial sonst nirgends angetroffen." Leupold got his information from an old manuscript, gave drawings of the rectilinear instrument, and promised to have it made. From this it appears clearly that the slide rule was, as yet, practically unknown in Germany in 1727. It first became known through the efforts of Johann Andreas von Segner (1704–1777), professor of mathematics in Göttingen and later in Halle, and of Johann Heinrich Lambert (1728–1777), member of the Berlin Academy of Sciences. Segner's efforts in this direction have been forgotten, no reference being made to him by German writers on the slide rule of the present day. Segner described a slide rule in 1750 and had it engraved upon copper.[2] In 1777 he was considering

[1] *Theatrum Arithmetico-Geometricum, Das ist: Schau-Platz der Rechen- und Mess-Kunst*, Leipsig, 1727.

[2] See Segner's letter to Lambert, March 22, 1777, printed in *Lambert's Briefwechsel*, Vol. IV, p. 379.

certain improvements in his instrument.[1] Much greater was the influence due to Lambert, who in 1761 brought out in Augsburg a booklet, *Beschreibung und Gebrauch der Logarithmischen Rechenstäbe*, which reached a new edition in 1772. Lambert realized fully the great practical value of the instrument and published a full and perspicuous account of its theory. Johann Bernoulli III. (1744–1807) based upon Lambert's publication the article "Logarithmiques," which he prepared for the *Encyclopédie Méthodique.* Through the medium of this article, Lambert made the theory of the instrument more widely known among French readers. Lambert's designs of the slide rule were executed in Augsburg, in wood and in metal, by the distinguished mechanic, G. F. Brander.[2] These rules were four feet long. There is no evidence to show that the slide rule secured any degree of popularity in Germany during the eighteenth century.

[1] *Lambert's Briefwechsel*, Vol. IV, p. 380, letter to Lambert, dated April 15, 1777.

[2] See letter from Lambert to Brander in *Lambert's Briefwechsel*, Vol. III, p. 9.

DEVELOPMENT IN FRANCE DURING THE
EIGHTEENTH CENTURY

Gunter's scale was introduced into France by Wingate in 1624, yet we have found no reference to any form of slide rule until about seventy-five years later. Lalanne [1] is authority for the statement that about 1700 Sauveur had constructed by the artisans Gevin and Le Bas slide rules having slides like those of Seth Partridge. In 1627 there was mentioned among the machines and inventions approved by the Royal Academy of Sciences of Paris "an instrument of Mr. Clairaut by means of which one can take angles, make arithmetical computations, such as multiplication, division, extraction of roots and the resolution of right triangles. It is a circle of cardboard, 21 in. in diameter, in which Mr. Clairaut has described a large number of concentric circles in order to express by the lengths of these circumferences the logarithms of numbers and those of sines. The instrument appears ingenious and very exact." [2] This

[1] Lalanne, *Instruction sur les règles à calcul*, 1851, préface, p. VII.; see Maurice d'Ocagne, *Calcul simplifié*, 2e éd., Paris, 1905, p. 114.

[2] *Histoire de l'académie royale des sciences*, année 1727, Méchanique p. 142: "un instrument de Mr. Clairaut par le moyen duquel on peut prendre les angles, faire les calculs arithmétiques, tels que la multiplication, la division, l'extraction des racines, et résoudre les triangles rectangles. C'est un cercle de carton, gradué de 21 pouces de diamètre, dans lequel Mr. Clairaut a décrit un grand nombre de ces circonférences concentriques pour exprimer par les longueurs de ces circonférences, les logarithmes des nombres, et ceux des sinus. L'instrument a paru ingénieux et assez exact."

Clairaut is Jean Baptiste Clairaut, sometimes called "Clairaut le Père," to distinguish him from his son, who attained great eminence as a mathematician. It would seem from the above extract that the elder Clairaut is the inventor of the instrument described, which is a circular slide rule. The circular form was to him an afterthought. He is said to have made his first designs in the year 1716, which were on a square of one foot, filled with parallel lines, constituting altogether a rule of 1500 French feet; and it was not till the year 1720 that he thought of the curvilinear form.[1] There is nothing to show that he was aware of the similar designs due to Oughtred and Biler. Nor is there any evidence to show that the instrument of Clairaut was ever constructed and used in France.

In 1741 Charles Étienne-Louis Camus (1699–1768) made known his *Instrument propre à jauger les tonneaux et les autres vaisseaux qui servent à contenir des liqueurs,*[2] and published two drawings of it. It was an octagonal rod with a slider, adopted, of course, to French units of measure. Camus makes no reference to earlier writers or earlier instruments. This gauge did not meet with success in France. The statement of Benoit[3] that it was welcomed in England and explained by Leadbetter in the *Royal Gauger* is incorrect. The first edition of the *Royal Gauger* appeared in 1739, two years before Camus wrote his article, and the slide rule of Leadbetter is a modification of Everard's, developed entirely upon English soil.

[1] *Mechanics Magazine*, Vol. V., London, 1802, p. 40.

[2] *Mémoires de l'académie royale des sciences de l'année* 1741, Paris 1744, p. 385.

[3] *Bulletin de la société d'encouragement pour l'industrie nationale*, Vol. 52, 1853, p. 587.

Our failure to find references to Sauveur, Camus, and Clairaut in French works of the eighteenth century leads to the belief that the slide rule was not known even to writers familiar with the "echelle angloise," as Gunter's scale was called in France. Saverien refers in his *Dictionnaire universel de mathematique et de physique*, Tome I, 1753, article "echelle angloise," to R. P. Pezenas as "seul Auteur François, qui ait parlé de ces sortes d'Echelles." Thus not only Clairaut and Sauveur, but also Camus, are overlooked. Saverien refers to two works of Pezenas, his *Elémens du Pilotage* and his *Pratique du Pilotage*. According to Saverien, Pezenas speaks not only of ordinary *echelles*, but also "of others more complicated, but more convenient. They are called *echelles doubles*. . . . When you proceed to find the fourth term of a proportion by these rules, you slide one rule against the other." Favaro [1] refers to a later work of Pezenas,[2] of the year 1768, in which the slide rule is described Favaro mentions also Lemonnier,[3] Fortin,[4] and Lalande.[5]

The article "Logarithmiques," written by Johann Bernoulli III., to which reference has already been made, was printed in the *Encyclopédie méthodique* and was translated into Italian in 1800.[6] It contained some historical references to Biler, Scheffelt, Leupold and Lambert, and a good account of the use of the instrument.

[1] Favaro, *op. cit.*, p. 505.

[2] *Nouveaux essais pour déterminer les longitudes en mer par les mouvements de la lune et par une seule observation*, Paris, 1768.

[3] *Abrégé du pilotage*, Paris, 1766.

[4] *Atlas céleste de Flamsteed*, translated by Fortin (Table 30), 1776.

[5] Encyclopédie méthodique (Marine), article "Echelle anglaise."

[6] *Dizionario enciclopedico delle matematiche delli signori Ab. Bossut, La Lande ec., Traduzione dal Francese*, Padova, 1800, Art. "Logaritmiche."

The time of the French revolution was a period of intense intellectual activity in France, during which mathematical studies received much attention. The establishment of the metric system gave impetus to the study of decimal arithmetic among the masses. In article 19 of the law of the "18 germinal an III," (April 7, 1795), was prescribed the construction of graphic scales, adapted for the determination, without calculation, of the ratios between the old and the new measures ("échelles graphiques pour estimer ces rapports sans avoir besoin d'aucun calcul").[1] One result of this legislation was the publication of Pouchet's *Arithmétique linéaire*. Due to this cause, no doubt, was also the appearance of *Cadrans logarithmiques adaptés aux poids et mésures*, published at Paris in 1799 by A. S. Leblond (1760–1811). These instruments, designed by Leblond, are circular slide rules, as are also those by François Gattey (1756–1819), who published *Instructions sur l'Usage des Cadrans logarithmiques*, Paris, 1799, and in after years brought out several publications on this subject and finally changed the name of the instrument to *arithmographe*.[2]

During the eighteenth century, France and Germany produced nothing in connection with the slide rule, which had not been worked out earlier in England. Nor were instruments of this type used there nearly as much as in England. It is also worthy of remark that, so far as we have observed, the early English designers of slide rules (Wingate, Oughtred, Partridge, Coggeshall, Everard) are never mentioned by continental writers of the eighteenth century. While Gunter's scale was known to be of English origin, German and French writers of the

[1] See G. Bigourdan, *Le Système Métrique des Poids et Mesures*. Paris, 1901, p. 65 69.

[2] Favaro, *op. cit.*, p. 506.

eighteenth century do not ascribe the *slide rule* to England. Even in England, books of the eighteenth century usually fail to mention Wingate and Oughtred in connection with the slide rule. The instruments, as originally planned, were never used extensively. When they were supplanted by new designs, they bore the names of the designers, and the names of Wingate and Oughtred were naturally forgotten.

DEVELOPMENT IN ENGLAND DURING THE NINE-TEENTH CENTURY (First Half)

The most conspicuous novelty advanced by English writers on the slide rule in the early part of the 19th century was invented by Peter M. Roget, M.D., who communicated to the Royal Society of London a *Description of an instrument for performing mechanically the involution and evolution of numbers*,[1] which solves a^b for integral or fractional values of b. This is done by denoting by the spaces upon the fixed rule, not logarithms, but *logarithms of logarithms*. Roget called it a "logometric scale." "Logometric" logarithms were used by Farey since 1807 in musical calculations.[2] The scale is now usually called a "logolog" or "log. log" scale. The operation of this rule may be seen from the following three settings:

Fixed Rule	a	a^b	a	$\sqrt[b]{a}$	a	$\sqrt[b]{a^c}$
Slider	1	b	b	1	b	c

The first setting yields a^b, the second $\sqrt[b]{a}$, the third $\sqrt[b]{a^c}$. In the first case we see the space $1-b$ on the slider to mean $\log b - \log 1 = \log b$, while the space $a - a^b$ on the fixed rule means $\log \log a^b - \log \log a$. Since the two spaces are equal to each other, we have $\log b = \log \log a^b - \log \log a$, or $\log b + \log \log a = \log \log a^b$, which relation is readily seen to hold. The instrument was constructed by Rooker of Little Queen Street, London. The loga-

---

[1] *Philosophical Transactions* (London) 1815, Part I., p. 9.

[2] *Phil. Mag.*, Vol. 45, p. 387; also art. "Logarithms" in Brewster's *Edinburgh Encyclopaedia*, 1st Am. ed., Philadelphia, 1832.

rithmic line representing a^b was divided into two parts, of which one was placed above the slider, the other below. On the middle of the upper scale stood 10; it ended on the right at 10^{10} and at the left at 1.25. The lower scale had 1.25 on the right and 1.0025 on the left. The slider had a double radius.

While, as Roget points out, questions relating to increase in population and the calculation of chances may be facilitated by this instrument, it is readily seen that its application would be limited. This fact explains why this rule was forgotten, being later re-invented as the demand for it in thermodynamic, electrical and other physical calculations arose. Roget applies this rule to two problems of interest to mathematicians: (1) He finds the system of logarithms in which the modulus is equal to the base; inverting the slider he reads off the answer 1.76315; (2) He solves $x^x = 100$, getting $x = 3.6$.

In the same article Roget explains a circular log-log rule and describes a log-log chart for the computation of powers and roots.

Slide rules were also designed by Sylvanus Bevan. In 1817, he explained an economic disposition of the numbers on the logarithmic scales.[1] "Instead of having, like the common sliding rule, a fixed and a movable line of numbers, each reaching from 1 to 10, and repeated to a second 10, mine has one line reaching from 1 to 10, and another reaching from 3 to 10, and thence onward to 3.3 . . . , one of these lines being inverted, or counting from right to left, whilst the other is placed in the usual manner. By this construction . . . the sliding rule is reduced to one half its usual bulk." The inversion of the scale was an old device, while the way of disposing

[1] *Philos. Magazine* (London), Vol. 49, 1817, p. 187.

of the logarithmic line was a rejuvenescence of an idea advanced 30 years earlier by Nicholson.

De Morgan refers to another modification of the principle of the slide rule, according to which the divisions are "all made equal, and the numbers written upon the divisions in geometrical proportion. . . . This modification of the principle has been applied in two very useful modes by Mr. McFarlane. In the first, two cylinders moving on the same axis, on one side and the other of a third, give the means of instantaneously proposing and solving any one out of several millions of arithmetical questions for the use of schools and teachers. In the second, one circle revolving upon another gives the interest upon any sum, for any number of days, at any rate of interest under ten per cent." [1] We have been unable to find other references to MacFarlane's designs.

J. W. Woollgar of Lewes, near London, designed different types of slide rules, in particular a six inch "Pocket calculator." With the view of extending the power of the slide rule, he made in another case the slider (or else the rule) bear, not the logarithms of the numbers marked on its graduation, but those of the values of a function of those numbers,[2] enabling him to compute the formula $a \cdot \phi(x)$. We are told that about 1860 these rules were no longer made.[3]

Various other modifications of the slide rule were made

---

[1] Art. "Slide rule" in the *Penny Cyclopaedia*, 1842. Who was McFarlane? Perhaps he was Donald McFarlane, the laboratory assistant to Lord Kelvin at Glasgow University, or perhaps he was Andrew Macfarlane, for many years secretary of the Mechanics' Institution of London.

[2] *Mechanics' Magazine*, Vol. 32, London, 1840, pp. 101, 102; "Slide Rule" in *Penny Cyclopaedia*.

[3] W. H. Bayley's *Hand-Book of the Slide Rule*, London, 1861, p. 340.

in different quarters, but, as previously pointed out, the newer designs met with little favor. The rules most commonly purchased failed to embody the use of the runner, suggested by Newton, Stone, Robertson and Nicholson. De Morgan never once mentions the runner in his article of 1842 in the *Penny Cyclopaedia*, which shows that this ingenious device had been completely forgotten. Peter Barlow, in his *Dictionary of Pure and Mixed Mathematics*, London, 1814, describes Everard's rule for gauging and Coggeshall's for timber-measurement, but makes no mention of the new rules of Nicholson and Pearson. Precisely the same course is taken by James Mitchell in his *Dictionary of Mathematical and Physical Sciences*, London, 1823. The novelties of Nicholson, Pearson and Roget were either ignored or forgotten. It is also worthy of remark that while Oughtred invented the circular rule, Milburne, Brown and Adams the spiral arrangement, and while Nicholson re-invented the circular form, this type of rule never until recently really secured a firm foothold in England.

In fact, the use of the slide rule in England during the second quarter of the nineteenth century appears to have diminished. About 1840 De Morgan complained that the instrument "has been greatly undervalued" in England.[1] This decline is doubtless due, in part, to the alteration in the system of weights and measures, which took place in 1824, introducing, for instance, an imperial gallon one fifth larger than the old wine gallon. Such changes rendered obsolete the old rules bearing gauge-points for the old units of measure. To be sure, new rules were designed. A large supply of new rules for the use of the exercise became necessary. This led a me-

---

[1] Art. "Slide Rule" in *Penny Cyclopaedia*.

chanic, Samuel Downing, to invent "more facile means of multiplying the logarithmic and other scales upon them, than by the old tedious method of transferring copies of the original divisions on the stocks and slides of the rules, by the help of the square and dividing knife, and the marking punches, etc., usually employed."[1] Thomas Young set himself to work to change the design of slide rules.[2] We surmise that the difficulty lay not in the design and manufacture of new rules, but rather in getting people to learn how to use them.

[1] Gill's *Technological Repository*, Vol. IV., London, 1829, p. 33.
[2] *Quarterly Journal of Science, Literature and Arts*, London, Vol. XVI, 1823, p. 357.

DEVELOPMENT IN GERMANY AND AUSTRIA DURING THE NINETEENTH CENTURY (First Half).

In Germany the slide rule was little known during the first half of the century. The efforts to popularize it, made in the eighteenth century by Lambert and Segner, bore little fruit. In the early volumes of J. G. Dingler's *Polytechnic Journal*, founded in 1820, occur numerous accounts of designs of slide rules, made in England,[1] but in 1829,[2] complaint is made that only few architects and Zimmerleute know what a logarithm is. In 1825, appeared in Berlin a book by Fr. w. Schneider, explaining the slide rule, which was modeled after a Swedish text of the year 1824. The English notation A, B, C, D of the four scales is used. On the cover of the book is an advertisement of the Berliner mechanic, F. Dübler, manufacturer of slide rules of boxwood or of brass. In 1847, C. Hoffmann published lectures on the slide rules, delivered by him before the Polytechnic Society of Berlin.[3] He mentions in his preface three makers of slide rules in Berlin, namely, Th. Baumann, C. T. Dörffel, and C. G. Grunow. Notwithstanding this activity, we are informed by a writer in 1859 that the slide rule was little used in Germany. Nor were new patterns of rules or new methods of construction attempted there during the first half of the century.

[1] Dingler's *Polyt. Journal*, Vol. 47, 1902, p. 489, Art. "Der Rechenschieber in Deutschland."
[2] *Idem*, Vol. 32, p. 173.
[3] *Idem*, Vol. 47, 1902, p. 490.

Hoffmann had drawn his inspiration from Vienna, where Adam Burg had interested himself in the slide rule, and for the popularization of which L. C. Schulz von Strassnitzki, professor at the Royal Polytechnic Institute in Vienna, prepared a small treatise [1] in 1843 and also delivered lectures before the Vienna Polytechnic Institute. In these lectures he used a huge slide rule eight feet long, probably similar to the two meter rules, used later by Tavernier-Gravet in Paris, and supplied for demonstration at the present time by Keuffel & Esser Co. and doubtless also by other manufacturing establishments. Strassnitzki designed a slide rule suited to the Austrian system of measures. Another lecturer in Vienna on this subject was E. Sedlaczek, the author of an important manual (1851) on the slide rule.

In Italy the instrument was first brought to notice in 1859 by Quintino Sella who wrote a text on it.[2] Favaro remarks that before the middle of the century Italy contributed little to its progress.

---

[1] *Anweisung zum Gebrauche des englischen Rechenschiebers.* . . . Wien, 1843; Dingler's *Polyt. Journal*, Vol. 47, 1902, p. 490.

[2] *Teorica e pratica del regolo calcolatore*, Torino, 1859; Favaro, *op. cit.*, p. 507.

DEVELOPMENT IN FRANCE DURING THE NINETEENTH CENTURY (First Half).

In France, the slide rule steadily gained in popularity, during the first half of the nineteenth century, until France became for a time a center of activity in the design and manufacture of rules. We have seen that, after the French Revolution and the adoption of the metric system, circular slide rules came to be appreciated somewhat. Nowhere has the circular rule secured as much of a hold as in France. The instruments of Leblond and Gattey, brought out at the close of the eighteenth century, were of the circular type. Gattey proposed a new circular instrument in 1810, with the name of "arithmographe."[1] Benoit says[2] that their construction was similar to the cardboard instrument of Clairaut, but less complete, that this and similar instruments were not much handled until after the National Society for the Encouragement of Industry, under the initiative of Jomard and Francoeur, interested itself in the popularization of the slide rule. It is worthy of notice that even in France the rectilinear rule gained ascendency over the circular type. Jomard described in the publications of this society a straight wooden slide rule, imported by him in 1815 from England.[3] Before this the straight edge type

[1] Gattey, *Explication et usage de l'arithmographe*, Paris, 1810, brought out later under the title *Usage du calculateur, instrument portatif au moyen duquel on peut en un instant, et sans etre obligé d'écrire aucune chiffre, se procurer les résultats de toutes sortes de calcul*, Paris, 1819; Favaro, *op. cit.*, p. 506.

[2] *Bulletin de la société d'encouragement pour l'industrie nationale*, Vol. 52, 1853, p. 588.

[3] *Idem*, p. 588.

had been seldom described in France. In another volume it is asserted that in 1816 Hoyau, a locksmith and inventor, constructed cylindrical slide rules of superior workmanship.[1] It is perhaps of this that De Morgan writes [2] in 1842, "Twelve or fifteen year sago, an instrument maker at Paris laid down logarithmic scales on the rims of the box and lid of a common circular snuff-box, . . . but either calculators disliked snuff, or snuff-takers calculation, for the scheme was not found to answer, and the apparatus was broken up."

About this time a large number of English rules were imported. In 1815 to 1818 Benoit secured rules constructed by the London optician, Bate, 28 and 56 inches long, and also carefully graduated rules from the workshop of W. & S. Jones in Lower Holborn, London. In 1821 Lenoir made the first of his copper rules, 35 cm. long, and constructed after designs of Jomard and Collardeau a machine which marked the divisions simultaneously upon 8 wooden rules 25 cm. long, and executing work as fine as that of the brothers Jones in London. Rules of different lengths were also constructed in 1821 by Clouet and by Isaac Sargent.[3] The rules of the latter commanded the lively admiration of the mathematician Prony. But all these efforts, says Benoit,[4] would have been long fruitless, if the government had not wisely imposed in its requirements for admission to the schools for public service a knowledge of the slide rule.[5] No doubt the ascendency of the slide rule in

---

[1] *Bulletin de la société d'encouragement pour l'industrie nationale,* Vol. 52, 1853, p. 588.

[2] Art. "Slide Rule," *Penny Cyclopaedia.*

[3] *Idem,* pp. 588, 589.

[4] *Idem,* p. 589.

[5] *Idem,* p. 589; Favaro, *op. cit.,* p. 508.

France is due mainly to this government provision. It is the experience of all that skill in the use of the rule is not attained, except as the result of considerable practice. But once this skill is acquired, the instrument is loved, and used persistently.

That French workmanship attained a high degree of skill is apparent from English comment. About 1841 De Morgan [1] received from Paris a circular logarithmic scale in brass, 4½ in. in diameter, consisting of two concentric plates, having a clamping screw on their common axis. De Morgan says that it "is so well divided that it will stand tests which the wooden rules would not bear without showing the error of their divisions. But here arise disadvantages which we had not contemplated. In the first place, no sub-division can be well made or read by estimation, unless the part of the scale on which it comes is uppermost or undermost, which requires a continual and wearisome turning of the instrument. In the next place, to make the best use of it, and to bring out all its power, requires . . . such care in setting and reading, as, unless a microscope and tangent screw were used, makes the employment of the four-figure logarithm card both shorter and less toilsome. For rough purposes, then, a wooden rule is as good; for more exact ones, the card is better." This is an interesting statement of comparative merits. It points out, also, a practical difficulty which has hindered the circular type from attaining wide use. Its vicissitudes in the struggle for existence are brought out in a statement of an Englishman who in 1841 saw in Montferrier's Mathematical Dictionary, article "arithmometre," a remark that these arithmometers were made and sold at the shop of the

[1] Art. "Slide Rule," *Penny Cyclopaedia*.

publisher of that dictionary in Paris.[1] He ordered one of them and received the last one in the shop—their manufacture was to be discontinued on account of insufficient sales.[2]

We have referred to the firm of Lenoir in Paris as skillful manufacturers of slide rules. It is interesting to see how that firm, then prominent in France for its excellent astronomical and geodetic instruments, gradually advanced until, for a time, it held the very first place in the world in the manufacture of slide rules. There were two Lenoirs, father and son. The father outlived his son and died in 1832.[3] The Lenoirs were succeeded by Collardeau and Gravet.[4] According to Maurice d'Ocagne, the name of the firm was first Gravet-Lenoir, then Tavernier-Gravet.[5]

---

[1] The first two volumes appeared in "Paris, chez Denain, Impr. de Locquin, 1835–37," "Tome 3. Supplément. Paris, Impr. de Mme Dondey-Dupré, 1840."

[2] *Mechanics' Magazine*, Vol. 35, London, 1841, p. 309.

[3] Favaro, *op. cit.*, p. 507.

[4] *Bulletin de la société d'encouragement pour l'industrie nationale*, Vol. 52, 1853, p. 589.

[5] D'Ocagne mentions in his *Calcul simplifié*, 2e éd., Paris, 1905, p. 116, the following French authors of works on the slide rule: Collardeau (1820), Ph. Mouzin (3e éd., 1837), J. F. Artur (1827, 2e éd., 1845), Aug. Hadéry (1845), L. Lalanne (1851), F. Guy 3e éd., 1885), P. M. N. Benoit (1853), Fr. René (1865), Montefiore Lévi (1869), Labosne (1872), Claudel (1875), Gros de Perrodil (1885), Leclair (1902), Jully (1903), Dreyssé (1903). Lévi's book is a translation from Italian into French of Quintino Sella's work.

DEVELOPMENT IN THE UNITED STATES DURING THE NINETEENTH CENTURY

In the United States, as previously pointed out, brief instructions for the use of the slide rule were printed in a few arithmetics of the latter part of the eighteenth century. An edition of Thomas Dilworth's *Schoolmaster's Assistant* (an English book) was brought out in Philadelphia in 1805 by Robert Patterson, professor of mathematics in the University of Pennsylvania. It devotes half a dozen pages to the use of the slide rule in gauging. Another English work, Hawney's *Complete Measurer* (1st ed., London, 1717) was printed in Baltimore in 1813. It describes the Carpenter's Rule as well as "Verie's Slide Rule" for gauging. Of American works, the *Arithmetic* of Nicolas Pike (1788) gives brief directions for the use of slide rules, while Bowditch's *Navigator*, 1802, gives one page to the explanation of the slide rule, but in working examples, Gunter's line alone is used. From these data it is difficult to draw reliable conclusions as to the extent to which the slide rule was then actually used in the United States. We surmise that it was practically unknown to the engineering profession as a whole. There were, no doubt, isolated instances of its use. The Swiss-American geodesist, F. R. Hassler, who was the first superintendent of the U. S. Coast and Geodetic Survey, possessed a slide rule—we shall describe it later. Mr. C. H. Progler, of Ripley, W. Va., informs me that in 1848–50 he was in the employ of Hassler's son in U. S. geodetic work in North Carolina, that they had a slide rule in camp, but did not use it in connection with the survey. I have seen a reference to the slide

FIG. 9.—THACHER'S CALCULATING INSTRUMENT.

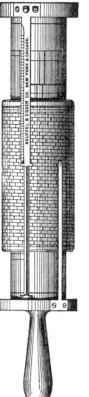

FIG. 13.—G. FULLER'S SLIDE RULE.

rule in a book issued about 1838 by a professor of the Rensselaer Polytechnic Institute.

It was in 1844 that Aaron Palmer's *Computing Scale* appeared in Boston. It was a circular slide. rule, 8 in. in diameter. The following year he brought out a *Pocket Scale*, 2⅝ in. in diameter. In 1846 the copyright of Palmer's scale was owned by John E. Fuller, who introduced changes in Palmer's original scale by the addition to it of non-logarithmic circles for determining the number of days between given dates. Fuller called this new part a *Time Telegraph* and the modified instrument as a whole a *Computing Telegraph*. Later the instrument may have been modified still further. About 1860 it was sold by subscription in New York under the name of *Telegraphic Computer*. We are not aware that Palmer's and Fuller's instruments were known outside of Massachusetts and New York.

An account of the rectilinear slide rule, which probably reached the engineering profession in America more widely than other accounts, is found in the *Mechanics' and Engineers' Book of Reference and Engineers' Field Book* (New York, 1856). This book was written by Charles Haslett, Civil Engineer, and Charles W. Hackley, Professor of Mathematics in Columbia College. It gives five pages to the description of the slide rule.

In spite of the facts just presented it appears that, before 1880 or 1885, the slide rule was little known and very little used in the United States. References to it are seldom found in engineering literature. Appleton's *Dictionary of Engineering*, Vol. I, New York, 1868, does not name the slide rule, but devotes three or four lines to a description of it under the head of "Gunter's line." Knight's *American Mechanical Dictionary*, Vol. II, 1881, describes Gunter's line; then, without naming the slide rule, describes it in four lines and ends with the statement to the effect that these "instruments" "are now common among intelligent workmen."

Wider interest in the slide rule was awakened about 1881. It was in that year that Edwin Thacher, a graduate of the Rensselaer Polytechnic Institute, now a bridge engineer, patented his well-known Cylindrical Slide Rule (Fig. 9). It was in 1881 that Robert Riddell published in Philadelphia his booklet on *The Slide Rule Simplified*, in which he describes a rule of Coggeshall's type. In the preface he points out that, though nearly unknown in this country, the slide rule was invented before the time when William Penn founded Philadelphia. Since 1881 the interest in the slide rule has been steadily increasing in America. Professor Calvin M. Woodward of Washington University writes that he does not remember having seen a slide rule while an undergraduate student, that his attention was first called to it by Professor C. A. Smith in the '70's and more strongly by Professor J. B. Johnson in the 80's; Johnson required every student in engineering to use it. Its popularity began with the introduction of the Mannheim type about the year 1890. At that time William Cox began his propaganda in the *Engineering News*. In recent years many of the rules for special purposes have originated in the United States. An inquiry instituted by C. A. Holden [1] showed that in about half of the engineering schools of the United States attention is given to the use of the slide rule.[2]

[1] *Engineering News*, Vol. 45, 1901, p. 405.

[2] For additional data of interest on the use of the slide rule in the United States, see *Transactions of the American Society of Mechanical Engineers*, Vol. VIII, New York City, 1886-7, pp. 707-709.

DEVELOPMENT DURING RECENT TIMES

Our limitations of space do not permit a detailed historical account of the very numerous modifications of the slide rule for special purposes which have been made during the last fifty years. We shall merely endeavor to touch upon a few of the leading facts.

It was about 1850 that a French army officer in Metz, then only about nineteen years old, designed a straight slide rule with a runner and with a disposition of the logarithmic scales, such as experience has shown to be admirably suited to the ordinary every-day uses of a slide rule. This officer was Amédée Mannheim (1831–1906) and his slide rules are known everywhere as Mannheim rules. In 1848 he entered the École Polytechnique in Paris, and then, as lieutenant of artillery, went to Metz and became a student at the École d'Application there.[1]

Mannheim has had a long and illustrious career as Professor of Geometry and Stereotomy at the École Polytechnique in Paris, where he has rendered long service and enriched geometry and mechanics with new researches. Homage was rendered to "Colonel Mannheim" by the École Polytechnique on the occasion of the celebration of his seventieth birthday in 1901.

[1] See C. A. Laisant: "La Vie et les Travaux d'Amédée Mannheim" in *L'ensignement mathématique*, IXe année, 1907, 169–179. From the *Journal de l'Ecole Polytechnique*, IIe série, *septième cahier*, Paris, 1902, p. 223, we quote:

"C'est ainsi qu' à Metz, étant encore élève à l'École d'Application vous avez imaginé la règle à calculs qui porte votre nom et qui fut adoptée par l'Artillerie sur la proposition du Capitaine Goulier Depuis, elle est employée partout à l'étranger."

Mannheim explained his rule and its use in a publication entitled *Règle à calculs modifiée. Instruction* (Metz, Imp. et lith. Nouvian, Décembre, 1851). Later an account appeared in the *Nouvelles Annales de Mathématiques*.[1] It is not generally known that Mannheim designed also a cylindrical slide rule which was more accurate than his straight rule.[2]

Mannheim had the good fortune to have his rectilinear slide rule made by Tavernier-Gravet, a firm of national reputation, and also of having this rule adopted as the one to be used by the French artillery. But many years elapsed before it acquired a foothold in other countries. Not until 30 or 40 years after its invention did it come to be used in England and the United States. Perhaps the first appreciation of it, outside of France, came from the Italian, Q. Sella, who published in Turin, in 1859, an excellent work on the slide rule, which was enlarged in the second edition, 1886. At the close of the last century, the Mannheim rule was known wherever instruments of this class were in use.

Mannheim is the first who succeeded in popularizing the use of the runner. The runner enables one to read corresponding numbers on scales that are not contiguous and also to compute the value of complex expressions without the necessity of reading intermediate results of computation. In England, where the runner was first invented nearly 200 years earlier, it met with slower adoption than in France, Italy or Germany. That the Mann-

---

[1] Iére série, tome XII, 1853, pp. 113–116. An exhaustive account of Mannheim's geometrical articles, 224 in number, is given by Gino Loria in the *Rendiconti del Circolo Matematico di Palermo*, Tomo 26, 1908, pp. 1–63.

[2] "Règle à calcul cylindrique," described in *Nouvelles Annales de Mathématiques*, Tome XIII, 1854, p. 36.

heim rule was unknown in England 20 years after its invention follows from the fact that the runner was re-invented in England by Erskine Scott in 1870.[1]

In Mannheim's rule (Fig. 10) the upper scale A on the rule and the upper scale B on the slide are marked alike, each having a double graduation from 1 to 10, as in the older rules. But the lower scale C on the slide and the lower scale D on the rule are also marked alike, both having a single graduation from 1 to 10, whereas, in the ordinary old Coggeshall's rules, C was marked the same as A and B, and in that form had enjoyed popular favor for 170 years. The new arrangement has its disadvantages in that squares and square roots require the use of the runner, while the use of the two lower scales C and D involves uncertainty as to the direction of the motion of the slide. Moreover, the inverted slide cannot be used in finding factors. But the rule enjoys the advantage of yielding a double accuracy when the lower lines are used for simple proportion, while the use of the runner in complex operations simplifies matters enormously. Protests against the Mannheim arrangement are seldom heard.[2]

And yet, it is far from certain that the Mannheim type will continue long in its undisputed supremacy as the best portable rule for popular use in ordinary computation to three significant figures. Even now there are signs of divided allegiance. In the technical schools in Paris a modification of the Mannheim rule is now used.[3]

---

[1] *Zeitschr. f. Mathematik. u. Physik.*, Vol. 48, 1903, p. 134. In France the runner was not wholly unknown in the first half of the nineteenth century. It is mentioned in Mouzin's *Instruction sur la manière de se servir de la règle à calcul*, 3ᵉ éd., Paris, 1837.

[2] For a recent protest, see *American Machinist*, Vol. 29, Pt. II, 1906, p. 256.

[3] See P. Rozé *Règle à calculs*, Paris, 1907, pp. 2, 3, 29–58.

This is called the "règle des écoles" (see Fig. 11), to distinguish it from the "règle du Colonel Mannheim." Greater simplicity as well as greater accuracy is claimed for the arrangement in the règle des écoles. It has also an adaption to the centesimal division of the quadrant. In this new rule the scales, familiarly known as C and D, are the same as in the Mannheim rule, being graduated from 1 to 10. But the scales A and B are different; A and B bear each a single graduation from 1 to 10, like C and D, but so placed that the figure 1 is not at the left end, but is in the middle of the scale and slide. From left to right the numbers A and B read 4, 5, 6, 7, 8, 9, 1, 2, 3. When the slide is so placed that the scales C and D coincide, then A and B coincide also. In computation, the slide need not be drawn further than half its length to the right or to the left. Use is made of the runner. The rule is constructed by Tavernier-Gravet, rue Mayet 19, Paris. Rozé remarks that with this rule one can perform multiplications and divisions, one after another, without interruption and with twice the precision possible with the Mannheim rule, that square roots are also gotten more accurately, though not as easily as with the Mannheim rule. Rozé says that in France the règle des écoles is being used more and more, while in England it has not been used until now. In the United States it has not acquired a foothold at all, as yet. In Germany this type of rule is just beginning to be offered for sale.

In France the règle des écoles goes also by the name of "règle Beghin," for it was Beghin [1] who suggested a disposition of the scales as it appears in the règle des écoles. Rozé adds, however, that no priority can be

[1] A. Beghin, *Règle à calcul, modèle spécial*, Paris, 1898, 2e éd., 1902.

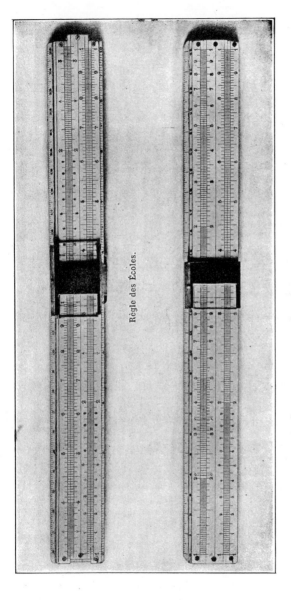

Règle des Écoles.

Fig. 10.—Règle du Colonel Mannheim. (Lower Illustration.)

Fig. 11.—Règle des Ecoles. (Upper Illustration.)

From P. Rozé, *Théorie et usage de la règle à calculs*, Paris, 1907.

To face page 66.

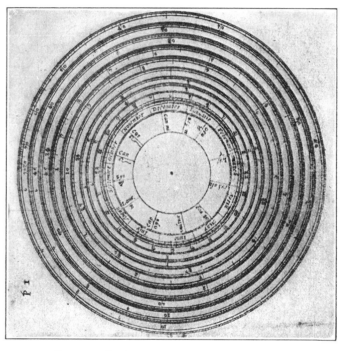

FIG. 17.—Oughtred's Circles of Proportion, 1632.

claimed for Beghin, for Professor Cherepashinskii [1] suggested this arrangement several years earlier. Cherepashinskii is a Russian, a professor at the Moscow Polytechnic. He designed the slide rule in 1882 and had the firm Tavernier-Gravet in Paris construct one instrument. The following year (1883) he published at Moscow in Russian a booklet on the slide rule, but his ideas were ignored by the public at that time.[2] It is of interest to observe that Cherepashinskii's modification of the Mannheim rule, by discarding the lines of two radii and using in their place only lines of one radius, is exactly the modification which, in the eighteenth century, Vero effected upon the Everard slide rule.[3]

Novelty cannot be claimed even for Cherepashinskii. In De Morgan's article "Slide Rule," in the *Penny Cyclopaedia* (1842), we find identically the same scale arrangement as Cherepashinskii's. It is attributed by De Morgan to Sylvanus Bevan (*Nicholson's Journal*, Vol. 49, 1817, p. 187), with the further remark that, thirty years before that, Nicholson had made somewhat similar dispositions (*Philosophical Transactions*, 1787, p. 246). We must remark, however, that while Nicholson employed the runner, this device was apparently unknown to Bevan.

Much ingenuity has been expended in recent years to increase the accuracy of the slide rule without unduly increasing its size. While E. Péraux took a longer scale and mounted it upon the rule in two parts, using

[1] Rozé transliterates the name as "Tserepachinsky," while d'Ocagne gives it as "Tchérépachinsky."

[2] Maurice d'Ocagne, *Calcul simplifié*, 2e éd., Paris, 1905, p. 116, note 2.

[3] See C. Leadbetter's *Royal Gauger*, 1755, p. 29.

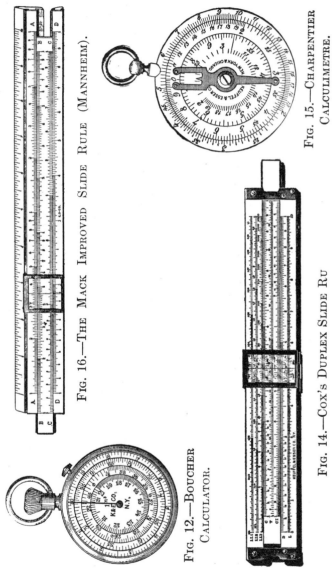

FIG. 16.—THE MACK IMPROVED SLIDE RULE (MANNHEIM).

FIG. 15.—CHARPENTIER CALCULIMETRE.

FIG. 12.—BOUCHER CALCULATOR.

FIG. 14.—COX'S DUPLEX SLIDE RU

two slides, Delamorinière adopted a rule one meter long.[1] Following out an idea advanced long before by W. Nicholson, the logarithmic scale was broken up into several parts of equal length and arranged side by side in a plane by J. D. Everett,[2] Hannyngton, Scherer, R. Proell, or upon the surface of a cylinder arranged parallel to its axis, as by J. D. Everett, Mannheim, E. Thacher. Thacher's instrument (Fig. 9) almost attains the accuracy of a five-place table of logarithms and ranks among the most accurate slide rules in practical use. It is the most important single contribution to the design of slide rules made in America.

Working on the plan of Oughtred, other designers adhered to the circular form, as, for instance, E. M. Boucher (Fig. 12), whose instrument resembles a watch, and Herrmann or P. Weiss, all the circles being coplanar and fixed, the sliding parts being pointers or hands. In other designs the circles slide relatively to each other. as in the old types of J. M. Biler and A. S. Leblond. Modern examples of the latter are the instruments of E. Sonne, F. M. Clouth, W. Hart, F. A. Meyer, E. Puller, A. Steinhauser, and others. Another variation in design is to place the logarithmic circles upon the rims of wheels, as in the instruments by Gattey and Hoyau at the beginning of the nineteenth century, and as in the more recent ones by MacFarlane, R. Weber, A. Beyerlen. The logarithmic line has also been mounted upon a cylinder in the form of a screw thread, as in designs by G. H. Darwin and Professor R. H. Smith, and in G. Fuller's well-known Spiral Slide Rule (Fig. 13). Still

---

[1] *Bull. de la société d'encouragement pour l'industrie nationale,* Paris, Vol. 62, 1863, p. 656.

[2] The references to the literature of each instrument are given later in the list of slide rules designed and used since 1800.

another idea is to place the logarithmic line upon metallic tapes, unwound from one roller or spool upon another, as in G. H. Darwin's designs and in B. Tower's instrument. What constitutes the best mechanical arrangement for accurate curvilinear or multilinear rules for common use is still a matter of speculation.

Generalizations of the slide rule, such as were introduced in the early part of the century by P. M. Roget, in his log-log rule have been re-invented by Burdon in France, by Captain Thomson of the British Army, by F. Blanc in Germany, and again by Professor John Perry of the Royal College of Sciences in London, and by Colonel H. C. Dunlap, Professor of Artillery at the Ordnance College, and C. S. Jackson, Instructor of Mathematics at the Royal Military College in England. When in $a^b = x$, the value of x is between 1 and 0, its logarithm is negative, a case first mechanically provided for by Blanc. Says C. S. Jackson, "The use of a log $(-\log x)$ scale for numbers less than unity was one fondly thought new, but in this idea, which Professor Perry also brought forward, we were all anticipated by Blanc.[1] Similar researches were made by Burdon, who proposed schemes for solving $xy^m = a$, $xy^n = b$, where m, n, a, b are given numbers. The introduction of still different scales, more general than that of $\log x$, was noticed by us in the case of Woollgar, and more recently has been studied by P. de Saint-Robert,[2] who solves equations of the form $f(z) = \phi(x) + \psi(y)$ by the use of slide rules graduated to f, ϕ, ψ. Studies along this line have been carried on by Ch. A. Vogler.[3]

With the aid of the ordinary Mannheim and similar

---

[1] *Mathematical Gazette*, Vol. II, London, 1904, p. 337.

[2] *Encyklopädie d. Math. Wiss.* Bd. I, 1898–1904, Leipzig, p. 1064.

[3] *Idem*, p. 1064; also *Zeitschr. Vermessungsw.* 10 (1881), p. 257.

slide rules it is possible to solve quadratic and cubic
equations. This has been pointed out by E. Bour,[1]
Paolo de Saint-Robert,[2] A. Genocchi,[3] Quintino Sella,[4]
Favaro and Terrier,[5] W. Engler,[6] H. Zimmermann,[7] H. C.
Dunlop and C. S. Jackson,[8] and A. Dreyssé.[9] The com-
putation of $\sqrt{a^2 \pm b^2}$, $\sqrt{a} \pm \sqrt{b}$, $(\sqrt{a} \pm \sqrt{b})^2$, and similar
expressions with a single setting of the rule was shown
by W. Ritter.[10] Fürle's general slide rule gives
$\sqrt{x^2 \pm y^2 \pm z^2}$.[11] Fürle generalizes the methods of Bour
and Burdon and describes a slide rule which has, besides
the ordinary scales, also scales for the functions x, x^2,
x^3, log-log x. This rule enables him to solve numerical
equations not higher than the fifth degree, also trinomial
equations of any degree and certain transcendental
equations.[12] It will be remembered that Newton out-
lined a method for solving equations of any degree by
the slide rule, which was described more fully, in somewhat modified form, by E. Stone. In recent times this
idea has been followed up also by the Spaniard L. Torres
for the solution of trinomial and higher equations, as

[1] *Par. Comptes rendus de l'Acad. d. Sci.*, 44 (1857), p. 22.

[2] *Mem. dell' Accad. d. Scie. di Torino*, T. XXV, Serie II.

[3] *Giornale di Matem. del Prof. Battaglini*, Napoli, 1867.

[4] *Regolo Calcolatore*, 2 ed. Ital., Torino, 1886, p. 88–94, 140–163.

[5] Favaro-Terrier, *Statique Graphique*, Paris, 1879.

[6] *Zeitschr. Vermessungsw.*, Vol. 29, 1900, p. 495.

[7] *Idem*, Vol. 30, 1901, p. 58.

[8] *Slide Rule Notes*, London, 1901, p. 17.

[9] *Règle à calcul Mannheim*, Paris, 1903, p. 151.

[10] *Schweizer. Bauzeitung*, Vol. 23, 1894, p. 37; quoted in *Ency-klopädie d. Math. Wiss.*, Vol. I, p. 1058.

[11] *Zur Theorie des Rechenschiebers*, Berlin, 1899.

[12] *Zur Theorie des Rechenschiebers*, Berlin, 1899; *Eycyklopädie der Math. Wiss.*, Bd. I, p. 1065.

well as by d'Ocagne,[1] and, as we have seen, by Fürle. In the same order of ideas are the modes of solving equations, advanced by F. W. Lanchester[2] and Baines.[3] Slide rules for use with complex quantities, $a + \sqrt{-1}\, b$, have been designed by R. Mehmke.[4]

Great activity has been shown during the last forty years in the direction of perfecting the mechanical execution of slide rules. In this, Germany took the lead. After the slide rules used in Germany had been mostly imported from France for a period of twenty or thirty years, German manufacturers gained the ascendency. In 1886,[5] Dennert & Pape in Altona began to mount the scales of numbers upon white celluloid, instead of boxwood or metal. Upon celluloid numbers appear so much more distinctly that the use of celluloid has become well nigh universal. In America celluloid rules were being sold by the Keuffel & Esser Co. as early as 1888.[6] Since 1895 the Keuffel & Esser Co. manufacture them in Hoboken, N. J. A prominent German firm, engaged in the manufacture of slide rules, is that of Albert Nestler of Lahr in Baden. The firm of A. W. Faber has manufactories in Germany, and houses in England, France, and the United States.[7] Slide rules are now usually engine-divided. Many mechanical devices have been patented by different manufacturers

[1] d'Ocagne, *Le calcul simplifié*, Paris, 1894; 2ᵉ éd., 1905. For fuller references, see *Encyklopädie d. Math. Wiss.*, Bd. I, pp. 1007, 1024, 1065.

[2] *Engineering*, Aug. 7, 1896, p. 172.

[3] *Engineer*, April 1, 1904, p. 346.

[4] Dyck's *Katalog, Nachtrag*, p. 21, Nr. 44 d.

[5] *Encyklopädie d. Math. Wiss.*, Vol. I, p. 1055.

[6] *Railroad Gazette*, Vol. 20, 1888, p. 149.

[7] C. N. Pickworth, *Instructions for the Use of A. W. Faber's Improved Calculating Rule*.

for ensuring the smooth and even workings of the slide in the stock of the rule and allowing compensation for wear, or obtaining material that will show little shrinkage or warping.

For the purpose of securing greater accuracy in the use of the slide rule, without increasing the length of the divisions—of securing, say, the third or fourth figure with a 25-cm. rule—attachments have been made, which go usually under the name of cursors. An early attempt along this line was a vernier applied in 1851 by J. F. Artur of Paris.[1] Similar suggestions were made by O. Seyffert in Germany.[2] Perhaps best known is the Goulding cursor, which allows the space between two consecutive smallest divisions of a rule to be divided into ten equal parts.[3] It is supplied by G. Davis & Son, Ltd., Derby, London, as is also a "magnifying cursor," enlarging by a plano-convex glass. A. W. Faber has a digit-registering cursor[4] with a semicircular scale, enabling the number of digits to be registered, these digits to be added or subtracted at the end of a lengthy operation. A radial cursor for multiplying or dividing a scale length mechanically has been introduced by F. W. Lanchester.[5]

We shall enumerate all the slide rules described and used since 1800, which have come to our notice. The number, though doubtless incomplete, is large and shows many types of rules designed for special kinds of com-

---

[1] *Bulletin de la société d'encouragement pour l'industrie nationale,* Vol. 50, Paris, 1851, p. 676.

[2] *Encyklopädie d. Math. Wiss.,* Bd. I, 1898–1904, p. 1058; *Cent alblatt Bauverwaltung* 8 (1888), p. 548.

[3] C. N. Pickworth *The Slide Rule,* 10th ed., 1906, p. 91.

[4] *Idem,* p. 92.

[5] *Idem,* p. 87; *Nature,* Vol. 52, 1895, p. 659.

putation, such as the change from one system of money, weight, or other measure, to another system, or the computation of annuities, the strength of gear, flow of water, various powers and roots. There are stadia rules, shaft, beam, and girder scales, pump scales, photo-expurse scales, etc.

SLIDE RULES DESIGNED AND USED SINCE 1800.

(Arranged approximately in chronological order.)

1. **Horton's New Improved Rule.**
   [Referred to by W. Pearson in *Nicholson's Journal*, London, Vol. I, 1802, p. 452. Reprint of Vol. I, 1797.]

2. **Roget's Slide Rule for Involution and Evolution.**
   Philosophical Transactions (London), 1815, Part I, pp. 9-29. Describes a linear log log slide rule.

3. **Roget's Logometric Circular Rule.**
   [*Philosophical Transactions* (London), 1815, Part I, p. 26. A log log rule in circular form.]

4. **Roget's Logometric Chart.**
   [*Philosophical Transactions* (London), 1815, Part I, p. 27. A chart with log log lines for computing roots and powers.]

5. **Wollaston's Slide Rule for Use in Chemistry.**
   [*Philosophical Transactions*, London, Year 1814; *Bull. de la Société d'encouragement pour l'industrie nationale*, Vol. 52, Paris, 1853, p. 581; cited by Favaro, *op. cit.*, p. 509, from *Journal des Mines*, Vol. 37, 1815, p. 101.]

6. **S. Bevan's Engineer's Rule.**
   [*Penny Cyclopaedia*, 1842, Art. "Slide Rule." This 12-in. rule has slides on both faces and serves for squares, cubes, square roots of cubes, etc. There are scales on the backs of the slides and in the grooves for sines, tangents, interest, annuities at 5%. Made by Cary, Strand. It is probably this rule that is referred to by C. Culmann in his *Die Graphische Statik*, Zürich, I., 1875, p. 75, as bearing the mark "W. Cary, 182 Strand, 1815."]

7. **Hoyau, boîtes à calculer.**

[*Bull. de la société d'encouragement pour l'industrie nationale*, Vol. 52, Paris, 1853, p. 588. Constructed these cylindrical instruments about 1816.]

8. **The Bate Rules.**

[*Bull. de la société d'encouragement pour l'industrie nationale*, Vol. 52, 1853, p. 588. Bate was an optician in London and his instruments were imported by the French about 1818. See also C. Culmann's *Die Graphische Statik*, Zürich, I., 1875, p. 67, where he gives a drawing of "Bate's Ready Reckoner."]

9. **S. Bevan's Improved Slide Rule.**

[A 6-in. rule, described in *Philosophical Magazine* (London), Vol. 49, 1817, p. 187. Without reversion of some of the lines that was suggested by Bevan, the rule was made by R. B. Bate of the Poultry. This is probably the rule mentioned by C. Culmann's *Die Graphische Statik*, Zürich, I., 1875, p. 75, as marked "17 Poultry, London, 1824."]

10. **B. Bevan's Circular Slide Rule.**

[Gill's *Technological Repository*, Vol. 4, London, 1829, p. 37; *Mechanic's Magazine*, London, Vol. 15, 1831, p. 164.]

11. **Clouet's règle à calcul.**

[*Bulletin de la société d'encouragement pour l'industrie nationale*, Vol. 52, 1853, p. 588. This rule was constructed by Clouet about 1821. See Vol. 20, p. 198.]

12. **Jomard règle a calcul.**

[*Bull. de la société d'encouragement pour l'industrie nationale*, Vol. 52, Paris, 1853, p. 588. Made by M. Collardeau, after 1815. See also *Calcul simplifié par* Maurice d'Ocagne, 2e ed., Paris, 1905, p. 115.]

13. **Thomas Young's Sliding Rule for Gauging Casks.**

[*Quarterly Jour. of Sci., Lit. and Arts*, London, Vol. 16, 1823, p. 357.]

14. **Lamb's Circular Slide Rule.**

[Gill's *Technological Repository*, Vol. 4, London, 1829, p. 37. Made by Mr. Lamb, a watch-maker in London.]

15. Downing's Slide Rule.
> [Gill's *Technological Repository*, Vol. 4, London, 1829, p. 33.]

16. Saddington's Rules.
> [*Mechanic's Magazine*, Vol. 12, London, 1830, p. 122. Rule made by Thomas Saddington of London.]

17. Henderson's Double Slide Rule.
> [*Penny Cyclopaedia*, Art. "Slide Rule." Solves at one operation most sets of multiplications and divisions not exceeding five operations. Made by Jones in Holborn, London.]

18. Arithmomètre made by Publisher of Montferrier's Dictionnaire.
> [Made and sold by these Publishers in Paris about 1840. See p. **57.**]

19. Woollgar's Calculator.
> [*Mechanic's Magazine*, Vol. 32, London, 1840, pp. 101, 102. See also Vol. 7, 1827; Vol. 15, 1831, p. 164; Vol. 17, 1832, p. 910. Designed by J. W. Woollgar, of Lewes, in Sussex, and made by Rooker, Little Queen Street, Holborn in London.]

20. Woollgar's Pocket-book Rule.
> [*Penny Cyclopaedia*, Art. "Slide Rule." Made by Rooker, Little Queen Street, in Holborn. See also W. H. Bayley's *Hand-Book of the Slide Rule*, London, 1861, p. 340.]

21. Hassler's Slide Rule.
> [A wooden slide rule of 25 in. effective length and width of $3\frac{1}{2}$ in. Consists of two parts sliding by one another. Brass guides at both ends. Each flat side carries lines of numbers. On one flat side are 21 parallel lines, 11 on one sliding part and 10 on the other. The 11 lines constitute a logarithmic line for numbers 1 to 1000; the 10 lines are a logarithmic line for numbers 892 to 89100. On the other flat side are 20 lines, 10 on each part. One part has logarithmic lines for numbers 1,000,000 to 100,000,000; the other part, for numbers 100,000 to 1,000,000,000. The instrument has the appearance of

being hand-made. It was used by F. R. Hassler, the
first Superintendent of the U. S. Coast and Geodetic
Survey and is now the property of his great-grandson,
F. R. Hassler, of Phillipsburg, Kansas.]

22. MacFarlane's Circular Interest Rule.

[Art. "Slide Rule," by De Morgan in the *Penny Cyclopaedia*, 1842.]

23. MacFarlane's Cylindrical Slide Rule.

[Art. "Slide Rule," by De Morgan in the *Penny Cyclopaedia*, 1842.]

24. Palmer's Endless, Self-Computing Scale.

25. Palmer's Pocket Scale.

[These instruments, composed of concentric circles (one
movable within the other), appear to be the first slide
rules designed, manufactured, and sold in the United
States. The title of Palmer's 1844 publication, comprising 50 pages, is as follows: "A Key to the Endless,
Self-Computing Scale, showing its application to the
different Rules of Arithmetic, etc. By Aaron Palmer,
Boston: Published by Smith & Palmer, 1844." On
page 3 this scale is declared to be "the result of three
years' incessant labor." No reference is made to similar
instruments designed by others. Twelve recommenda-
tions of Palmer's Scale are printed in the booklet, one of
them by Benjamin Peirce, Professor of Astronomy and
Mathematics at Harvard University. Peirce says that
the scale is "simple and most ingenious." It is stated
in the booklet that the scale is made in three different
styles and numbers: No. 1, for common business calculations, at $2; No. 2, for higher branches of mathematics
at $3; No. 3, for nautical and astronomical calculations,
at $5. The circles (two or more) were about 8 in. in
diameter. There is also announced the manufacture of
metallic scales. In 1845 appeared a new edition of the
book: "Palmer's Pocket Scale, with Rules for its use in
solving Arithmetical and Geometrical Problems. Boston:
Published by Aaron Palmer. D. H. Ela, Printer, 37
Cornhill. 1845." The Pocket Scale is of cardboard and

contains two circles, 2⅝ in. in diameter; it is pasted,
inside, against the rear cover of the book. "All the errors
which have been discovered in the former editions, have
been corrected in this." We have seen only one "former"
edition, namely, the one of 1844, quoted above. But
Favaro, *op. cit.*, p. 509, names "Palmer's Computing
Scale, New York, 1843." I am indebted to Dr. Artemas
Martin, of Washington, D. C., for copies of the two editions of Palmer's booklets, described here. For a fuller
account of Palmer's Computing Scale, see the *Colorado
College Publication*, Engineering Series, Vol. I, No. 6
(1909).]

26. Lalanne, Arithmoplanimètre.

[Cited by Favaro, *op. cit.*, p. 510, from *Comptes rendus des
séances de l'académie des sciences*, 1840 (April 27, May 24),
and from Lalanne's "Mémoire sur l'Arithmoplanimètre,
machine arithmétique et géométrique donnant facile-
ment les résultats des opérations les plus compliquées de
calcul et de planimétrie" in the *Annales des Ponts et
Chaussées.* 1er semestre, 1840.]

27. Lalanne, Règle à calcul à enveloppe de verre.

[Favaro, *loc. cit.*, p. 510, cites *Instruction sur les règles à
calcul et particulièrement sur la nouvelle règle* à *enveloppe
de verre* par. L. Lalanne, Paris, 1851, 1854, 1863. Translated into English under the title *A Treatise on the slide
rule with description of Lalanne's glass slide rule*, London,
1851; transl. into German, *Gebrauchs-Anweisung für
Rechenstäbe*, etc., Paris, 1852, and into Spanish, *Instruction sobre las reglas de calculo*, etc., Paris, 1852. This
slide rule was designed as a cheap rule.]

28. Lalanne, tableau graphique.

[*Bull. de la société d'encouragement pour l'industrie nationale*, Vol. 45, Paris, 1846, p. 153. Designed by Léon
Lalanne, ingénieur des ponts et chaussées. Favaro,
op. cit., p. 510, refers to the following publications: *Notice
sur les travaux et titres scientifiques*, de M. Léon Lalanne,
Paris, 1876, p. 32, and to *Méthodes graphiques pour l'expression des lois empiriques on mathématiques à trois
variables, avec des applications à l'art de l'ingènieur et à la*

résolution des équations numeriques d'un degré quelconque.
Par M. Léon Lalanne, Paris, 1878.]

29. Eschmann-Wild's Tachymeterschieber.

[Cited by Favaro, *loc. cit.*, p. 512, from *Der topographische Distanzmesser mit Rechenschieber* von J. Stambach, Aarau, 1872. See also *Engineering News*, New York, Vol. 54, 1905, p. 486; E. Hammer, *Der logarithmische Rechenschieber*, 4te Auflage, Stuttgart, 1908, p. 10. Was used in the Canton Zürich, Switzerland, as early as 1847.]

30. Bradford's Sliding Rule.

[Cited by Favaro, *loc. cit.*, p. 512, from a publication *On Bradford's Sliding Rule*, London, 1845.]

31. Porro's Scale Logaritmiche Centesimali.

[Cited by Favaro, *op. cit.*, p. 512, from *La Tachéométrie*, ecc., par J. Porro, Turin, 1850, p. 75.]

32. Regolo Calcolatorio di Oesterle.

[Cited by Favaro, *op. cit.*, p. 508, from Ernest Sedlaczek, *Neber Visir- und Recheninstrumente*, Wien, 1856, pp. 3, 4, and from Ernest Sedlaczek, *Anleitung z. Gebrauche einiger logarith. getheilter Rechenschieber*, Wien, 1851.]

33. Altmütter's Rechenschieber.

[*Zeitschr. f. Mathematik und Physik*, Vol. 47, 1902, p. 491. Designed by G. Altmütter and printed on cardboard in Vienna before 1851.]

34. Werner's Rechenschieber.

[*Zeitschr. für Mathematik und Physik*, Vol. 47, 1902, p. 491. F. Werner was a mechanic in Vienna, about 1850, who made rules of boxwood.]

35. Werner's Tachymeterschieber.

[E. Hammer, *Der logarithmische Rechenschieber*, 4te Aufl., Stuttgart, 1908, p. 10.]

36. Règle Mannheim.

[Mannheim, *Règle à calculs modifiée. Instruction*, Metz, Imp. et. lith. Nouvian, Décembre, 1851; also in Nouvelles Annales de Mathématiques, Ière Série, tome XII, 1853, pp. ?27–329. See also P. Rozé, *Théorie et usage de la règle à calculs*, Paris, 1907, pp. 21, 58–82; E. Hammer, *Der logarithmische Rechenschieber und sein Gebrauch*, Stuttgart, 1908, p. 6; Pickworth, *op. cit.*, 1906, p. 14; *De Ingenieur* 18e Jaargang, 1803, p. 88, ff.; *Engineering News*, Vol. 25, 1891, p. 16. Made by Tavernier-Gravet of Paris, and goes also under the name of the "Tavernier-Gravet Slide Rule" and the "Gravet Slide Rule." Rules of the Mannheim type are now made and sold by nearly all slide rule manufacturers of the present time. Favaro, *loc. cit.*, p. 511, refers for description to *Teorica e pratica del regolo calcolatore* per Quintino Sella, Torino, 1859, p. 100–109; Wm. Cox, *The Mannheim Slide Rule*, published by Keuffel & Esser Co., New York, 1891, pp. 1–10; C. W. Crockett, *Explanation of the Principles and Operation of the Mannheim Slide Rule*, Troy, N. Y., 1891. See Fig. 11.]

37. Mannheim Règle à Calcul Cylindrique.

[*Nouvelles Annales de Mathématiques*, tome XIII, 1854, p. 36; *Encyklopädie d. Math. Wiss.*, Bd. I. Leipzig, 1898–1904, p. 1060. Made of wood in 1871, since 1873 in metal.]

38. Lenoir's Règle à Calcul.

[*Bull. de la société d'encouragement pour l'industrie nationale*, Vol. 52, 1853, p. 588; also Vol. 20, p. 77, and Vol. 23, p. 129. Lenoir constructed his instruments about 1821 and later. See also E. Sedlaczek, *Anleitung z. Gebrauche einiger logar. getheilter Rechenschieber*, Wien, 1851, who is cited by Favaro, *op. cit.*, p. 509.]

39. Sargent's Règle à Calcul.

[*Bull. de la société d'encouragement pour l'industrie nationale*, Vol. 52, Paris, 1853, p. 589; also Vol. 21, p. 12.]

40. Prestel's Arithmetische Scheibe.

[*Mittheilungen des Gewerbevereins f. d. Königreich Hannover*, 1854, p. 169; *Zeitschr. des Architecten- u. Ingenieur-Vereins f. d. Königr. Hannover*, Vol. 10, Hannover, 1864, p. 454.]

41. Regolo di Higgison.

[Cited by Favaro, *op. cit.*, p. 509, from E. Sedlaczek, *Ueber Visir- und Recheninstrumente*, Wien, 1856, pp. 3, 4.]

42. Regolo per iscopi costruttivi e geodetici del Prof. L. C. Schulz von Strassnicki.

[Cited by Favaro, *op. cit.*, p. 509, from E. Sedlaczek, *Ueber Visir- und Recheninstrumente*, Wien, 1856, pp. 3, 4.]

43. Regolo Calcolatorio di Schwind.

[Cited by Favaro, *op. cit.*, p. 509, from E. Sedlaczek, *Ueber Visir- und Recheninstrumente*, Wien, 1856, pp. 3, 4, and E. Sedlaczek, *Anleitung zum Gebrauche einiger logar. getheilter Rechenschieber*, Wien, 1851.]

44. Bouché, Hélice à Calcul.

[*Calcul simplifié*, par Maurice d'Ocagne, seconde éd., Paris, 1905, p. 109; *Comptes rendus*, 2e sem. 1857, p. 437.]

45. Regolo di Sedlaczek per i calcoli d'interpolazione.

[Cited by Favaro, *op. cit.*, p. 509, from E. Sedlaczek, *Ueber Visir- und Recheninstrumente*, Wien, 1856, pp. 3, 4, and E. Sedlaczek, *Anleitung zum Gebrauche einiger Logarith. getheilter Rechenschieber*, Wien, 1851.]

46. Dubois, Arithmograph.

[Cited by Favaro, *loc. cit.*, p. 511, from *Comptes Rendus hebdomadaires des séances de l'acad. d. sciences*, T. LI, 1860, p. 293, and from *Atti dell' Imp. Reg. Istituto veneto di scienze*, etc., Novembre, 1860, all' ottobre, 1861. Tomo sesto, serie terza. Venezia, 1860–61, p. 376.]

47. Carrett's Slide Rule.

[W. H. Bayley's *Hand-Book of the Slide Rule*, London, 1861, Preface.]

48. Delaveleye's Règle à Calcul.

[*Bull. de la société d'encouragement pour l'industrie nationale*, Vol. 62, Paris, 1863, p. 659. Designed a rule 2.30 m. long.]

49. Delamorinière Règle à Calcul.

[*Bull. de la société d'encouragement pour l'industrie nationale*, Vol. 62, Paris, 1863, p. 659. Designed an instrument 1.20 m. long.]

50. Burdon Règle à Calcul.

[*Comptes rendus*, Paris, Vol. 58, 1864, pp. 573–576. A log-log rule.]

51. Péraux, Échelle Logarithmique.

[*Bull. de la société d'encouragement pour l'industrie na-itonale*, Vol. 62, 1863, p. 513; also *N. Annales de mathé-matiques*, 2d S., Vol. 18, Paris, 1869, pp. 283–5. M. Péraux was a merchant in Nancy. Favaro, *loc. cit.*, p. 512, refers to an article *Instruction sur la règle à calcul à deux réglettes*, par E. Péraux (Extrait des *Annales du Gènie Civil*, juin 1874), Paris, 1874, also Paris, 1885.]

52. Everett's Universal Proportion-table, or Gridiron Slide Rule.

[The Universal-proportion-table was published by Long-mans, Green and Dyer. See Pickworth, *The Slide Rule*, 10th ed., p. 102; *Report British Ass'n* for 1866, p. 2; *Philosophical Magazine* (4), Vol. 32, 1866, p. 350; C. V. Boys "The Slide Rule" in *Van Nostrand's Engin. Maga-zine*, Vol. 33, 1885, p. 513. Invented by Professor J. D. Everett, Professor of Mathematics in Glasgow University.]

53. Everett's Cylindrical Slide Rule.

[Only in model; see references to his "Universal Propor-tion-table."]

54. Derivry, Carte à Calcul.

[M. d'Ocagne, *Calcul simplifié*, 2ᵉ éd., Paris, 1905, p. 120.]

55. Sonne's Rechenscheibe.

[*Zeitschr. d. Architecten- u. Ingenieur-Vereins f. d. Königr. Hannover*, Vol. 10, 1864, p. 451–458. Made by Lands-berg and Parisius, mechanicians in Hannover. Favaro, *op. cit.*, 510, refers to *Annales du Génie Civil*. Cinquième année, 1866, and to *Instruments et machines à calculer*, Paris, 1868, p. 75.]

56. Coulson's Slide Rule.

[J. F. Heather, *Drawing and Measuring Instruments*, London, 1871, p. 144, with a figure of the rule; it has four slides. See also Coulson's book on the Slide Rule.]

57. Heather's Cubing Rule.

[J. F. Heather, *Drawing and Measuring Instruments*, London, 1871, p. 147. Three feet long, containing four lines, *A*, *B*, *C*, *E*.]

58. Kentish Slide Rule.

[J. F. Heather, *Drawing and Measuring Instruments*, London, 1871, p. 144. Was mnaufactured by Messrs. Dring & Fage.]

59. Bayley's "One-Slide" Rule.

[*English Cyclopedia* (Arts and Sciences), Art. "Sliding Rule." Was made by Elliot, Strand, in London. See also W. H. Bayley's *Hand-Book of the Slide Rule*, London, 1861, Preface, and p. 338; J. F. Heather's *Drawing and Measuring Instruments*, London, 1871, p. 143.]

60. Bayley's "Two-Slide" Rule.

[W. H. Bayley's *Hand-Book of the Slide Rule*, London, 1861, Preface, and p. 340. Was made by Elliot, 30 Strand, in London.]

61. The Timber-contenting Rule.

[J. F. Heather, *Drawing and Measuring Instruments*, London, 1871, p. 149. Usually two feet long, one side containing the lines A, B, C, D, and the other side A, B, C, E (inverted).]

62. Hoare's Slide Rule.

[*The Slide Rule and How to Use it*, by Charles Hoare, C.E., with a slide rule in tuck of cover. Sixth edition, London, 1890. Date of preface, 1867. Rule has two slides.]

63. Ipsologista di Paola de Saint-Robert.

[*Torino Acc. Sci. Memorie* (2), Vol. 25, 1871, p. 53; *Eycyklopädie d. Math. Wiss.*, Bd. I, 1898–1904, p. 1064. See also Q. Sella *Regolo Calcolatore*, 2 ed., Ital., Torino, 1886, p. 159.]

64. Regolo Soldati per i calcoli di celerimensura.

[Cited by Favaro, *loc. cit.*, p. 511, from "Cenni intorno ad un saggio di celerimensura applicata alla compilazione dei progetti ferroviarii e descrizione di tavole grafiche e numeriche pel calcolo delle coordinate, per l'ing. V. Soldati," in *Atti della Società degli Ingegneri e degli Industriali di Torino*. Anno V, 1871, p. 38. See also Quintino Sella *Regolo Calcolatore*, 2 ed., Ital., Torino, 1886, p. 163.]

65. Routledge's Slide Rule.

[Cited by Favaro, *loc. cit.*, p. 512, from *Catalogue of instruments manufactured by W. F. Stanley*, 14th ed., London, 1877, p. 30. See also J. F. Heather's *Drawing and Measuring Instruments*, London, 1871, p. 142; W. H. Bayley's *Hand-Book of the Slide Rule*, London, 1861, Preface.]

66. Weber's Rechenkreisen.

[R. Weber, *Anleitung zum Gebrauche des Rechenkreises* Aschaffenburg, 1872; *Encyklopädie d. Math. Wiss.*, Bd. I, 1898–1904, p. 1063.]

67. Goulier, Règle pour les Levers Tachéométriques.

[*Calcul simplifié*, par Maurice d'Ocagne, 2e éd., Paris, 1905, p. 118. Made by Tavernier-Gravet as early as 1873.]

68. Rechenstab von Dennert und Pape.

[*Deutsche Bauzeitung*, Bd. 8, 1874, p. 136.]

69. Darwin's Slide Rules.

[*Proceed. London Math. Soc.*, Vol. 6, 1875, p. 113. G. H. Darwin here proposes two types of slide rules, to be small enough for pocket rules, and yet powerful.]

70. Culmann's Rechenschieber für Distanzmessern.

[Designed by C. Culmann and described in his *Die Graphische Statik*, Zürich, Vol. I., 1875, p. 65.]

71. Coggeshall's Slide Rule.

[J. F. Heather, *A Treatise on Mathematical Instruments*, London, 1874, p. 55. Favaro, *loc. cit.*, p. 512, refers to a publication *On Coggeshall's Sliding Rule*, London, 1844.]

72. De Montrichard, Règle pour le Cubage des Bois.

[*Calcul simplifié*, par Maurice d'Ocagne, 2e éd., Paris, 1905, p. 118. Made by Tavernier-Gravet in 1876 and later.]

73. Pestalozzi's Rechenschieber.

[See C. Culmann, *Die Graphische Statik*, Zürich, Vol. I., 1875, p. 69. Designed for agiotage by Banquier L. Pestalozzi.]

74. Puscariu's Stereometer.

[Cited by Favaro, *loc. cit.*, p. 511, from *Das Stereometer, Körper-Messinstrument* von Johann Ritter von Puscariu, Budapest, 1877.]

75. Hawthorn's Slide Rule.

[Cited by Favaro, *loc. cit.*, p. 512, from *Catalogue of Instruments manufactured by W. F. Stanley*, 14th ed., London, 1877, p. 30. See also W. H. Bayley's *Hand-Book of the Slide Rule*, London, 1861, Preface.]

76. Moinot, Règle Logarithmique pour la Tachéometrie.

[Cited by Favaro, *loc. cit.*, p. 512, from *Leves de Plans à la Stadia. Notes pratiques pour études de tracés* par I. Moinot. Troisième édition, Paris, 1877, p. 41–67. Constructed by Tavernier-Gravet as early as 1868; see *Calcul simplifié* par Maurice d'Ocagne, 2e éd., Paris, 1905, p. 118.]

77. Boucher Calculator.

[Pickworth, Charles N., *The Slide Rule; A Practical Manual*, 10th ed., Manchester, London, New York, 1906, p. 93. Manufactured by W. F. Stanley & Co., Holborn, London. It is a circular slide rule with two dials. Is made by H. Chatelain in Paris in improved form; by Messrs. Manlove, Alliott, Fryer and Co. of Nottingham; by J. F. Steward, Strand, London; also by Keuffel & Esser Co. in New York. See also *La Nature*, 6e année, 8 juin, Paris, 1878, pp. 31, 32. See Fig. 12.]

78. Herrmann's Rechenknecht.

[*Zeitsch. des Vereins Deutscher Ingenieure*, Vol. 21, 1877, p. 455. This circular rule was made by Wiesenthal u. Cie. in Aachen. Favaro, *loc. cit.*, p. 511.]

79. G. Fuller's Spiral Slide Rule.

[Pickworth, Charles N., *The Slide Rule; A Practical Manual*, 1906, p. 100; Blaine, R. G., *Some Quick and Easy Methods of Calculating*, 2d ed., London, 1903, p. 91. Made by Stanley. See also Fuller, George, *Spiral Slide Rule, Equivalent to a straight slide rule 83 feet 4 inches long, or a circular rule 13 feet 3 inches in diameter*. London, 1878. George Fuller, Professor of Engineering, Queen's University, Ireland. See Fig. 13.]

80. J. Fuller's Computing Telegraph.

[This instrument consists of a "Time Telegraph," designed by Fuller, which he added to or united with Aaron Palmer's "Computing Scale." The "Time Telegraph" was a non-logarithmic circular scale for determining the number of days between given dates. See *Improvement to Palmer's Endless Self-Computing Scale and Key; . . . with a Time Telegraph, making, by uniting the two, a Computing Telegraph*. By John E. Fuller, New York, 1846. See also the *Colorado College Publication*, Engineering Series, Vol. I, No. 7 (1909).]

81. J. Fuller's Telegraph Computer.

[*Telegraphic Computer, a most wonderful and extraordinary instrument, by which business questions, of every possible variety, are instantly performed; a safe and speedy check to avoid vexatious errors, affording at the same time a greater amount of practical business knowledge than can be obtained for ten times the cost of this work*. Sold only by subscription. John Fuller, New York (about 1860). Cited by Favaro, *op. cit.*, p. 510. A circular slide rule.]

82. Thacher's Calculating Instrument.

[*Thacher's Patent Calculating Instrument or Cylindrical Slide Rule*, by Edwin Thacher, M. Am. Soc. C.E., New York, Keuffel & Esser Co., 1903. An edition of 1884 was brought out by D. Van Nostrand, New York. The rule was patented in 1881, and is manufactured by Keuffel & Esser Co. Approaches closely to a five-place table of logarithms in accuracy. See also Thacher's article in the *Proceeds. Engineers' Society of Western Pennsylvania*, Vol. I, Pittsburgh, Pa., 1880, pp. 289–310. See Fig. 9.]

83. Ruth's Rechenschieber.

[Dingler's *Polytechnisches Journal*, Vol. 242, Augsburg, 1881; also *Theorie der logarithmischen Rechenschieber* von Franz Ruth.]

84. ЧЕРЕПАШИНСКІЙ, М. М. Slide Rule.

[Черепашинскій, М. М., Теоріа и употребленіе карманной счетной линейки собственной системы. Москва, 1883. See also P. Rozé, *Règle à Calculs*, Paris, 1907, p. 2. See Fig. 11.]

85. Ganga Ram's Special Rules.
    [*Van Nostrand's Engin. Magazine*, Vol. 33, 1885, pp. 516, 517.]

86. Thomson's Log-Log Rule.
    [*Van Nostrand's Engin. Magazine*, Vol. 33, 1885, p. 516. Thomson was then a British lieutenant, later became captain.]

87. Lebrun, Règle pour les Calculs de Terrassements.
    [*Calcul simplifié*, par Maurice d'Ocagne, 2e éd., Paris, 1905, p. 118. Made by Tavernier-Gravet as early as 1886.]

88. Tower's Slide Instrument.
    [*Van Nostrand's Engin. Magazine,* Vol. 33, 1885, p. 516. Mr. Beauchamp Tower, well knc vn in connection with the spherical engine.]

89. Dixon's Rules.
    [*Van Nostrand's Engin. Magazine*, Vol. 33, 1885, pp. 515, 517. His "triple radius double-slide rule" allows complex operations.]

90. Hannyngton's Extended Slide Rule.
    [Pickworth, *The Slide Rule*, 10th ed., p. 102; C. V. Boys, "The Slide Rule" in *Van Nostrand's Engin. Magazine*, Vol. 33, 1885, p. 513; manufactured by Aston & Mauder in Soho, W. London.]

91. Cherry's Calculator.
    [Pickworth, *The Slide Rule*, 10th ed., p. 102. Designed by Henry Cherry in 1880.]

92. M. Kloth's Apparat.
    [*Encyklopädie d. Math. Wiss.*, Bd. I., 1898–1904, p. 1059; D. R. P. Nr. 26695, V. 1883; Dingler's *Polyt. Jour.*, Vol. 260, 1886, p. 170.]

93. Toulon, Règle pour les Calculs de Terrassements.
    [*Calcul simplifié*, par Maurice d'Ocagne, 2e éd., Paris, 1905, p. 118; Durand-Claye, *Cours de Routes*, 2e éd., p. 561.]

94. Rechenschieber von Zellhorn.

[*Dennert & Pape* of Altona was the first firm to manufacture slide rules of white celluloid or Zellhorn, in 1886.
Now all manufacturers in the world face the rules with
celluloid. *Encyklopädie d. Math. Wiss.*, Bd. I, 1898–
1904, p. 1055.]

95. Regolo psicrometrico di A. Prazmowski.

[See Q. Sella, *Regolo Calcolatore*, 2 ed., Ital., Torino, 1886,
p. 161. Prazmowski was an astronomer of Warsaw in
Poland.]

96. Pouech, Échelles Enroulées en Spirales pour les Racines Carrées et Cubiques.

[M. d'Ocagne, *Calcul simplifié*, 2ᵉ éd., Paris, 1905, p. 121.
Designed before 1890.]

97. Beyerlen's Rechenrad.

[*Zeitsch. f. Vermess. W.*, Vol. 15, 1886, p. 382; *Gewerbeblatt aus Würtemberg*, 1886, pp. 201–206. Designed by
A. Beyerlen of Stuttgart and made in Stuttgart by the
mechanician Tesdorpf.]

98. Paulin, Règle pour les Calculs Terrassements.

[*Portefeuille des Conducteurs des Ponts et Chaussées*, T.
XXI, 1889, p. 133; see also *Calcul simplifié*, par Maurice
d'Ocagne, 2ᵉ éd., Paris, 1905, p. 118.]

99. Regolo di F. Stapff.

[Described by Quintino Sella in his *Regolo Calcolatore*,
2 ed., Ital., Torino, 1886, pp. 163, 164. This rule was
used in computing an equation with four variables, ex-
pressing the volume of certain excavations of earth.]

100. Sanguet, Règle pour les Levers Tachéométriques.

[*Calcul simplifié*, par Maurice d'Ocagne, 2ᵉ éd., Paris, 1905,
p. 118. Made by Tavernier-Gravet as early as 1888.]

101. K. & E. Patented Adjustable Slide Rule (Mannheim).

[Wm. Cox, *The Mannheim Slide Rule*, published by
Keuffel & Esser Co., New York, 1891, p. 12. Patented
June 5, 1900.]

102. Hasselblatt's Rechenschieber.

[Dingler's *Polytechnisches Journal*, Vol. 278, 1890, p. 520. Hasselblatt was then docent at the Technological Institute in St. Petersburg. The rule was of cardboard and was made in St. Petersburg. Hasselblatt published, in Russian, a book on his slide rule.]

103. Kern Règle à Calcul pour la Stadia Topographique.

[J. Stambach, *Instruction pour la détermination de la distance et de la différence d'altitude d'un objet à un point de Station*, Aarau, 1890. Made by Kern & Cie, Aarau, Switzerland.]

104. Pollit's Hydraulic Slide Rule.

[Designed by C. T. Pollit of Adelaide, South Australia. Made by Elliot Brothers, St. Martins-lane, London. See *Engineering and Mining Journal*, New York, Vol. 54, 1892, p. 130.]

105. Bosramier, Règle pour les Levers Tachéométriques.

[*Calcul simplifié*, par Maurice d'Ocagne, 2e éd., Paris, 1905, p. 118. Made by Tavernier-Gravet in 1892.]

106. Wingham's Slide Rule for Calculating Blast-Furnace Charges.

[Designed by A. Wingham of the British Mint. See *Engineering and Mining Journal*, New York, 1892, Vol. 54, p. 487.]

107. Scherer's Rechentafel.

[*Zeitschr. für Vermessungsw.*, 1892, p. 153; also 1894, pp. 54–60; W. Jordan, *Handbuch der Vermessungskunde*, Bd. II. Stuttgart, 1897, p. 134; Scherer's *Logarithmisch-graphische Rechentafel*, Kassel, 1893.]

108. W. H. Breithaupt's Reaction Scale and General Slide Rule.

[*Engineering News*, Vol. 32, 1894, p. 103. Made and sold by E. G. Soltmann, 119 Fulton St., New York City.]

109. A. Steinhauser's Rechenscheibe.

[*Encyklopädie d. Math. Wiss.*, Bd. I, 1898–1904, p. 1063; Dyck's *Katalog, Nachtrag*, p. 3, Nr. 11 c. Designed in München in 1893.]

110. F. W. Lanchester's Rule for Solving Equations.
> [*Calcul simplifié* par Maurice d'Ocagne, 2ᵉ éd., Paris, 1905, p. 118; *Engineering*, August 7, 1896, p. 172.]

111. Omnimeter.
> [*Engineering News*, Vol. 38, 1897, p. 291. Sold by Theodore Alteneder & Sons, 945 Ridge Ave., Philadelphia, Pa.]

112. J. Crevat, Ruban Logarithmique.
> [M. d'Ocagne, *Calcul simplifié*, 2ᵉ éd., Paris, 1905, p. 119; *Nature*, 1893, p. 378.]

113. Cox's Duplex Slide Rules.
> [*Catalogue of Keuffel & Esser Co.*, New York, 1906, p. 324. Patented October 6, 1897, designed by William Cox. See *American Machinist*, Vol. 27, Pt. II, 1904, p. 1376. See Fig. 14.]

114. Faber's Rechenstab.

114 (a). Faber's Improved Calculating Rule for Electrical and Mechanical Engineers.
> [*Der Praktische Maschinen-Constructeur* (Uhland), Vol. 27, 1894, p. 8; originally made by A. W. Faber in Stein near Nürnberg; now this firm has houses also in England, France, and the United States (Newark, N. J.). See C. N. Pickworth, *Instructions for the Use of A. W. Faber's Improved Calculating Rule*, London, E. C.; Rudolf Krause, *Rechnen mit dem Rechenschieber nach dem Dreiskalensystem der Firmen Dennert & Pape, A. W. Faber, Nestler u. A.*, Mittwerda (no date).]

115. Gallice, Règle pour les Calculs Nautiques (en employant la division de la circonférence en 240 degrés proposée par M. de Sarrauton).
> [*Calcul simplifié* par Maurice d'Ocagne, 2ᵉ éd., Paris, 1905, p. 118. Made by Tavernier-Gravet in 1897.]

116. Johnson's Rule for Unit Strains in Columns.
> [*Engineering Record*, 1894, Vol. 30, p. 31. Designed by Thomas H. Johnson, of Pittsburgh, Pa., M. Am. Soc. C.E.]

117. Crane's Sewer Slide Rule.
> [*Catalogue of Keuffel & Esser Co.*, New York, 1906, p. 328. Patented Oct. 6, 1891. See also *Engineering* (London),

Vol. 62, 1896, p. 655. Designed by A. S. Crane, of Brooklyn, New York, and introduced into England by A. Wollheim.]

118. **L. Torres, Machine for Solution of Equations.**

[M. d'Ocagne, *Calcul simplifié*, 2ᵉ éd., Paris, 1905, pp. 95, 123. Torres is a Spanish engineer who invented this logarithmic machine in 1893.]

119. **Schuermann's Computing Instrument.**

[*Engin. Ass'n. of the South*, Vol. 7, Nashville, Tenn., 1896, pp. 92–99.]

120. **Jordan Rechenschieber.**

[Designed by W. Jordan and described in his *Handbuch der Vermessungekunde*, Bd. II, Stuttgart, 1897, p. 130, Fig. 4. It is manufactured by Dennert Pape in Altona.]

121. **Landsberg's Rechenscheibe.**

[*Zeitsch. f. Instrumentenkunde*, Vol. 20, p. 336. See also W. Jordan, *Handbuch der Vermessungekunde*, Bd. Il, Stuttgart, 1897, p. 134. After the design due to Sonne. Landsberg was a mechanic in Hannover.]

122. **F. A. Meyer's Taschenschnellrechner.**

[*Mechaniker*, Vol. 5, 1897; *Encyklopädie de Math. Wiss.*, Bd. I, 1898–1904, p. 1063.]

123. **Règle pour les Vitesses, Poids et Calibres des Projectiles.**

[*Calcul simplifié*. par Maurice d'Ocagne, 2ᵉ éd., Paris, 1905, p. 118. Made in 1895 for La Société des Forges et Aciéries de Saint-Chamond.]

124. **Naish's Logarithmicon.**

[*The Logarithmicon; A mechanical contrivance for facilitating calculations*. Described by Edmund Naish, Dublin, 1898.]

125. **Lallemand, Règle à Calcul.**

[*Zeitschr. Vermessungsw.*, Vol. 29, 1900, p. 233; *Encyklopädie Math. Wiss.*, Bd. I, Leipzig, 1898–1904, p. 1059.]

126. **Hart's Proportior.**

[*Techniker*, Vol. 12, 1889–1890, p. 34; *Encyklopädie d. Math. Wiss.*, Vol. I, Leipzig, 1898–1904, p. 1063.]

127. Renaud-Tachet, Règle Circulaire.
   [M. d'Ocagne, *Calcul simplifié*, 2e éd., Paris, 1905, p. 121;
   Génie civil, 21 Janvier, 1893, p. 191.]

128. Clouth Rechenscheibe.
   [F. M. Clouth, *Anleitung zum Gebrauch der Rechenscheibe*,
   Hamburg, 1872; Dyck's *Katalog, Nachtrag*, p. 3, Nr. 11 d;
   Encyklopädie d. Math. Wiss., Bd. I, Leipzig, 1898–1904,
   p. 1062.]

129. F. J. Vaes, Règle pour la Traction des Locomotives.
   [M. d'Ocagne, *Traité de Nomographie*, Paris, 1899, p. 361;
   M. d'Ocagne, *Calcul simplifié*, 2e éd., Paris, 1905, p. 119.]

130. Sickman Scale.
   [*Yale Scientific Review*, Vol. 5, 1898, p. 47.   To determine
   mill water-power.]

131. F. J. Vaes, Échelles Binaires.
   [M. d'Ocagne, *Calcul simplifié*, 2e éd., Paris, 1905, p. 119.
   Vaes is a Dutch engineer.]

132. Sexton's Omnimetre.
   [*Yale Scientific Review*, Vol. 5, 1898, p. 47.   This is a
   circular type.]

133. Piper's Logarithmische Skale.
   [Referred to by E. Naish in his *Logarithmicon*, Dublin,
   1898, p. 43.   Designed by Dr. Piper, of Lemgo, Germany.]

134. Wichmann's Rechenschieber.
   [*Zeitschr. für Mathematik and Physik*, Vol. 47, 1902, p. 491.
   Paper scales mounted on wood, about 1895; made by
   Gebr. Wichmann in Berlin.]

135. Honeysett's Hydraulic Slide Rule.
   [Pickworth, *The Slide Rule*, 10th ed., p. IV; made by
   W. F. Stanley & Co., Ltd., Holborn, London.   Based on
   Bazin's formula.]

136. J. Billeter, Rechenwalze.
   [M. d'Ocagne, *Calcul simplifié*, 2e éd., Paris, 1905, p. 120;
   Zeitschr. f. Vermessungsw., Vol. 20, 1891, p. 346; *Encyklo-
   pädie d. Math. Wiss.*, Bd. I, p. 1059, Note 558.]

137. Hamann's Proportional-Rechenschieber.

[*Zeitschr. Vermessungsw.*, Vol. 28, 1899, p. 660; see also *Encyklopädie d. Math. Wiss.*, Vol. I, 1898–1904, p. 1066.]

138. Hales' Slide Rule for Indicator Diagrams.

[Pickworth, *The Slide Rule*, 10th ed., p. IV; made by W. F. Stanley & Co., Ltd., Holborn, London.]

139. Fürle's Rechenschieber.

[Hermann Fürle, *Zur Theorie der Rechenschieber* (*Jahresbericht der Neunten Realschule zu Berlin. Ostern*, 1899); Berlin, 1899. This rule has eleven scales and a runner, and in general construction resembles Robertson's slide rule of 1778. But the scales are differently graduated. Besides the four scales on the Mannheim rule, it has scales for the functions x, x^2, x^3, log log x.]

140. Froude's Displacement Rule.

[Pickworth, *The Slide Rule*, 10th ed., p. IV; made by W. F. Stanley & Co., Ltd., Holborn, London.]

141. Cox's Strength of Gear Computer.

[F. A. Halsey, *The Use of the Slide Rule*, New York, 1899, p. 74.]

142. G. Charpentier's Calculimètre.

[*De Ingenierer*, Vol. 18, 1903, p. 94; F. A. Halsey, *The Use of the Slide Rule*, New York, 1899, p. 66. Fig. 15.]

143. Règle des écoles.

[P. Rozé, *Théorie et usage de la règle a calculs*, Paris, 1907, pp. 2, 22. This rule, used in technical schools in Paris, is after the designs of Cherepashinskii and of Beghin. See Fig. 11.]

144. Mehmke Rechenschieber für Komplexe Grössen.

[Designed by R. Mehmke in Stuttgart. See Dyck's *Katalog, Nachtrag*, p. 21, Nr. 44 d; *Encyklopädie d. Math. Wiss.*, Bd. I, 1898–1904, p. 1065.]

145. Beghin's Règle à Calcul.

[A. Beghin, *Règle à calcul, modèle spècial*, . . . Paris, 1898, 2e éd., 1902. See also *Encyklopädie d. Math. Wiss.*, Bd. I, Leipzig, 1898–1904, p. 1058; P. Rozé, *Règle à calculs*, Paris, 1907, pp. 2, 3, 113.]

146. Peter's Universal Rechenschieber.
[*Instructions for the Calculating Slide Rule*, by Albert Nestler, Lahr, Baden, p. 63; E. Hammer, *Der logarithmische Rechenschieber*, 4te Aufl., Stuttgart, 1908, p. 10.]

147. "Peter and Perry" Rule.
[*Instructions for the Calculating Slide Rule*, by Albert Nestler, p. 56. It has a log-log scale and is manufactured by Albert Nestler in Lahr, Baden.]

148. Pickworth's Power Computer.
[Pickworth, *The Slide Rule*, 10th ed., p. VII. Sold by the designer C. N. Pickworth, Fallowfield, Manchester.]

149. Precision Slide Rule.
[C. N. Pickworth, *op. cit.*, p. 88; *Instructions for the Calculating Slide Rule*, Albert Nestler, Lahr, Baden, p. 32. Made by Albert Nestler in Lahr, Baden.]

150. Puller's Rechenscheibe.
[*Zeitsch. f. Instrumentenkunde*, Vol. 20, 1900, p. 336. Designed by Ingenieur E. Puller in St. Johann (Saarbrücken.]

151. Röther's Rechenscheibe.
[*Zeitsch. f. Instrumentenkunde*, Vol. 20, 1900, p. 335. Manufactured with diameter of 80 mm. and also 220 mm. Designed by Bezirksgeometer Röther in Weiden, Bayern.]

152. Sheppard's Cubing and Squaring Slide Rule.
[Pickworth, *The Slide Rule*, 10th ed., p. IV; made by W. F. Stanley & Co., Ltd., London.]

153. Herrgott, Règle à Deux Réglettes.
[*Calcul simplifié*, par Maurice d'Ocagne, 2e éd., Paris, 1905, p. 116. Designed in 1900.]

154. Simplex Slide Rule.
[Sold now by John Davis & Son (Derby), Ltd.]

155. The Smith-Davis Premium Calculator.
[Pickworth, *The Slide Rule*, 10th ed., p. 104. Made by John Davis & Son, Derby.]

156. The Smith-Davis Piecework Balance Calculator.
[Pickworth, *The Slide Rule*, 10th ed., p. 103.   Made by John Davis & Son, Derby.]

157. Sperry's Pocket Calculator.
[Pickworth, Charles N., *The Slide Rule; A practical manual*, 10th ed., Manchester, London, New York, 1906, p. 99.   Manufactured by Keuffel & Esser Co., New York. A circular rule with two rotating dials.]

158. Burnham's Circular Slide Rule.
[Designed by the astronomer S. W. Burnham of the Yerkes Observatory, divided for him by Warner & Trasey; is 7½ in. in diameter and divided into 1000 parts, thus giving four places, the last by estimation.   Has accuracy of a four-place table.   A movable arm (runner) has a lens for close reading and a stop which can be pressed down and movable inner circle brought to coincidence with the arm, without looking at the divisions.   This saves time in continuous multiplications, etc.]

159. The Davis Log-Log Rule.
[Pickworth, *The Slide Rule*, 10th ed., p. 79.   Made by Messrs. John Davis & Son, Ltd., Derby.]

160. The Faber Log-Log Rule.
[Pickworth, *The Slide Rule*, 10th ed., p. 84.   Manufactured by A. W. Faber in Stein near Nürnberg.   See also C. N. Pickworth, *Instructions for the Use of A. W. Faber's Improved Calculating Rule*, London, E. C., p. 46.]

161. Hall's Nautical Slide Rule.
[Pickworth, *The Slide Rule*, 10th ed., p. 91.   Made by J. H. Steward, Strand, London.   This rule is designed by the Rev. William Hall, R.N.   It has two slides and eight scales.]

162. Hudson's Horse-power Scale.
[Pickworth, *The Slide Rule*, 10th ed., p. IV.   Made by W. F. Stanley & Co., Ltd., Holborn, London.]

163. Hudson's Shaft, Beam and Girder Scale.
[Pickworth, *The Slide Rule*, 10th ed., p. IV.   Made by W. F. Stanley & Co., Ltd., Holborn, London.]

164. Hudson's Pump Scale.

165. Hudson's Photo-Exposure Scale.

166. The Jackson-Davis Double Slide Rule.
   [Pickworth, *The Slide Rule*, 10th ed., p. 84.   Enables the log-log slide to be temporarily attached to the ordinary rule.]

167. Müller's Hydraulischer Rechenschieber.
   [*Oesterreich. Wochensch. f. d. öffentl. Baudienst*, Vol. 7, 1901, p. 72.]

168. Riebel's Geodetischer Rechenschieber.
   [*Oesterreich Wochensch. f. d. öffentl. Baudienst*, Vol. 7, 1901, p. 680.]

169. Schweth's Rechenschieber.
   [*Zeitsch. des Vereins Deutscher Ingenieure* (Peters), Vol. 45, 1901, Pt. I, pp. 567–8, 720; *Encyklopädie d. Math. Wiss.*, Bd. I., Leipzig, 1898–1904, p. 1064, Note 580.]

170. Slide Rule for Electrical Calculations.
   [*American Machinist*, New York, Vol. 24, 1901, p. 339. Instrument is made by A. E. Colgate, 36 Pine St., New York.]

171. Thacher-Scofield Engineer's Slide Rule.
   [E. M. Scofield, *The Slide Rule*, published by Eugene Dietzgen Co., Chicago, 1902, p. 21.   This rule is designed by Edwin Thacher and E. M. Scofield, bridge and consulting engineers.   Patented in 1901.]

172. Pierre Weiss, Règle à Calcul.
   [*Comptes rendus*, Vol. 131, 1900, p. 1289; *Journal de Physique*, Sept., 1901; *Nature*, Vol. 64, 1901, p. 523.]

173. Baines' Slide Rule for Solving Equations.
   [*Calcul simplifié*, par Maurice d'Ocagne, 2e éd., Paris, 1905, p. 118; *Engineer*, April 1, 1904, p. 346.]

174. A. Wüst Taschenrechenschieber.
   [*Zeitschr. für Mathematik and Physik*, Vol. 47, 1902, p. 491. Printed on cardboard in Halle about 1880.]

175. Barth's Slide Rule for Lathe Settings for Maximum Output.

> [*Engineering News*, New York, Vol. 50, 1903, p. 512; also Vol. 46, 1901, p. 461. A rule designed by Carl G. Barth and Fred W. Taylor in the shop of the Bethlehem Steel Co. It is a rectilinear rule.]

176. Barth's Rule for Strength of Spur Gears.

> [*Engineering News*, New York, Vol. 50, 1903, p. 514. A circular rule, according to formula of Wilfred Lewis, by Carl G. Barth. Copyright, 1902.]

177. Barth's Speed Slide Rule (lathe No. 43).

> [*Engineering News*, Vol. 50, 1903, p. 514. In *American Machinist*, Vol. 25, 1902, p. 1685, are described Barth's "General Speed Slide Rule" and also his "Special Speed Slide Rule." Copyright, 1902.]

178. Barth's Time Slide Rule.

> [*Engineering News*, New York, Vol. 50, 1903, p. 514. Copyright, 1902. A circular rule designed by Carl G. Barth, of Swarthmore, Pa., and Fred W. Taylor in the shop of the Bethlehem Steel Co. See also *Railway and Engineering Review*, Vol. 44, March, 1904, p. 152.]

179. Leven, Règle pour les Reports de Bourse.

> [*Calcul simplifié* par Maurice d'Ocagne, 2e éd., Paris, 1905, p. 118. Made by Tavernier-Gravet in 1903.]

180. F. Blanc's Rechenschieber.

> [*Zeitschr. des Vereins Deutscher Ingenieure*, Vol. 45, 1901, Pt. I, p. 720. A log-log rule designed in 1890.]

181. Cox's High Pressure Fluid Discharge Computer.

> [*American Machinist*, Vol. 25, 1902, p. 1515.]

182. Fürle's Rechenblätter.

> [Hermann Fürle, *Rechenblätter* (*Jahresbericht der Neunten Realschule zu Berlin.* Ostern. 1902), Berlin, 1902. As an example, we mention "Rechenblatt für photographische Zwecke," published by Mayer & Müller in Berlin, which solves the equations for lenses
> $$\frac{1}{a}+\frac{1}{b}=\frac{1}{f};\ \frac{a}{f}=1+\frac{\alpha}{\beta};\ \frac{b}{f}=1+\frac{\beta}{\alpha}.]$$

183. Matthes' The U. S. Geological Survey Topographic Slide Rule.

[*Technological Quarterly*, Boston, Vol. XV, 1902, pp. 250–259. Designed by Gerard H. Matthes and made by Kern & Cie., Aarau, Switzerland.]

184. The Perry Log-Log Rule.

[*Nature*, Vol. 67, 1902, p. 141; Pickworth, *The Slide Rule*, 10th ed., p. 85; R. G. Blaine, *Some Quick and Easy Methods of Calculating*, 2d ed., London, 1903, p. 69.]

185. Proell's Rechentafel.

[*Verhandl. d. Vereins z. Beförderung d. Gewerbefleisses*, Berlin, Vol. 21, 1902, p. 48; *Zeitsch. f. Math. u. Physik*, Vol. 46, p. 218; Pickworth, *Slide Rule*, 10th ed., p. 102. Designed by Reinhold Proell, an engineer in Dresden. See also *Rechentafel System Proell*, Berlin, 1901.]

186. Rietz's Rechenschieber.

[*Zeitschr. d. Vereins Deutscher Ingenieure*, Vol. 47, 1903, p. 1163; C. N. Pickworth, *The Slide Rule*, 10th ed., p. 88. Made by Albert Nestler in Lahr, Baden.]

187. Simplex Taschenrechenschieber.

[*Zeitschr. f. Instrumentenkunde*, Vol. 23, 1903, p. 158. Made by Dennert & Pape.]

188. Frank's Einscala-Rechenschieber.

[*Zeitschr. f. Instrumentenkunde*, Vol. 23, 1903, p. 159. Sold by A. Martz in Stuttgart.]

189. Hazen-Williams' Hydraulic Slide Rule.

[*Engineering Record*, New York, Vol. 47, 1903, pp. 321 and 667. Designed by Allen Hazen, of New York, and Professor Gardner S. Williams, of Cornell Univ. For sale by G. G. Ledder, 9 Province Court, Boston.]

190. Knowles' Calculating Scale.

[W. Knowles, *Calculating Scale; a Substitute for the Slide Rule*, Spon & Chamberlain, 1903; see also *Nature*, Vol. 69, 1904, p. 485.]

191. Mougnié, Règle pour le Calcul des Conduites d'eau, d'après la Formula de Flamant.

[*Calcul simplifié*, par Maurice d'Ocagne, 2ᵉ éd., Paris, 1905, p. 118. Made in 1904.]

192. Goldschmidt's Rule with Two Runners.
[*American Machinist*, New York, Vol. 27, Pt. II, 1904, pp. 1303, 1376, 1616.   Designed by Daniel Goldschmidt.]

193. Anthony's Improved Circular Hydraulic Calculator.
[See *H. Catalogue*, 1905, of W. F. Stanley & Co., Holborn, London.   Based on Manning's formula.]

194. Fuller-Bakewell Calculating Slide Scale.
[Like Fuller's Calculating Slide Scale, with the additional scales of sin² and sin × cos on the fixed cylinder.   See *H. Catalogue*, 1905, of W. F. Stanley & Co., Holborn, London.]

195. Moehlenbruck's Instrument.
[*Comptes rendus*, Paris, Vol. 138, 1904, pp. 1266–1268. A circular slide rule with double runner, enabling the various change gears for screw-cutting to be selected without computation.]

196. Stanley-Boucher Calculator.
[Differs from the Boucher Calculator in having a third index hand which indicates the total movement of the front hand.   See *H. Catalogue*, 1905, of W. F. Stanley & Co., Holborn, London.]

197. Union Slide Rule (Mannheim).
[L. W. Rosenthal, *Mannheim and Multiplex Slide Rules*, published by Eugene Dietzgen Co., Chicago, 1905, p. 60.]

198. Gravet's Tacheometer Slide Rule.
[See *H. Catalogue*, 1905, of W. F. Stanley & Co., Holborn, London.]

199. Mack Improved Slide Rule (Mannheim).
[L. W. Rosenthal, *Mannheim and Multiplex Slide Rules*, published by Eugene Dietzgen & Co., manufacturers and importers of drawing materials, Chicago, 1905, p. 60.] See Fig. 16.   This rule has a new mechanical construction, devised in 1898 by Professor John G. D. Mack of the University of Wisconsin, to allow the slide to move freely regardless of weather, temperature, etc.   It is manufactured in Chicago by Dietzgen & Co.]

200. Würth-Micha, Règle pour le Calcul des Distributions de Vapeur.

> [M. d'Ocagne, *Calcul simplifié*, 2e éd., Paris, 1905, p. 119. Designed in 1904 by Würth-Micha, an engineer in Liège.]

201. Masera's Rechenschieber.

> [*Schweizerische Bauzeit.* (Waldner), Vol. 45, Zürich, 1905, p. 189; also *Zeitschr. f. Instrumentenkunde*, Vol. 25, Berlin, 1905, p. 385.]

202. Bell's Stadia Slide Rule.

> [Designed by Arthur L. Bell. See *Engineering News*, Vol. 54, 1905, p. 487.]

203. The "R. H. S." Calculator.

> [Pickworth, Charles N., *The Slide Rule; A practical manual*, Manchester, London, New York, 1906, p. 101. This rule is designed by Professor R. H. Smith. The scale line is arranged on a cylinder in a spiral form. It is made by J. H. Steward, Strand, London.]

204. Universal Slide Rule.

> [C. N. Pickworth, *op. cit.*, p. 90; *Instructions for the Calculating Slide Rule*, Albert Nestler, p. 42. Made by Albert Nestler in Lahr, Baden. A rule by this name is manufactured by Keuffel & Esser Co. in New York under patent of March 21, 1899. See their catalogue for 1906, p. 326.]

205. Webb's Stadia Slide Rule (cylindrical).

> [Catalogue of Keuffel & Esser Co., New York, 1906, p. 327.]

206. Colby's Sewer Computer.

> [Catalogue of Keuffel & Esser Co., New York, 1906, p. 327; *Engineering News*, Vol. 37, 1897, p. 5. Designed by B. H. Colby of St. Louis, Mo.]

207. Cox's K. & E. Stadia Slide Rules.

> [Catalogue of Keuffel & Esser Co., New York, 1906, p. 327. Designed by William Cox.]

208. Cox's Stadia Computer (circular rule).

> [*Engineering News*, Vol. 43, 1900, p. 232. Purchased by W. & L. E. Gurley, Troy, N. Y.]

209. Favorite Slide Rule (Mannheim type).
[Catalogue of Keuffel & Esser Co., New York, 1906, p. 323.]

210. Goodchild Mathematical Chart.
[Catalogue of Keuffel & Esser Co., New York, 1906, p. 317.]

211. Halden Calculex.
[W. H. Harling's *Drawing Instruments*, 13th ed., London, 1906, p. 75. Manufactured in Manchester, England, by J. Halden & Co. See also *Rules, Tables and Formulæ for Patent Circular Slide Rule (Halden Calculex)*, Manchester.]

212. W. H. Harling's Calculating Rule.
[W. H. Harling's *Drawing Instruments*, 13th ed., 1906, p. 73.]

213. W. H. Harling's Calculating Rule, Rietz Pattern.
[W. H. Harling's *Drawing Instruments*, 13th ed., London, 1906, p. 74.]

214. Mechanical Engineer Pocket Calculator (Circular).
[W. H. Harling, *Mathematical Drawing and Surveying Instruments*, 13th ed., London, 1906, p. 75.]

215. Miggett's Cost-estimating Slide Rule.

216. Miggett's Cost-estimating Slide Rule in Conical Form.
[*American Machinist*, Vol. 29, Pt. II, 1906, p. 803. Designed by W. L. Miggett.]

217. Rosenthal's Multiplex Slide Rule.
[L. W. Rosenthal, *Mannheim and Multiplex Slide Rules*, published by E. Dietzgen & Co., Chicago, 1905. Invented and patented by L. W. Rosenthal, electrical engineer. The manufacture of this rule was begun in Chicago in 1906.]

218. Nickel's Runnerless Slide Rule.
[*American Machinist*, Vol. 29, Pt. II, 1906, p. 256; also *The Runnerless Slide Rule*, by F. F. Nickel. Published by the author, East Orange, New Jersey. This is a protest against the prevailing Mannheim construction.]

219. Roberts' Slide Rule for Wiring Calculations.

> [*Electric Journal*, Pittsburg, Pa., Vol. 3, 1906, pp. 116–118. Mr. E. P. Roberts, the designer, says that it was patented in 1894, and sold for a time, though not on the market now.]

220. Slide Rule for Calculating Sag in Wires.

> [Designed by R. J. C. Wood. See *Electrical World*, New York, Vol. 50, 1907, p. 402.]

221. Tilsley's Slide Rule for Strength of Gear Teeth.

> [*American Machinist*, Vol. 30, Pt. II, 1907, p. 76. A straight rule graduated according to formula of Wilfred Lewis, designed by Harry Tilsley.]

222. Younger's Logarithmic Chart for Computing Costs.

> [*American Machinist*, Vol. 30, Pt. II, 1907, p. 91. Designed by John Younger as a substitute for Miggett's Cost-estimating Slide Rule.]

223. Niethammer's Präzisions-Schulstab.

> [*Zeitschr. f. Mathem. u. Naturwissensch. Unterricht*, 38. Jahrgang, 1908, p. 528. For articles on the use of the slide rule in German schools, see this *Zeitschrift*, Vol. 3, 1872; Vol. 27, 1897, pp. 568, 594; Vol. 28, 1897, p. 180.]

224. Neuer Präzisions-Rechenstab.

> [Made by Dennert & Pape in Altona, "mit federndem Stahlrücken und seitlicher Justierschraube." See *Zeitschr. f. Mathem. u. Naturwissensch. Unterricht*, Vol. 38, 1908, p. 580.]

225. Griffin and Son's Card Slide Rule.

> [Made by J. J. Griffin & Sons, Ltd., of Kingsway, London See *Nature*, Vol. 77, 1908, p. 500.]

226. Malassis, Cercles Logarithmiques.

> [M. d'Ocagne, *Calcul simplifié*, 2e éd., Paris, 1905, p. 121.]

227. Viaris, Ruban Calculateur.

> [M. d'Ocagne, *Calcul simplifié*, 2e éd., Paris, 1905, p. 122. Marquis de Viaris was a French navy officer.]

228. Chadwick's Improved Slide Rule.

> [John Chadwick's *Slide-Rule Instructor for Instruction on Chadwick's Improved Slide Rule*, London (no date).]

229. Dämen-Schmid's Rechenwalze.

[E. Hammer, *Der logarithmische Rechenschieber*, 4te Aufl., Stuttgart, 1908, p. 9. The instrument is sold in Örlikon.]

230. Niehans' Metalltachymeterschieber.

[E. Hammer, *Der logarithmische Rechenschieber*, 4te Aufl., Stuttgart, 1908, p. 10. See also *Zeitschr. für Vermess.*, Vol. 35, 1906, p. 237.]

231. Koppe's Barometerhöhenrechenschieber.

[E. Hammer, *op. cit.*, p. 10.]

232. Bischoff's Barometerhöhenrechenschieber.

[E. Hammer, *op. cit.*, p. 10.]

233. Vogler's Barometerhöhenrechenschieber.

[E. Hammer, *op. cit.*, p. 10.]

234. Hammer's Barometerhöhenrechenschieber.

[E. Hammer, *op. cit.*, p. 10.]

235. J. L. Hall's Structural Slide Rule (Column Slide Rule, Beam Slide Rule, and Mannheim Slide Rule in one).

[*American Architect*, February 12, 1908; see also *Slide Rule Manual*, by John L. Hall. Manufactured and sold by the *Slide Rule Club*, Box 12, Station J, New York City. In use since 1907.]

236. Edge's Weight Computer for Structural Shapes.

[*American Machinist*, Vol. 31, 1908, p. 613. Sold by Edge Computer Sales Agency, St. Paul Building, New York City.]

237. Perry's New Slide Rule.

[*Engineering Record*, Vol. 58, 1908, Current News Supplement, p. 37. Devised by John Perry and placed on market by A. G. Thornton of Manchester, England. Solves expressions with fractional indices.]

238. Wynne-Roberts' Pocket Hydraulic Calculator.

[*Engineering Record*, Vol. 58, 1908, p. 679. A compound circular slide rule devised by R. O. Wynne-Roberts.]

239. Eichhorn's Trigonometric Slide Rule.
   [*American Machinist*, Vol. 31, 1908, p. 818.   Put on the
   market by M. J. Eichhorn, 5759 Aberdeen St., Chicago,
   Ill.]

240. Celluloid Slide Rules, with spare Logologarithmic
   Slide, as arranged by H. C. Dunlop and C. S.
   Jackson.
   [*Slide Rule Notes*, by Lt.-Col. H. C. Dunlop, R.F.A., and
   C. S. Jackson, M.A., London, 1901.   Made by John Davis
   & Son (Derby), Ltd., London.]

241. M. Schinzel's Logarithmischer Kubizierungsmass-
   stab.
   [*Encyklopädie d. Math. Wiss.*, Bd. I, 1898–1904, p. 1057.]

242. Scheve's Artillerist Rechenschieber.
   [*Encyklopädie d. Math. Wiss.*, Bd. I, 1898–1904, p. 1060;
   Arch. Artill. Ingen. Off. 88; Sonderabdruck dieses Artikels,
   Berlin, 1881.]

243. Fearnley's Universal Calculator.
   [C. N. Pickworth's *Slide Rule*, 10th ed., 1906, p. 100.]

244. "Midget" Slide Rule.
   [*Catalogue of Drawing Materials*, Kolesch & Co., New
   York, 1907, p. 88.   See also Kolesch & Co., *Slide Rule
   Instructions*.]

245. "Vest Pocket" Slide Rule.
   [*Catalogue of Drawing Materials*, Kolesch & Co., New
   York, 1907, p. 88.]

246. "Triplex" Slide Rule.
   [*Catalogue of Drawing Materials*, Kolesch & Co., New
   York, 1907, p. 89.]

247. The L. E. Knott Slide Rule.
   [Made by L. E. Knott Apparatus Co., Boston, Mass.
   Directions for use of rule by W. B. Carpenter.]

248. The K. & E. Polyphase Slide Rule.
   [*Catalogue of Keuffel & Esser Co.*, New York, 1909, p. 310.]

249. The K. & E. Adjustable Duplex Slide Rules.
   [*Catalogue of Keuffel & Esser Co.*, New York, 1909, p. 311.]

250. The K. & E. Adjustable Log-Log Duplex Slide Rule.
[*Catalogue of Keuffel & Esser Co.*, New York, 1909, p. 312.]

251. The K. & E. Circular Calculator.
[*Catalogue of Keuffel & Esser Co.*, New York, 1909, p. 307.]

252. Nestler's Slide Rule for Wiring Calculations.
[*Electrical Review and Western Electrician*, Vol. 54, 1909, p. 399; *Elektrotechnischer Anzeiger*, 1909. Made by Albert Nestler, of Lahr, in Baden, Germany.]

253. Woodworth's Slide Rule for Electrical Wiremen.

254. Woodworth's Slide Rule for Calculations with Volts, Amperes, Ohms and Watts.
[*Electrical Review and Western Electrician*, Vol. 54, 1909, p. 399. Both rules are designed by Professor P. B. Woodworth, of the Lewis Institute, Chicago.]

255. Nordell's Slide Rule for Computing Run-off to Sewers.
[*Engineering News*, Vol. 61, 1909, p. 266. Designed by Carl H. Nordell of New York City and manufactured by the Keuffel & Esser Co. Based on Kutter's formula.]

256. Schumacher's Rechenschieber mit Teilung in gleiche Intervalle.
[Dr. Soh. Schumacher, Professor am Kgl. Bayer. Kadettenkorps, *Ein Rechenschieber mit Teilung in gleiche Intervalle auf der Grundlaged er zahlentheoretischen Indizes. Für den Unterricht konstruiert*, München, 1909. See also *Zeitschr. f. Math. u. Naturwiss. Unterricht*, Vol. 40, 1909, p. 59.]

BIBLIOGRAPHY OF THE SLIDE RULE

With Index to pages where referred to.

1723. Construction and Principal Uses of Mathematical Instruments. M. Bion (Translated by E. Stone),

3, 15, 18, 32

1726, 1743. New Mathematical Dictionary. E. Stone (London) 3

1727. Histoire de l'académie royale des sciences. Jean Baptiste Clairaut........................... 43

1727. Theatrum Arithmetico-Geometricum. Jacob Leupold (Leipzig) 24, 41

1733. The Description and Use of an Universal and Perpetual Mathematical Instrument. Benjamin Scott (London)............................ 34

1740. Lives of the Professors of Gresham College. Ward. 5

1740. Theory and Practice of Gauging. Robert Shirtcliffe (London) 25, 29, 39

1744. Mémoires de l'académie royale des sciences de l'année, 1741 (Paris) 44

1753. Dictionnaire universel de mathematique et de physique. Tome I, Saverien.................. 45

1755. Royal Gauger. C. Leadbetter 29, 67

1755. The Royal Gauger. Leadbetter. 4th Ed. (London) 17, 29, 44

1761. Beschreikung und Gebrauch der Logarithmischen Rechenstäbe. Johann H. Lambert (Augsburg). New edition published in 1772................ 42

1766. Abrégé du Pilotage. Lemonnier (Paris).......... 45

1768. Nouveaux essais pour déterminer les longitudes en mer par les mouvements de la lune et par une seule observatione. Pezenas (Paris) 45

1768. (Treatise on Slide Rule—no name). Flower (London) 32

1775. Treatise on Mathematical Instruments. John Robertson 32

1776. Atlas céleste de Flamsteed, translated by Fortin.. 45

18—. Theorie du logarithmischen Rechenschieber. Franz
       Ruth...................................... 87

1800. Dizionario enciclopedico delle matematische delli
      signori. Art. "Logaritmiche" (Padova) 45

1802. "Mechanics' Magazine," Vol. 5 (London)......... 44

1802. Navigator. Bowditch 59

1802. Nicholson's Journal, Vol. 1, p. 452.............. 75

1803. De Ingenieur 81

1805. "Schoolmaster's Assistant," by Thos. Dilworth,
      brought out in Philadelphia by Robert Patterson. 59

1808. Mathematisches Wörterbuch, I. Abtheilung, 3. Theil
      (Leipzig).................................... 15

1810. Explication et usage de l'arithmographe. Gattey
      (Paris) 55

1811. Mathematical Tables. Hutton iii

1813. Complete Measurer. Hawney (1st Edit. London,
      1717) (Baltimore) 59

1813. Complete Measurer. Hawney (Baltimore). (The
      first edition of this book appeared in London in
      1717) 30

1814. Dictionary of Pure and Mixed Mathematics. Peter
      Barlow (London) 51

1815. Mathematical Dictionary. Charles Hutton...... 3, 15

1815. "Journal des Mines," Vol. 37, p. 101 75

1815. "Philosophical Transactions," Part I (London) 48, 75, 76

1817. "Nicholson's Journal," Vol. 49, p. 187 67

1817. "Philosophical Magazine," Vol. 49, p. 187 (London) 49

1820. (Treatise on Slide Rule—title not given). Collar-
      dean (Paris) 58

1823. Dictionary of Mathematical and Physical Sciences.
      James Mitchell (London)..................... 51

1823. Quarterly Journal of Science, Literature and Arts, Vol. XVI, p. 357 (London).................. 52, 76

1827. Treatise on the Steam Engine. John Farey (London) 31

1827. (Treatise on Slide-Rule—no title given). J. F. Artur (2ᵉ éd., 1845) (London) 58

1829. Gill's Technological Repository, Vol. IV, p. 33 (London) 52, 76, 77

1831. "Mechanics' Magazine" (London) 76, 77

1832. Brewster's Edinburgh Encyclopædia, 1st Am. Ed. (Philadelphia) 48

1837. Instruction sur la manière de se servir de la règle à calcul. Mouzin. 3ᵉ éd. (Paris) 65

1837. (Treatise on Slide Rule—no title given). 3ᵉ éd. Ph. Mouzin (Paris) 58

1840. "Annales des Ponts et Chaussées".............. 79

1840. "Mechanics' Magazine," Vol. 32, pp. 101, 102 (London)....................................... 50

1841. Mathematical Dictionary. Montferrier.......... 57

1841. "Mechanics' Magazine".................... 58, 77

1842. Penny Cyclopaedia. (Article on "Slide Rule" by De Morgan) .... iii, 9, 50, 51, 56, 67, 75, 77, 78

1843. Anweisung zum Gebrauche des englischen Rechen-schiebers. L. C. Schulz von Strasnitzki (Wien).. 54

1844. On Coggeshall's Sliding Rule (London) 85

1845. Palmer's Pocket Scale, with Rules for its use in solving Arithmetical and Geometrical Problems (Boston) 78

1845. (Treatise on Slide Rule—no title given). Aug. Hadéry (Paris) 58

1845. On Bradford's Sliding Rule (London) 80

1846. Improvement to Palmer's Endless Self-Computing Scale and Key; . . . John G. Fuller (New York). 87

1847. Arithmetical Books from the Invention of Printing
to the Present Time. De Morgan (London).... 5, 8

1850. La Tachéométrie. J. Parro (Turin) 80

1851. A Treatise on Slide Rule. L. Lalanne (London) ... 58

1851. Instruction sur les règles à calcul. Lalanne...... 43

1851. Règle à calculs modifiée. Mannheim (Metz).... 64, 80

1851. Auleitung z. Gebrauche einiger logarith. getheilter
Rechenschieber (Wien) 80, 81, 82

1852. Gebrauchs-Anweisung für Rechenstäbe (Paris) 76

1852. Instruction sobre das reglas de calculo. (Paris)... 79

1853. Régle à Calcul expliquée. M. P. M. N. Benoit
(Paris) 7, 15

1853. Bulletin de la sociéte d'encouragement pour l'industrie nationale 44, 55, 56, 58, 75, 76, 79, 81

1853. (Treatise on Slide Rule—no title given). P. M. N.
Benoit (Paris) 58

1853. Nouvelles Annales de Mathématiques, 1ére série,
Tome XII, pp. 113–116 64

1854. Nouvelles Annales de Mathématiques, Tome XIII,
p. 36 .... 64, 81

1854. Mittheilungen des Gewerbevereins f. d. Königreich
Hannover, p. 169........................... 81

1856. Ueber Visir- und Recheninstrumente. Ernest Sedlaczek (Wein) 15, 80, 81, 82

1856. Mechanics' and Engineers' Book of Reference and
Engineers' Field Book. Charles Haslett and
Chas. W. Hackley (New York) 61

1857. Par. Comptes rendus de l' Acad. d. Sci. 44, p. 22.. 71, 82

1859. Teorica e practica del regolo calcolatore. Quentino
Sella (Torino) 54, 81

1860. Encyclopædia Brittannica. (Eighth Ed.)........ 3

1860. Atti dell' Imp. Reg. Istituto veneto di scienze
(Venice) 82, 84

1861.   Handbook of the Slide Rule. W. H. Bayley
        (London).................... 50, 77, 82, 84, 85, 86

1863.   Bull. de la sociéte d'encouragement pour l'industrie
        nationale (Paris) 69, 73, 82, 83

1864.   "Zeitschr. des Architecten- u. Ingenieur-Vereins f. d.
        Königp." Hannover, Vol. 10, p. 454........ 81, 83

1865.   (Treatise on Slide Rule—no title given). Fr. René
        (Paris) 58

1866.   Report British Assn. (London) 83

1867.   Giornale di Matem. del Prof. Battaglini (Naples).. 71

1868.   Appleton's Dictionary of . . . Engineering, Vol. I
        (New York) 4, 61

1868.   Instruments et machines à calculer (Paris)........ 83

1869.   (Treatise on Slide Rule—no title given. Transla-
        tion of Q. Sella's book—1859). Montefiore Lévi
        (Paris)..................................... 58

1871.   Drawing and Measuring Instruments. J. F.
        Heather (London) 83, 84

1871.   Torino Acc. Sci. Memorie 84

1872.   (Treatise on Slide Rule—no title given). Labosne
        (Paris) 58

1872.   Der Topographische Distanzmesser mit Reschen-
        schieber. J. Stambach (Aaran) 80

1872.   Auleitung zum Gebrauche des Rechenkreises. R.
        Weber..................................... 85

1872.   Amleitung zum Gebrauch der Rechenscheibe.
        F. M. Clouth (Hamburg)..................... 92

1874.   "Annales du Gènie Civil " (Paris).............. 83

1874.   "Deutsche Bauzeitung," Bd. 8, p. 136 85

1874.   A Treatise on Mathematical Instruments. J. F.
        Heather (London) 85

1875.   Die Grahpische Statik. (Zurich) 75, 76, 85

1875. (Treatise on Slide Rule—no title given). Claudel (Paris) 58

1875. Proceed. London Math. Soc., Vol. 6, p. 113 (London)   85

1876. Notice sur les travaux et titres scientifiques. M. Léon Lelanne.............................. 79

1877. Geschichte der Astronomie. R. Wolfe (München).   15

1877. Catalogue of Instruments manufactured by W. F. Stanley (London) 85, 86

1877. Das Stereometer, Körper-Messinstrument (Budapest) 86

1877. Notes pratiques pour études de tracés. I. Moinot (Paris)...................................... 86

1877. "Zeitschr. des Vereins Deutscher Ingenieure   86

1878. Méthodes graphiques pour l'expression des lois empiriques, etc............................. 79

1878. Veneto Istituto Atti. A. Favaro. .Numerous references

1878. "La Nature" (Paris) 86

1878. Spiral Slide Rule. George Fuller (London) 86

1879. Statique Graphique. Favaro-Terrier. (Paris).... 71

1880. Proc. Engineers' Society of Western Penna........ 87

1881. Knight's American Mechanical Dictionary, Vol. II   61

1881. The Slide Rule Simplified. Robert Riddell (Phildelphia) 62

1881. "Zeitschr f. Vermessungsw"............... 70, 71, 89

1881. Dingler's "Polytechnisches Journal" (Augsburg)..   87

1883. (Booklet on Slide Rule—no title given). Prof. Cherepashinskii (Moscow) 67

1885. Leçons de statique graphique, 2ième partie, calcul graphique. A. Favaro, Translated into French by P. Terrier (Paris)   6

1885. (Treatise on Slide Rule—no title given). F. Guy, 3e éd. (Paris).............. 58

1885. (Treatise on Slide Rule—no title given). Gros de
      Perrodil (Paris)   58

1885. Van Nostrand's "Engineering Magazine" 83, 88

1886. Regolo Calcolatore. Quintino Sella. 2 ed. Ital.
      (Torino) 71, 84, 89

1886. Dingler's "Polytechnisches Journal"   88

1886. Gewerbeblatt aus Würtemberg   89

1886–7. Transactions of Am. Soc. M. E., Vol. VIII, pp.
      707–709   62

1888. "Centralblatt Bauverwaltung"   73

1888. "Railroad Gazette."   (New York)   72

1889. A New and General Biographical Dictionary. Art.
      by Oughtred, quoted in "Nature," Vol. 40, 1889,
      p. 458.   12

1889. Portefeuille des Conducteure des Ponts et Chaussées
      (Paris)   89

1889–90.   "Techniker," Vol. 12, p. 34   92

1890. The Slide Rule and How to Use it.   Charles Hoare
      (London)   84

1890. Instruction pour la determination de la distance
      et de la différence d'altitude d'un objet à un
      point de Station.   J. Stambach (Aarau)   90

1890. Dingler's "Polytechniches Journal"   90

1891. "Zeitschr. f. Vermessungsw.".   93

1891. "Engineering News"   81

1891. The Mannheim Slide Rule. W. M. Cox (New
      York) 81, 89

1891. Explanation of the Principle and Operation of the
      Mannheim Slide Rule. C. W. Crockett (Troy,
      N. Y.)   81

1892. International Cyclopædia. (New York)   iv

1892. "Engineering and Mining Journal" (New York),
      Vol. 54, p. 130   90

1892–4. "Zeitschr. für Vermessungsw"................ 90

1893. Scherer's Logarithmischgraphische Rechentafel
        (Kassel) 90

1894. "Schweizer. Bauzeitung," Vol. 23................ 71

1894. "Engineering News," Vol. 32, p. 103............. 90

1894. Der Praktische Maschinen-Constructeur, Vol. 27,
        p. 8 91

1894. "Engineering Record," Vol. 30, p. 31 91

1895. "Nature." (London)......................... 73

1896. "Engineering," Aug. 7p 172 (London) 72, 91

1896. Engin. Ass'n of the South, Vol. 7 (Nashville, Tenn.) .
        pp. 92–99 92

1897. Handbuch der Vermessungskunde. W. Jordan, Bd.
        II, p. 134 (Stuttgart) 90, 92

1897. "Engineering News," Vol. 38, p. 291............. 91

1897. "Mechaniker," Vol. 5 92

1898. Règle à calcul, modèle spécial. A. Beghin (2ᵉ éd.,
        1902, Paris) 66, 94

1898. "Yale Scientific Review," Vol. 5, p. 47........... 93

1898. Logarithmicon. E. Nash, p. 43 (Dublin) 93

1898–1904. Encyklopädie d. Math. Wiss, (Leipzig)
                6, 38, 70, 71, 72, 73, 81, 83, 88, 89, 90, 92, 105

1899. Zur Theorie des Rechenschiebers. (Berlin)..... 71, 94

1899. Traité de Momograpĥie. M. d'Ocagne (Paris), p.
        361 93

1899. "Zeitschr. f. Vermessungsw.," Vol. 28, p. 660...... 94

1899. The Use of the Slide Rule. F. A. Halsey, p. 74
        (New York) 94

19—. Instructions for the Use of A. W. Faber's Improved
        Calculating Rule. C. N. Pickworth (London),
                                           91, 95, 101

19—.   Instructions for the Calculating Slide Rule. Albert
        Nestler, p. 63 (Lahr, Baden)................... 95

19—.   Slide Rule Instructor for Instruction on Chad-
        wick's Improved Slide Rule. John Chadwick
        (London) 103

19—.   Some Quick and Easy Methods of Calculating.
        R. G. Blaine (London).

19—.   The Runnerless Slide Rule. F. F. Nickel 102

19—.   Treatise on a Box of Instruments. T. Kentish
        (Philadelphia).

19—.   Engineers' Slide Rule. W. Tonkes (New York) ...

1900.   " Zeitschr. f. Vermessungsw.," Vol. 29, p. 233 92

1900.   "Zeitsch. f. Instrumentenkunde," Vol. 20, p. 336 .. 95

1900.   "Comptes rendus," Vol. 131, p. 1289............ 97

1900.   "Engineering News," Vol. 43, p. 232 101

1901.   Le Système Métriques des Poids et Mesures. G.
        Bigourdan (Paris) 46

1901.   Oesterreich. Woch. ensch. f. d. offentl. Baudienst,
        Vol. 7, p. 72 97

1901.   "American Machinist," Vol. 24, p. 339 (New York) 97

1901.   "Journal de Physique," Sept. 97

1901.   "Nature," Vol. 64, p. 523 97

1901.   Rechentafel System Proell (Berlin) 99

1901.   Slide Rule Notes. Lt.-Col. H. C. Dunlop, R.F.A.
        and C. S. Jackson, M.A. (London)........ iv, 71, 105

1901–1903.   "Engineering News" (New York)........ 62, 98

1902.   (Treatise on Slide Rule—no title given). Leclair
        (Paris) 58

1902.   "Journal de l'Ecole Polytechnique" IIᵉ séné,
        septième cahier (Paris, p. 223)................ 63

1902.   The Slide Rule. E. M. Scofield (Chicago)........ 97

1902.   "American Machinist," Vol. 25, p. 1515 98

1902.   "Rechenblätter" (Berlin) 98

1902.   "Technological Quarterly," Vol. XV, pp. 250–259
(Boston)   98

1902.   "Nature," Vol. 67, p. 141   98

1902.   "Verhandl. d. Vereins z. Beforderung d. Gewerbefleisses" (Berlin), Vol. 21, p. 48   99

1903.   (Treatise on Slide Rule—no title given). Jully
(Paris)   58

1903.   Treatise on Slide Rule—no title given). Dryssé
(Paris)   58

1903.   Règle à calcul Mannhiem (Paris)   71

1903.   "Zeitschr. f. Mathematik. u. Physik." Vol. 48, p.
134 .... 65, 80, 93, 97

1903.   "De Ingenierer," Vol. 18, p. 94   94

1903.   "Engineering Record" (New York)   99

1903.   Calculating Scale; a Substitute for the Slide Rule.
W. Knowles (New York).....................   99

1903.   Some Quick and Easy Methods of Calculating.
R. G. Blaine (London)   86

1903.   Thacher's Patent Calculating Instrument. Edwin
Thacher (New York)   87

1904.   "Engineer," April 7, p. 346 (London)   72

1904.   "Mathematical Gazette," Vol. II, p. 337 (London).   70

1904.   "American Machinist," Vol. 27, Pt. II, p. 1376
(New York)   91

1904.   "Nature," Vol. 69, p. 485   99

1904.   "American Machinist" (New York)..............   100

1904.   "Comptes rendus," Vol. 138, pp. 1266–1268 (Paris)   100

1904.   Slide Rule.   E. M. Scofield (New York).

1905.   Calcul simplifié. Maurice d'Ocagne, 2ᵉ éd. (Paris)
7, 58, 67, 72, 76, 82, 83, 88, 89,
90, 91, 92, 95, 97, 98, 101, 103

1905.   "Engineering News"   80

1905. Mannheim and Multiplex Slide Rules. L. W.
       Rosenthal (Chicago) 100

1905. "Schweizerische Bauzeit," Vol. 45 (Zürich) 101

1905. "Zeitschr. f. Instrumentenkunde," Vol. 25, p. 385
       (Berlin)..................................... 101

1905. "Engineering News," Vol. 54, p. 487 101

1906. "American Machinist," Vol. 29, Pt. II, p. 256
       (New York) 65

1906. The Slide Rule: a Practical Manual. C. N. Pick-
       worth (London) 73, 81, 83, 86, 88, 93, 94, 98, 99, 105

1906. Catalogue of Keuffel & Esser Co. (New York) ... 91, 101

1906. Drawing Instruments. W. H. Harling (London).. 102

1906. Mathematical Drawing and Surveying Instruments.
       W. H. Harling (London) 102

1906. "American Machinist" 102

1906. "Electric Journal," Vol. 3, pp. 116–118 (Pitts-
       burg, Pa.)................................... 103

1907. Règle à calculs. P. Rozé, pp. 2, 3, 29–58 (Paris).. 65

1907. Theorie et usage de la règle à calculs. P. Rozé
       (Paris) 66, 80, 87, 94

1907. "Electrical World," Vol. 50, p. 402 (New York)... 103

1907. "American Machinist," Vol. 30, Pt. II, p. 76 103

1907. Slide Rule Manual. John L. Hall (New York).... 104

1907. Catalogue of Drawing Materials. Kolesch & Co.
       (New York) 105

1907. Complete Mechanical Slide Rule and How to Use it.
       F. T. Hodgson (New York).

1908. Der logarithmische Rechenschieber. E. Hammer.
       4te Aufl. (Stuttgart) 7, 80, 81

1908. Rendiconti del Circolo Matematico di Palermo,
       Tomo 26, pp. 1–63 64

1908. Der logarithmische Rechenschieber. E. Hammer
       (Stuttgart) 80, 95, 103

1908. "Zeitschr. f. Mathem. u. Naturwissensch." (Unterricht)....................................... 103

1908. "Nature," Vol. 77, p. 500..................... 103

1908. "American Architect," Feb. 12................. 104

1908. "American Machinist," Vol. 31, p. 613....... 104, 105

1908. "Engineering Record," Vol. 58................. 104

1908. How to Use Slide Rules. D. Petrie Palmedo (New York).

1908. Mannheim and Multiplex Slide Rules. L. W. Rosenthal (New York).

1908. Slide Rule Calculator.

1909. Catalogue of Keuffel & Esser Co. (New York)..... 105

1909. "Colorado College Publication," Vol. I, No. 6... 79, 87

1909. "Electrical Review and Western Electrician," Vol. 54, p. 399.................................. 106

1909. "Elektrotechnischer Anzeiger".................. 106

1909. "Engineering News," Vol. 61, p. 266........... 106

1909. Ein Rechenschieber mit Teilung in gleiche Intervalle auf der Grundlaged er zahlentheoretischen Indizes. Für den Unterricht Konstruiert (München) 106

1909. "Zeitschr. f. Math. u. Naturwiss." Unterricht, Vol. 40, p. 59............................... 106

1909. History of the Slide Rule. F. Cajori (New York)..

1909. "Engineering News," Vol. 62, p. 40

ADDENDA *

To Page 10. I have received from Professor Antonio Favaro of the Royal University of Padua, whose history of the slide rule we have often quoted, a communication which indicates that he has not had the opportunity himself to examine Wingate's *Of Natural and Artificial Arithmetic*, London, 1630. This fact throws doubt upon the correctness of my conclusion, that Wingate was the inventor of the slide rule, for I went on the supposition that the statement in Favaro's history was the result of his own personal inspection, and could, therefore, be relied upon implicity. I learned later that a copy of Wingate's text of 1630 is in the Bodleian Library at Oxford in England. I have before me a *verbatim* copy of Wingate's description of the instrument in that book. The instrument is not a slide rule, but a "Line of Proportion" which, as he himself says, is "nothing else but a mechanicall Table of Logarithmes." It is the same scale that is described in his *Construction and Use of the Line of Proportion*, 1628. It appears, therefore, that De Morgan's inference, that Wingate never wrote on the slide rule, is certainly correct for those publications of Wingate that appeared before 1632. But De Morgan's inference was drawn from incomplete data and was of

* Copy received from the author after foregoing sheets were printed.—PUB-LISHERS.

the nature of a guess, even if it is applied merely to the period preceding 1632. For he admits never having seen Wingate's book of 1630 and he nowhere mentions the text of 1628, just quoted. But the findings of De Morgan and those due to myself, when taken together, establish conclusively that THE INVENTION OF THE SLIDE RULE IS NOT DUE TO WINGATE, BUT TO WILLIAM OUGHTRED, WHOSE INSTRUMENTS WERE DESCRIBED IN PUBLICATIONS BROUGHT OUT BY WILLIAM FORSTER IN 1632 AND 1653. The question remains, did Wingate write on the slide rule since 1632? I have now received reports on all of Wingate's mathematical books, except his *Use of the Guage-rod*, 2. ed., 1658, and I have found in them no trace of the slide rule.

To Page 11. From the 1660 Oxford edition of Oughtred's *Circles of Proportion* I copy the description of the circular slide rule and supply a photograph (Fig. 17) of the diagram. This passage is said to be an exact reprint from the 1632 edition, and is of interest as being the description of the earliest slide rule invented. The passage is, pp. 1–3 (using the modern notation for decimal fractions):

"1. There are two sides of this Instrument. On the one side, as it were in the *plain of the Horizon,* is delineated the *projection of the Sphaere.* On the other side there are diverse kindes of Circles, divided after many severall waies; together with an *Index* to be opened after the manner of a paire of Compasses, and of this side we will speake in the first place.

"2. The *First,* or outermost circle is of *Sines,* from 5 degrees 45. minuts almost, untill 90. Every degree till 30 is divided into 12 parts, each part being 5 min.: from thence untill 50 deg. into six parts which are 10 min. a peece: from thence untill 75 degrees into two parts

which are 30 minutes a peece.   After that unto 85 deg.
they are not divided.

"3. The *Second circle* is of *Tangents*, from 5 degrees
45 min; almost, untill 45 degrees.   Every degree being
divided into 12 parts which are 5 min: a peece.

"4. The *Third circle* is of *Tangents*, from 45 degrees
untill 84 degrees 15 minutes.   Each degree being divided
into 12 parts, which are 5 min: a peece.

"5. The *Sixt circle* is of *Tangents* from 84 degrees till
about 89 degrees 25 minutes.

"The *Seventh circle* is of *Tangents* from about 35 minutes
till 6 degrees.

"The *Eight circle* is of *Sines*, from about 35 min: till
6 degrees.

"The *Fourth circle* is of *unequall Numbers*, which are
noted with the Figures 2, 3, 4, 5, 6, 7, 8, 9, 1.   Whether
you understand them to be single numbers or Tens, or
Hundreds, or Thousands, etc.   And every space of the
numbers till 5, is divided into 100 parts, but after 5 till
1. into 50 parts.

"The *Fourth circle* also sheweth the *true* or *naturall*
Sines, and *Tangents*.   For if the *Index* be applyed to any
Sine or Tangent, it will cut the *true Sine* or *Tangent* in
the fourth circle.   And we are to know that if the *Sine*
or *Tangent* be in the *First*, or *Second circle*, the figures
of the *Fourth circle* doe signifie so many thousands.   But
if the *Sine* or *Tangent* be in the *Seventh* or *Eight circle*,
the figures of the *Fourth circle* signifie so many hundreds.
And if the *Tangent* be in the *Third circle*, the figures of
the *Fourth circle* signifie so many times tenne thousand,
or whole *Radii*.   And if the Tangent be in the sixt circle,
so many times, 100000 and by this meanes the Sine of
23°, 30′ will be found 3987: and the Sine of it's complement
9171.   And the Tangent of 23°, 30′ will be found 4348:

and the Tangent of it's complement, 22998. And the Radius is 10000, that is the figure one with foure ciphers or circles. And hereby you may find out both the summe, and also the difference of Sines and Tangents.

"7. The *fift circle* is of equall numbers noted with 1 2 3 4 5 6 7 8 9 0, and every of these parts is subdivided into 10 parts; and again each of them into 10: so that the whole circle conteineth 1000 equall parts, beginning the line noted 10, which therefore I call the initiall line. This fift circle serveth for finding the Logarithmes of the true numbers upon the fourth circle, by a right line out of the center. Thus the Log: of 21.6 in circle IV, will be found 1.33445 in circle V. And so contrarily.

"For example if the space betwixt 20 & 21.6 which is also the space betwixt 1 & 1.08 (because 20:21.6::1:1.08 is to be septuplyed that is multiplyed into it selve for 7 times: Apply the Index unto 1.08 reconed in circle IV from the initiall line; and it will in circle V cut 0.03342, the Log. of 1.08; which multiplyed by 7 makes 0.23396; a Logarithme also: for the valor whereof, apply unto it an Index; and it will be in circle IV cut 1.71382, which is the Ratio of 1 to 1.08, or $\frac{1.08}{1}$ multiplyed into it selfe for 7 times. And the like manner is to be used in septupartion of the Ratio 1.08; or multiplying the subratio $\frac{1}{1.08}$ into it selfe for 7 times."

In the dedication, printed in the work of 1632 and quoted by us, reference is made to the rectilinear slide rule, but a description was not printed until 1633, in the *Addition unto the Use of the Instrument, called the Circles of Proportion*, where the description is given in an appendix bearing the title, *The Declaration of the Two Rulers for*

Calculation. No diagram of the instrument is given. I quote the description.

"The *Rulers* are so framed and composed, that they may not only be applyed to the *calculation of Triangles*, and the *resolution of Arithmeticall quaestions:* but that they may also very fitly serve for a *Crosse staffe* to take the height of the Sunne or any Starre above the Horizon, and also their distances: in which regard I call the longer of the *two Rulers* the *Staffe*, and the *Shorter* the *Transversarie.* And are in length one to the other almost as 3 to 2.

"The *Rulers* are just foure square, with right angles: and equall in bignesse: they are thus divided.

"The *Transversarie* at the upper end noted with the letters, S, T, N. E, on the severall sides hath a *pinnicide* or *sight*: at the lower edge of which sight is the *Line of the Radius*, or *Unite line*, where the divisions beginne.

"On the left edge of one of the sides are set the Degrees from 0 to 33 degrees or as many above 30 as the side can containe. And on the right edge of the same side is set the *Line of Sines* from 90 to 1 degree. Those 33 degr. are tangents measured according to a Radius of 173205, which is the tangent of 60 on the staff.

"In the next side are set *two lines of Tangents*, that on the right edge goeth upward from 1 to 45 degr. and that on the left edge goeth downward from 45 to 89 degrees.

"In the third side, on the right edge is set the *line of Numbers*, having these figures in descent 1, 9, 8, 7, 6, 5, 4, 3, 2, 1, 9, 8, 7, 6, 5, 4, 3, 2, 1.8.

"In the fourth side on the right edge is the set *line of Æquall parts*: And on the left edge are diverse *chords* for the dividing of Circles.

$$10, 9, 8, 7, 6, 5, 4, 3, 2, 1, 10$$
$$9, 8, 7, 6, 5, 4, 3, 2\tfrac{1}{2}$$

"The *Staffe* at the farther end of it hath a *socket* with a *pinnicide* or *sight:* at which beginneth the 30 degree, and so goeth on to 90 degrees at the end of the *Staffe* next your eye: which degrees from 30 to 90 are set on the right edge of one of the sides of the Staffe.

"Then applying your *Transversarie* to the *Staffe* with the lower end set to 90, mark on the foure sides of the staffe the *line of the Radius* or *Unite:* at which on every left edge must begin the *single line of Sines, Tangents,* and *Numbers,* the very same which were in the *Transversarie* (that of the Sines being on that side where the degrees are) only the *line of Tangents and Numbers are continued* beyond the line of the *Radius* to the further end of the Staffe, by turning your transversary that way.

" And on the fourth side of the staffe in the middle are *double divisions:* that on the right hand is *a line of Æquall parts* to 100, reaching the whole length of the Staffe: And on the left hand contiguous to the former, is the *line of latitudes* or *Elevations of the Pole* unto 70 degrees marked with the letter L.

"The *degrees* both of the Staffe and Transversarie, and also of the Sines and Tangents may be divided into 6 parts which containe 1 minutes a piece: or rather into 10 parts containing 6 minutes a piece: for so they may serve also for decimals.

"Thus have you on the *two Rulers* the very same lines which are in *Circles of Proportion*: and whatsoever can be done by those Circles, may also as well be performed by the two Rulers." The rulers were kept together by the hand.

To Page 16. I have secured a copy of Seth Partridge's *Double Scale of Proportion*, London, 1662. The copy in the British Museum is dated 1671. His instrument was of brass or box. "It consisteth of three pieces, or Rulers, each one about half an inch in breadth, and about a quarter of an inch in thicknesse, more or lesse, as the Maker and User of them pleaseth; and for their length, they may be made to what length you will, either one foot, two foot, three foot, or more or lesse. . ." (p. 2). The rulers had "at each end a little plate of Brasse, or wood fitted to hold them close together, & so fastened to the two out-side pieces, that they may be kept steady, and the middle Ruler to slide to and fro between them" (p. 3). The instrument was of the duplex type. It had four pairs of logarithmic lines. The lines in each pair were identical and contiguous, one line being on the fixed part of the rule, the other on the slide. On the front side was the pair with the logs. 1–10, 1–10, and a second pair with the log. sine 1°. . . 90°. On the back side was a pair with logs. 1–10, 1–10, and a pair with log. tan. 1° (89°). . . 45°. Partridge tells how to solve $a:b=c:x$, $a:b=\sin C:\sin X$, $a:b=\tan C:\tan X$, $\tan A:\tan B=\sin C:\sin X$. There is no diagram of the instrument. On p. 188 he mentions Anthony Thompson in London as the maker of it.

Leupold in his *Theatrum Arithmetico-Geometricum*, Leipsig, 1727, Cap. XIII, p. 71, gives a description of a slide rule which is almost word for word that of Partridge. Leupold said he did not know who the inventor was, that he possessed a MS. of 10 sheets describing it.

To Page 17. Hunt describes his rule in his *Mathematical Companion*, London, 1697, p. 7, thus:

"This *Rule* consists of three Peices, viz. One fixed, called the *Stock* (which is twelve Inches long) in which the other two Slide, and the *Lines* graduated thereon are these:

"I. Upon one *Edge* on the *Stock* is a *Double Line of Numbers* marked *D*, and a *Triple Line of Numbers* marked *E*.

"And on the *First Side* of this *Slider* are two *Single Lines of Numbers* marked *C*, one Facing *D*, and the other Facing *E*.

"On the *Second, Third,* and *Fourth Sides,* are six Lines *of Segments,* viz. Three for the three *Forms of Casks* in the *Clavis Stereometriœ,* Lying, marked 1.*L*; 2.*L*; 3.*L*; to Slide by *D*, and Three for the three *Forms of Casks Standing,* marked 1.*S*; 2.*S*; 3.*S*; to Slide by *A*.

"II. Upon the opposite Edge on the *Stock* is a *Line of Artificial Sines* marked *SS*, and a *Double Line of Numbers* marked *A*.

"And on the *First Side* of this *Slider* is a *Line of Sines* marked *S*, Facing *SS*, and a *Double Line of Numbers* marked *B*, Facing *A*.

"On the *Second Side* is a *Line of Tangents* marked *T*, to Slide by *SS*, and a Line for finding the *Perifery of an Ellipsis* marked 0, to Slide by *A*.

"On the *Third Side* are two *Lines of Segments,* one of a *Cone,* marked *A*, Facing *D*, the other of a *Parabolick Spindle Standing,* marked ( ) Facing *A*.

"On the *Fourth Side* are two *Lines of Segments,* one of a Sphere marked o, to Slide by *D*, the other of a *Circle* marked 0, to Slide by *A*." There is no diagram of the instrument. It is worthy of notice that, on page 87, Hunt finds the length of rectangle whose area is unity and whose breadth is known, *by inverting the slider.* Hunt did this exactly one hundred years before Pearson taught the use of the inverted slider. Using the lines *B* and *D* (both double lines of numbers) Hunt says: "Draw out the *Slider* marked *BS*, and put it in the contrary way, setting 1 on *B* to 10 on *D*; Then against any *Bredth* in *Feet,* or *Yards* on one Line (it matters not which) is the *Length* on the other."

To Page 17. I have secured the 5th ed. of Everard's

Stereometery, or, The Art of Gauging Made easie, by the Help of a Sliding-Rule, London, 1705. From the preface: ". . . many Thousands that have been Sold, and a Fifth Edition of this Tract, are so good evidence of its Utility, that it is as needless as unbecoming for me to say any thing in its Commendation. . . . the Principal Lines upon this Instrument are put [also] upon a TOBACCO-Box, to slide one by another, as they do upon the Rule. . . ." Thus, the English anticipated the French in the effort to interest in the slide rule those who use snuff. Everard and Hunt appear to be the first to use the term "sliding-rule." Both used lines of single, double and triple radius, convenient for square and cube root. Everard gives no diagram.

To Page 20. The 5th edition (London, 1732) of Coggeshall's work has the title changed to *The Art of Practical Measuring by the Sliding Rule.* On page 25 we read: "This rule is different from that described by Mr. *Coggeshall,* and which was all along made use of in the former Editions, but now is laid aside, as not being so compleat; for his made use of both Sides of the Rule in working Proportions, whereas this makes use but of one. . ." Mark the departure from the duplex type. The lines described are as follows: Three log. lines (two of them on the slide) are graduated 1–10, 2–10; the fourth (on the fixed part) carries the figures 4, 5, 6, 7, 8, 9, 10, 20, 30, 40.

To Page 61. Later there appeared the following publications on Palmer's and J. E. Fuller's instruments: Fuller's *Computing Telegraph,* New York 1852 (copy in the New York Public Library); Fuller's *Time Telegraph, (Palmer's Improved by Fuller) Computing Scale,* Boston, 1852; Fuller's *Telegraphic Computor* (being letter press description of above), New York, 1852. The copy in the New York Public Library (1852) gives a reference to a London edition of the work. The instrument appears to have been used later in England than in America, as is shown by the following publications: Fuller's *Multiplication Chart*, London, 1870, 1880, 1885; *The Computer*, London, 1871, brought out by G. V. Marsh of Manchester and explaining Fuller's instrument.

To Page 67. Recently the following details about the slide rule in Russia have been received from Professor Cherepashinskii of the Imperial Technical School of Moscow. He says that he wrote his booklet, *Instruction in the Use of the Slide Rule, New System*, in 1878, that it was published in 1880 and was exhibited that year in the educational department of the Industrial Exposition in Moscow. He has no knowledge of Russian publications on the slide rule earlier than his own. His rule was introduced in 1886 in the intermediate schools of the Russian Communication-Ministerium. Now it is used quite extensively in Russian technical schools and in offices of engineers. Directions for the use of the slide rule in tacheometric work were issued by Professor Bogustawski in a book in the Russian language. In 1890 Professor Gasselblatt (elsewhere transliterated Hasselblatt) of St. Petersburg brought out a publication which we have mentioned earlier, in which a card-board slide rule of the old type, without a runner is described. Also in 1890, A. Berle brought out in Wyshni Wolotchek (city near St. Petersburg) a work entitled *Systematic Collection of Exercises and Problems on the Slide Rule, System Cherepashinskii*. A second edition of Cherepashinskii's book of 1880 appeared in 1898.

INDEX